ENVIRONMENTAL
SCIENCE

Richard Genn

iNSIGHT &
PERSPECTIVE

Insight and Perspective Ltd, 701 Stonehouse Park, Sperry Way, Stonehouse, Glos, GL10 3UT

www.insightandperspective.co.uk

Insight and Perspective Ltd 2017

First published 2017
10 9 8 7 6 5 4 3 2

ISBN 13: 978-1-912190-00-3

Designed and typeset by Wooden Ark
Printed by TJ International, Padstow, Cornwall, UK

Acknowledgements

The author and publishers would like to thank the following for permission to use the photographs/copyright material:
Amber Collinson & Carys Jones Entrance to Global Seed Vault 37, Glacier 94; Annette Boenke-Jarek Turtle egg collection x2 24; Chris Hatten Honeycreeper 45; Cochlias SAM Maltese Falcon 209; Gordon Genn Power station 22, Harpoon gun 31, Dead albatross 70, Stainless steel 132, Coal excavator 185, Steel wheels 227, Power station256; Jonny Vere Hodge Adelie 68, Penguin Elephant Seal pup 68, Chinstrap Penguin 68 Snow fed river in South America 96; Keith Betton Red Kites 37; Lindsey Death Rat eradication 46; Louise Porter Iceberg 95; Michael Sharp Shipwreck on rock 258; MOD Military low flying military flight paths https://www.gov.uk/government/publications/uk-military-low-flying-presentation https://www.nationalarchives.gov.uk/doc/open-government-licence/version/3/288; NASA Landsat 8 satellite image 143, Aster satellite image 143, Overhead sprinklers 310; Irrigation circles 310; National Oceanic and Atmospheric Administration/Department of Commerce NOAA Photo Library Albatross chick 23, Coral reef fish 58, Deep water reef 63, Krill 68, Shark 80, Coral drifting 102, Finetooth Shark 343; R. Waller NOAA Photo Library Orange Roughy 349; Ross Primmer Plants colonising lava flow 76; Susan Cox Buffalo 11; Ted Scambos NSIDC Research station 69, Ice core 69; Vladimir Rodrigues Frogs 43, Yellow Tree Frog 91. All other photographs Richard Genn.

The publishers have made every effort to trace the copyright holders. If they have inadvertently overlooked any they will be pleased to acknowledge these at the first available opportunity.

Contents

Introduction

Planet Earth is the only planet we can all live on, so it seems like a good idea to look after it. However, Earth did not come with an Owner's Manual. So, if we are to manage it well, we must:

- ▼ study Earth to see how it works;
- ▼ understand how we rely on environmental resources and services for our survival;
- ▼ understand that human actions are reducing the ability of Earth to support us and the other species with which we share the planet;
- ▼ develop sustainable lifestyles.

To achieve the above we must study how the Earth and human society interact to gain a better understanding on which we can make better decisions.

This is what Environmental Science is about.

We cannot afford to delay in acting.

The time gap between human action and the consequences becoming clear can be long, so the problems we are now experiencing may have been caused by human actions in the past, when there were fewer of us having smaller individual impacts. So, our current actions may be committing us to even bigger problems in the future. Even when the consequences of our actions are very clear, it can take a long time to develop new technologies and gain the support of politicians, industry, and the wider society so that we can tackle the problems.

The environmental impacts of human society and our awareness of them have changed as society has developed. As people have moved from rural to urban areas the environmental impacts of individual lifestyles become less and less obvious as the locations of resource exploitation become ever more distant. Over-exploitation of your local forest or pollution of your local river soon become obvious, but over-exploitation of resources to support urban communities are often less evident as resource exploitation moves from area to area as each becomes depleted. The consumers do not realise what is happening. Associated problems such as habitat destruction and pollution may also not be appreciated.

As scientists, we must be objective in our approach to issues, without presuming an outcome. This is especially important in areas where strong opinions exist such as nuclear power, agriculture, and wildlife conservation.

In the early days of environmentalism there were often clear divisions between the environmental movement and the economists, industrialists, and political decision-makers that were often judged to be a big part of the problem.

This is changing. With the growth in understanding of the importance of the environment and our reliance upon it, there is an increasing willingness of politicians to prioritise environmental protection. Economic systems increasingly recognise how natural systems support economic systems. There is an increasing focus on technological solutions to environmental problems, for example, in new energy technologies, pollution control, and environmental research.

We have the ability to solve the problems, but we must also be responsible in how we live and the demands we place on the planet.

"Earth provides enough to satisfy every man's needs, but not every man's greed."
Mahatma Gandhi (Indian politician and activist)

We must not be complacent, but there are genuine reasons for optimism regarding humanity's ability to develop a sustainable lifestyle. We can all play a part in this, no matter which path we follow. We need environmentally motivated scientists, engineers, architects, teachers, farmers, politicians, lawyers, economists, home-makers etc etc.

"Never doubt that a small group of thoughtful, committed citizens can change the world; indeed, it's the only thing that ever has."
Margaret Mead (American anthropologist)

"The future will either be green or not at all."
Bob Brown (Australian politician)

The conditions for life on Earth

Chapter topics
▼ Conditions on Earth and how these developed over time
▼ The physical features of Earth which enabled life to be created
▼ How the development of life on Earth changed conditions

Early conditions on Earth

The Earth was formed about 4.6 billion years ago as gravity pulled rock fragments in space together. The huge amount of energy absorbed as the rocks joined, created heat and produced a ball of molten rock. The surface gradually cooled to produce a surface crust of solid rock.

The physical features of Earth made it suitable for the eventual development of life by controlling the abiotic factors that are needed by living organisms.

▶ This 'Blue marble' image was taken from Apollo 17 while travelling to the Moon in 1972

Features of Earth that created suitable conditions for life

A range of features of the structure, position and behaviour of Earth made the development of life possible.

Mass

The mass of the Earth was great enough to prevent most gases from escaping into space. This atmosphere included the elements essential for life: carbon, hydrogen, oxygen, and nitrogen. They were present in compounds such as methane, ammonia, and carbon dioxide. The atmospheric pressure was high enough to prevent all the liquid water from boiling. Water is vital for living organisms as it is the general physiological solvent in which most biological reactions take place. It is also important in transport and temperature regulation.

Distance from the Sun

The light emitted from the Sun and the distance from the Sun were suitable to produce temperatures on Earth that would be suitable for life. Being too close or too far away from the Sun would prevent liquid water being present. The time taken for the Earth to rotate on its axis produced a day/night cycle that was fast enough to minimise excessive heating or cooling.

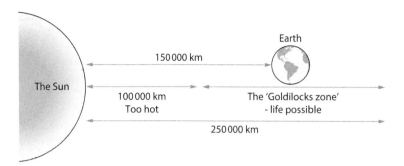

Axis of rotation

The axis of rotation is at an angle to its orbit around the Sun which produces seasonal variations in conditions as the Earth orbits the Sun.

▲ *How Earth's position in the Solar System affects the survival of living organisms*

Speed of rotation

The temperature of the Earth's surface rises when it is exposed to sunlight and falls when it is not. The 24-hour period of rotation of Earth around its axis reduces temperature extremes.

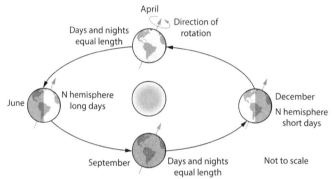

▶ *How the Earth's orbit around the Sun produces seasonal changes.*

Magnetic field

The molten layers beneath the crust produce the Earth's magnetic field that deflects the 'solar wind' and prevents biologically damaging radiation reaching the Earth's surface.

▶ *How the features of the Earth create conditions that are suitable for life*

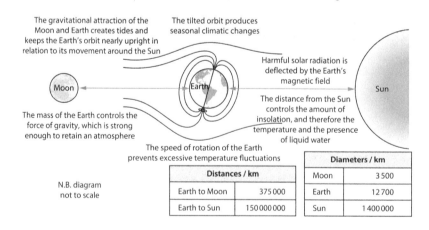

Distances / km	
Earth to Moon	375 000
Earth to Sun	150 000 000

Diameters / km	
Moon	3 500
Earth	12 700
Sun	1 400 000

Life first developed on Earth about 3.5 billion years ago. The conditions on Earth then were very different from those that exist now. The atmosphere contained some toxic gases, like ammonia, but no oxygen. The solar energy reaching the ground included high levels of ultra-violet radiation.

The chemical composition of the sea included increasingly complex organic molecules.

Development of life on Earth

Eventually, simple single-cells formed, possibly around volcanic geothermal vents on the seabed where the warm temperatures and rich mix of chemicals made biological processes more likely. These Archaea were single-celled organisms similar to bacteria. They still survive in many habitats, especially the oceans. Some are anaerobic, such as the methanogenic archaea that live in intestines and marshes.

Early conditions on Earth that allowed life to develop

After the formation of the Earth about 4.6b years ago, the conditions changed, eventually becoming suitable for life to develop.

Presence of liquid water

All living organisms require water for survival. It performs essential physiological functions and controls many environmental conditions.

- **Solvent water:** the 'general physiological solvent'. Most chemical reactions in living organisms involve reactants that are dissolved in water.
- **Transport within organisms:** water is the solvent in blood and sap where it transports dissolved gases, sugars, amino acids, mineral nutrients, waste products, etc.
- **Temperature control:** the evaporation of water absorbs heat, causing temperatures to decline.
- **Anomalous expansion on freezing:** water is most dense at 4°C so water that is cooler than this floats, stopping the convection current that may have cooled the whole water body.
- **High specific heat capacity:** water warms up and cools down slowly, which helps to moderate the rate and size of temperature changes.
- **Aquatic habitats:** oceans, seas, lakes, marshes, and rivers.
- **Absorption of UV radiation:** this protected living organisms in the oceans before the ozone layer developed which absorbed UV in the stratosphere.

Temperature range

Most areas of Earth have temperatures between 0°C and 35°C, so most areas are warm enough to have liquid water but not hot enough to denature proteins.

Atmospheric gases

- Carbon dioxide for photosynthesis and the synthesis of carbohydrates, proteins, and lipids.
- Nitrogen for protein synthesis.

Solar insolation

Sunlight provides the energy for photosynthesis. The heat produced by the absorption of sunlight provides the energy that drives the water cycle and warms the Earth's surface and the oceans. The amount of sunlight that is absorbed by the Earth's surface depends upon the albedo of the surface. The composition of the atmosphere controls the amount of infrared energy that is absorbed and converted to heat.

How life on Earth caused environmental change

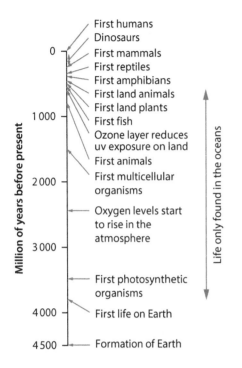

Graph axis label (left): Million of years before present

First humans
Dinosaurs
0 — First mammals
First reptiles
First amphibians
First land animals
First land plants
1 000 — First fish
Ozone layer reduces uv exposure on land
First animals
2 000 — First multicellular organisms
Oxygen levels start to rise in the atmosphere
3 000 —
First photosynthetic organisms
4 000 — First life on Earth
4 500 — Formation of Earth

Life only found in the oceans

▲ *A history of life on Earth*

As life developed and became more abundant, it started to change the environmental conditions which eventually made it possible for new life forms to evolve and new habitats to be colonised.

Atmospheric oxygen

By 2.7 billion years ago, some of the Archaea in the oceans had developed the ability to photosynthesise and release oxygen. For millions of years, all the oxygen produced reacted with iron in the oceans. Once all the iron had reacted with oxygen, the surplus dissolved oxygen built up in the oceans. Much of this was released into the atmosphere where concentrations started to rise about 2.45 billion years ago.

Oxygen in the atmosphere absorbed ultra-violet light, producing a dynamic equilibrium of reactions involving O_3, O_2 and O. The absorption of ultra-violet light made life on the Earth's surface possible. The time period when oxygen in the atmosphere was building up lasted until about 540m years ago and was called the Proterozoic. Many anaerobic Archaea and bacteria died out but more complex aerobic organisms evolved including animals and plants.

Carbon sequestration

Carbon dioxide is a greenhouse gas and helps to retain heat energy in the atmosphere. Photosynthetic organisms, photoautotrophs, absorbed carbon dioxide, some of which was stored in geological sediments such as carbonate rocks and fossil fuels. This reduction in atmospheric carbon dioxide levels helped to prevent a long-term temperature rise even though the brightness of the Sun increases by about ten per cent every billion years.

Biogeochemical cycles

As a greater variety of organisms evolved, inter-connected biological processes developed which produced biogeochemical cycles. These meant that relatively small amounts of some nutrient elements could support life over long periods of time without the resources becoming depleted.

Transpiration

Once plants had evolved and colonised the land, transpiration returned water vapour to the atmosphere and increased the amount of rainfall in other areas, making the growth of even more plant life possible.

The development of methods to research past conditions on Earth

Detailed, comprehensive, scientific knowledge of the planet and its past has developed relatively recently. Proxy data is often used as direct measurements of past conditions cannot be taken. This requires an understanding of how natural systems work and the development of new analytical techniques.

Increasing understanding of continental drift, ocean currents, ocean chemistry and atmospheric processes have been very important in understanding why and how conditions changed.

New analytical techniques have been developed that can be used to estimate past climate, for example:

- radioisotope composition can be used to date samples such as the ratio of carbon-12 to carbon-14;
- the ratio of oxygen-18 to oxygen-16 can be used to estimate past temperatures;
- the composition of past atmosphere can be analysed from air bubbles collected from ice cores;
- the ratio of magnesium to calcium in calcite deposits can be used to estimate the temperature. More magnesium is incorporated at higher temperatures.

More details of monitoring techniques can be found in other sections, for example, global climate change and research methods.

Key principles

- The structure and movement of Earth, and its position in the Solar System, control the abiotic conditions on Earth that make life possible.
- The presence of life has changed the conditions on Earth and made it more suitable for life to become more varied and abundant.
- Living systems have responded to environmental changes, such as the increasing intensity of sunlight. This has maintained the conditions that allow living organisms to survive.

Chapter 2

Conservation of biodiversity

Chapter topics
▶ The importance of the conservation of biodiversity.
▶ Threats to biodiversity.
▶ Methods of conserving biodiversity.
▶ Selected habitats.

The importance of conserving biodiversity

Global biodiversity is the variety and abundance of life on Earth. As humans, our survival depends on the other species with which we share planet Earth. They provide a wide range of ecological life-support services as well as resources that we exploit. Sustainable development and conservation are required to maintain these resources.

Resources

A wide variety of materials is collected from plants and animals.

▶ **Wood**: used in the manufacture of buildings, tools, furniture.
▶ **Fibres**: cotton, wool, paper, silk, rayon.
▶ **Oils**: vegetable and animal oils are used in foods, lubricants, soaps.
▶ **Fuel**s: wood, charcoal, alcohol, vegetable oils.
▶ **Food**: plants, animals, algae, fungi.

❶ *Cotton growing in a tropical rainforest*
❷ *Charcoal*

Fruit from tropical rainforests with the potential for commercial cultivation;
❸ *Custard apple from West Africa,*
❹ *Cohune Palm nuts from Central America,*
❺ *Stemmedenia from Central America*

New food species

Relatively few of the known species of plant or animal are used for human food. Some of these are kept in areas to which they are not well adapted so productivity is reduced.

Indigenous species are usually better adapted than introduced species to local conditions such as climate, pests and soil conditions and therefore may have higher survival rates. Selective breeding may be needed to enhance desirable characteristics and eliminate undesirable ones.

Most of the species that are currently farmed were first cultivated a long time ago but there are attempts to domesticate new species.

Many plant species have the potential for commercial cultivation.

- The Potato Bean of North America has a high protein content.
- The Morama Bean from dry areas of Southern Africa has a protein content similar to soya and is drought resistant.
- The Yeheb Tree from Somalia produces edible nuts, is drought-resistant, and can grow in poor soils.
- Many species in the spinach family can grow in soil with a high salt content. They may be used in crop breeding programmes to increase the salt tolerance of crops grown in areas where irrigation has caused soil salinisation.
- A perennial variety of maize was discovered in Mexico. Being perennial, it grows year after year so there is no need to buy new seeds each year. It also reduces the need for ploughing, which reduces the risk of soil erosion.
- Kernza is a perennial cereal with similar advantages to perennial maize.

A range of animal species has been investigated for domestication including American Bison, Common Eland, Common Ostrich, Cane Rats, Emu, and Giant Land Snails. They are often better adapted to the local conditions than traditional livestock species.

❶ *American Bison graze grasslands that are too poor for cattle*
❷ *Common Eland browse from trees and bushes as well as grazing grass so they can be kept with cattle without severe competition*

Biomimetics

Biomimetics involves the use of knowledge of the adaptations of other species, to improve the designs of manufactured items.

All species have evolved over long periods of time, developing adaptations that increase their chances of survival. Some of these involve structural features that help us to design improved engineering structures and equipment.

Vehicle design

The splayed wingtip feathers of soaring birds reduce wind turbulence and drag. Copying the feather structures has improved aircraft wing designs to help increase fuel efficiency.

❶ *The wing tip feathers of an eagle*
❷ *Aircraft wingtip fin*

Humpback Whale fin tubercles allow them to turn in tight circles

Humpback whale flippers have tubercles (bumps) on their flippers that channel water flow, increasing hydrodynamic efficiency and allowing them to turn in tight circles when swimming around shoals of fish. This has been applied to designs of ship rudders and aerogenerator blades. The new rudder design allows ships to turn in tighter circles. The aerogenerator blades can start to rotate at lower wind speeds than other designs, so they can generate more electricity.

Shark skin has scales that reduce friction while swimming. The ridges created by the scales have been copied in new designs for aircraft and ship surface coatings to reduce fuel consumption.

▶ *Shark skin scales reduce friction with the surrounding water*

Infection control

Bacteria do not stick easily to shark skin. A coating material that imitates shark skin is used in hospital operating theatres to help control bacterial infections.

Architecture

The mounds that termites construct above the ground absorb sunlight and become hot. The hot air inside rises creating a convection current. This draws stale air out of lower parts of the nest and creates a natural solar-driven ventilation system. Air, blowing over the mound, has a lower air pressure and draws air out of the mound. This system has been copied in shopping complexes and office blocks to create natural ventilation and cooling without the need for air conditioning.

① Moving air reduces air pressure and creates an updraft in the termite mound.

Solar warming creates a convection current in the termite mound.

Nursery gallery and fungus combs.

① Natural ventilation in a termite mound
② The external structure of the 'Gherkin' is based on the external skeleton of a marine sponge. The ventilation system is based on the circulatory system for water in the sponges

Many plants and animals have structural features that provide strength but are light. Bird wing bones must be light and strong. They are hollow and have internal struts that prevent the bones from bending too much or breaking. This lightweight, strong structure has been copied in the design of lightweight bridges and roofs.

Adhesion

High and low adhesion are both important for survival in different situations.

- The toes of gecko lizards have pads that provide strong adhesion. Attempts are being made to copy this to provide adhesion without the need for glue.
- The seeds of some plants have burrs with hooks that can stick to the fur of passing animals and aid seed dispersal. This was copied in the development of Velcro.
- Lotus flowers have water-repelling properties. This has been copied to produce self-cleaning glass.

◄ A lightweight roof support using cross-struts to increase strength

Materials

Some natural materials have properties that can be applied to the manufacture of synthetic materials. The lightweight, flexible, strong silk produced by spiders is being copied to produce better car airbags and body armour.

Medicines

Plants need to protect themselves from herbivores. Some plants use thorns, spikes, and bad tastes but others produce chemicals that are toxic to the animals that may eat them. Many of these chemicals are alkaloids. In carefully controlled amounts, these chemicals may have beneficial medical effects in humans.

- Poppies are cultivated to produce the painkillers, morphine and codeine.
- The cinchona tree of South American rainforests was used to produce quinine for malaria protection.

- Aspirin was extracted from the bark of willow trees. It is now manufactured synthetically.
- Taxol is extracted from the yew tree and is used to treat a range of cancers including breast, ovarian, lung, bladder, and prostate.
- The Mexican yam from Central American rainforests was the source of diosgenin that has been used to make steroid medicines including the contraceptive pill and cortisone to reduce inflammation and allergic reactions.
- The drug AZT was discovered in a tropical marine sponge found in the Caribbean. It is used to treat HIV/AIDS.
- The alkylglycerols and polyunsaturated fatty acids found in shark liver lipids can suppress the growth of cancer tumours.
- The drug AD 114 is being tested as a cure for fibrosis of the lungs. It is based on an antibody extracted from shark blood.

❶ The painkiller codeine is extracted from poppies cultivated in the UK
❷ The drug Taxol is extracted from the bark and leaves of the yew tree
❸ A tropical marine sponge

Only a very small proportion of the species that exist have been studied for the medicinal substances they may contain. This is a powerful argument for conserving the other species, or preferably entire habitats, for the medicinal substances they may contain.

Physiological research

Some species have evolved to become adapted to specific environmental conditions. Studying these could give a greater understanding of human health problems.

- Marsupials give birth to their young at a very early stage of development: they then develop in their mother's pouch. Studying a developing kangaroo or wallaby in a pouch is easier than studying a human baby of the same age inside its mother's womb. This has helped in understanding developmental problems in unborn babies.
- Hippopotamus skin secretes hipposudoric acid which is a natural sunscreen and antimicrobial agent. This is being studied to help improve the treatment of burns victims.
- Marine sponges produce proteins that prevent the rejection of grafts from other individuals. These proteins are being developed to prevent the rejection of human organs after transplant surgery.

- Embryos of the Purple Sea Urchin are used to test whether new medicines are teratogenic and could cause abnormal embryo development in humans. This does not threaten sea urchin populations as the sea urchin is a common species and a single female can produce half a million eggs. It is not ethically acceptable to carry out the tests directly on humans.
- Studying dolphins and bats that use high frequency sound to echo-locate their food has enabled the development of new ultrasound scanners that give better 3-D images for medical diagnosis.
- Human nerve cells are very small and difficult to study, particularly the sodium/potassium pump across cell membranes. Squid nerves are much larger and therefore easier to study. This has provided a better understanding of human heart disease, stroke, cancer, Alzheimer's disease, and kidney disease.
- Armadillos are among the few animals that can catch the bacterial disease leprosy. They are used in the study of the disease and in vaccine production.

❶ *Bennet's Wallaby*
❷ *Squid*

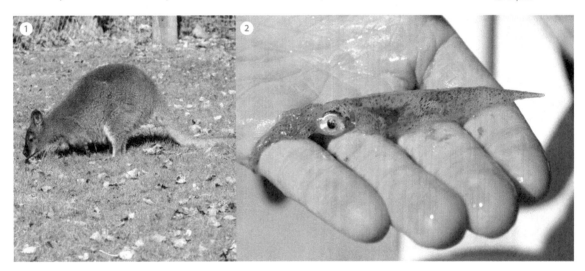

Pest control species

A wide range of predators, herbivores, parasites, and pathogens are used to control agricultural pests. Some may be indigenous species, while others may have to be introduced.

- The populations of natural predators such as ladybirds and ground beetles can be increased by providing suitable habitats such as hedgerows and beetle banks.
- Herbivores may be introduced to control weeds, especially if the weed species is non-indigenous and is not eaten by the indigenous herbivores. The prickly pear cactus became a weed after its introduction to Australia from South America. The *Cactoblastis* moth was successfully introduced from South America to control it.
- *Encarsia formosa* is a parasitic wasp that is released in greenhouses to control whitefly pests on crops such as tomatoes.
- *Bacillus thuringiensis* (Bt) is a pathogenic bacterium that has been used to control insect crop pests as it produces proteins that are toxic to insects.

Genetic resources

Many populations of wild plants have genetic characteristics that may be used in breeding programmes to improve cultivated crop varieties.

Crop breeding programmes

Domesticated crops often lack genetic diversity because they have been produced from a limited number of original plants. The search for new characteristics that can be bred into the commercial crops focuses on wild plants of the same species or close relatives. These are often called Crop Wild Relative species (CWR). Many CWR species are naturally found in areas where environmental degradation threatens their survival, for example, the Middle East, Central America, and South East Asia. Traditional varieties, grown in subsistence farming areas, are also likely to hold desirable characteristics which are not found in the commercial varieties.

▲ Beetle banks provide habitats for the predators of crop pests

Characteristics introduced from CWR species

Disease resistance

- ▼ Sugar cane has been protected from the sugar cane mosaic virus by cross-breeding with a wild sugar cane variety from Indonesia.
- ▼ A single wild species of tomato has provided the genetic characteristics for resistance to nine major diseases of commercially grown tomato varieties.

Salt-tolerance

- ▼ The introduction of salt-tolerant characteristics from wild varieties of rice and barley has led to the breeding of commercially cultivated varieties that can be grown in saline soil.
- ▼ Sea kale is salt tolerant and has been studied for possible use in breeding programmes with closely related crop species.

▲ Sea kale has salt-tolerant characteristics which may be bred into commercial crop varieties

Resistance to drought

- ▼ Varieties of cacao, the source of chocolate, that are more drought-tolerant have been developed by cross-breeding with wild plants from the Amazon rainforest.

High yield

- ▼ Oil palm yields have been increased by 25% by cross-breeding with wild varieties found in central Africa.

Improved taste or appearance

- ▼ Selective breeding for characteristics such as post-harvest shelf life or improved appearance may result in the loss of other desirable qualities such as a good taste. These characteristics may be re-introduced by further selective breeding.
- ▼ More attractive, sweeter pineapples with yellower flesh have been produced by selective breeding since the 1990s.

Nutrient uptake

- ▼ Many recently developed wheat varieties do not form a strong link with mycorrhizal fungi in the soil. This reduces their ability to absorb nutrients, such as phosphates, from the soil. Breeding programmes with wild wheat are increasing nutrient uptake efficiency by forming better associations between the wheat plants and the mycorrhizal fungi.

Centres of diversity

The Russian Biologist Nikolai Vavilov studied crop genetics in the early 1900s. He realised that some areas of the world had high concentrations of the close relatives of important crop species. These were named Centres of Diversity, Centres of Origin, or Vavilov Centres.

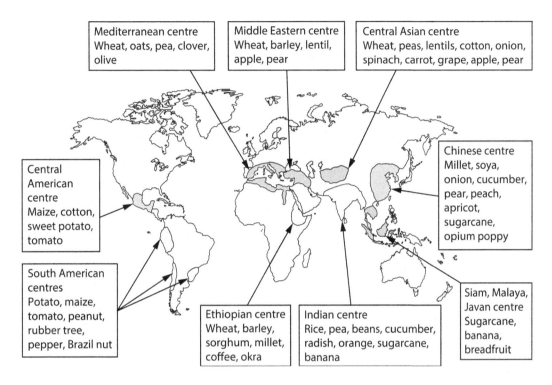

Mediterranean centre
Wheat, oats, pea, clover, olive

Middle Eastern centre
Wheat, barley, lentil, apple, pear

Central Asian centre
Wheat, peas, lentils, cotton, onion, spinach, carrot, grape, apple, pear

Chinese centre
Millet, soya, onion, cucumber, pear, peach, apricot, sugarcane, opium poppy

Central American centre
Maize, cotton, sweet potato, tomato

South American centres
Potato, maize, tomato, peanut, rubber tree, pepper, Brazil nut

Ethiopian centre
Wheat, barley, sorghum, millet, coffee, okra

Indian centre
Rice, pea, beans, cucumber, radish, orange, sugarcane, banana

Siam, Malaya, Javan centre
Sugarcane, banana, breadfruit

▲ World map of Centres of Diversity

Unfortunately, many Vavilov Centres are in parts of the world where environmental degradation threatens the survival of the remaining wild plants.

Gene-pool problems

A gene-pool is the total number of different genes present in all individuals in a population of a particular species. A large population does not always have a large gene pool as they may all be descendants of closely related individuals so they are all genetically similar.

Domesticated species have often been produced from a very small number of original ancestors. They lack the wide variety of characteristics found in wild or traditional subsistence cultivars (varieties). If they are genetically similar they will have similar adaptations and may all be susceptible to the same environmental changes. There is also a greater risk of inbreeding where disadvantageous recessive genes could cause problems.

The desirability of a large gene-pool means that conserving a few representatives of each species is not enough. A wide range of genetically different, comparatively distantly-related individuals must be protected.

Each region, within the geographical range of a particular species, is likely to have some genes that are unique to that area. These will exist because of the need to be adapted to the specific local conditions in each region. So, to protect all the genes in the gene pool, each species should be protected over its entire range, not just in a few convenient areas.

❶ An amelanistic zebra. Amelanism is the genetic inability to produce pigments and is caused by a recessive gene. Inbred populations are more likely to produce the homozygous recessive individuals that show the condition.

❷ These lion cubs are the offspring of two closely related parents. The cub on the right has poor muscle development caused by inbreeding. It has an abdominal hernia and weak back legs.

Ecosystem services

Other species often influence the conditions on Earth that are beneficial to humans. The importance of their actions is often not appreciated so their conservation may be a low priority.

Atmospheric composition

The composition of the atmosphere is regulated by many abiotic and biotic processes which act to cancel each other out, creating a 'dynamic equilibrium'. Because the processes may be balanced, with no overall change, their actions and importance often go unnoticed. For example, concentrations of carbon dioxide and oxygen are largely regulated by photosynthesis and aerobic respiration.

The hydrological cycle

Evapotranspiration from vegetation produces a large amount of the water vapour that forms clouds, controls surface temperatures, and increases precipitation.

Biogeochemical cycles

Living organisms are involved in many of the processes in the biogeochemical cycles such as the carbon, nitrogen, and phosphorus cycles. Many of these are done by microbes such as bacteria and fungi. Without these processes, waste products would build up and important nutrient resources would become depleted.

Soil maintenance

Soil is vital for the growth and survival of almost all plants, providing support, water, and nutrients. Soil also regulates the water cycle, producing more even river flow, and reducing flooding. The processes involved in the breakdown and decomposition of dead organic matter involves invertebrate animals, fungi, and bacteria. The organic matter and humus produced help to hold the soil together, while decomposition produces organic acids which aid the weathering and breakdown of rocks, helping to produce more soil and release more nutrients.

Interspecies relationships

No species can live in ecological isolation because their survival relies on other species for a range of resources and ecological services.

Food

All heterotrophs rely on other organisms as a source of energy and nutrients.

Pollination

◤ Pollination of flowers by insects allows plants to have dispersed populations as the insects search over long distances for the the flowers. Insect pollination is more successful than wind pollination which is very unreliable over long distances. Plants with insect-pollinated flowers save energy because they don't need to produce as much pollen as wind-pollinated plants.

◤ Pollination by animals is especially important in habitats such as forests where the trees reduce wind velocity so wind pollination would not be effective.

◤ Most of the animal species that pollinate flowers are insects, especially bees, but butterflies, moths, beetles and wasps are also important. Other pollinators include some species of birds, bats, and monkeys. The animals visit the flowers to drink the sugar-rich nectar, picking up pollen when they do so.

◤ Many plants have evolved flowers that attract particular insects and many insects have evolved to be able to feed from the flowers of particular species. These specialisations give the pollinating insects an exclusive source of food and reduce the risk of the pollen being carried to other plant species.

Darwin's Orchid is found in Madagascar. The nectar that attracts insects is found at the end of a 30cm long tube. The only insect that has a tongue long enough to reach it is the Sphinx Moth, which carries pollen between the flowers of Darwin's Orchid. This specialism means that there is no risk of less specialised feeders wasting the pollen by carrying it to the flowers of other plant species.

▲ Darwin's Orchid

Seed dispersal

◤ Seed dispersal by animals has many advantages over dispersal by the wind because it is not haphazard and the seeds may be carried longer distances. Since the animals live in the same habitat as the plant, they are likely to carry the seeds to locations where the seeds can survive. The seeds can also be larger than could be carried by the wind. This increases survival as the seeds contain more nutrients for the growth of the young plants produced when the seeds germinate.

◤ Plants often attract animals using fruit that is brightly coloured and tastes good.

◤ The seeds may be dropped by the animal or the seeds may pass through the animal's gut and be carried to a suitable habitat in faecal material which acts as a fertiliser. The seeds of many plant species are stimulated to germinate by their passage through the intestines of the animals that disperse them.

Habitat provision

One species may provide habitats for other species:

◤ trees provide nest sites for birds;

◤ hermit crabs live inside the shells of dead molluscs;

◤ trees control the abiotic conditions beneath the canopy, such as light levels, humidity, wind velocity, and temperature. This may provide conditions that are suitable for species that cannot survive in more exposed locations.

Threats to biodiversity

Direct exploitation

The populations of many species have declined as they been exploited for a wide range of products, or they are considered to be harmful. Some of these species now have legal protection although, in many cases, an illegal trade continues.

Food

Many species have been overexploited to provide food for humans, for example, turtles, cod, swordfish, tuna, many sharks, and many herbivores. Some species have become extinct including the Dodo, Great Auk, and Passenger Pigeon. See page 341, The environmental impacts of fishing.

❶ Swordfish steak
❷ Mako shark steaks for sale (illegal under EU law)

Fashion

Animal skins have been used for clothing throughout human history. However, certain animals have been over-exploited for fashion, for example:

  ▟ fur coats and accessories: leopard, snow leopard, ocelot, tiger, fur seals (fur seals were nearly hunted to extinction for their skins in the 1900s);
  ▟ leather bags and shoes: crocodiles and alligators;
  ▟ feathers from kingfishers, parrots and ostriches.

◀ A bag made from crocodile skin

Pets and entertainment

  ▟ Pets: parrots, lizards, snakes, tortoises, tropical fish.
  ▟ House plants: 'air plants' (Tillandsia), some tropical exotics and many insectivorous plants are collected in the wild to be sold.
  ▟ Zoos: it used to be common to collect wild animals for zoo collections. This is rarer now and normally only occurs for conservation reasons, such as a need to increase the gene pool for a captive breeding programme.
  ▟ Aquaria: marine fish do not breed well in captivity because the conditions they require are not understood. Most captive marine fish have been taken from the wild.
  ▟ Marine life centres: many of the dolphins and Orcas (killer whales) that are kept in captivity were caught in the wild.

▲ The Banggai Cardinal fish is endemic to the Banggai Islands of Indonesia. It is endangered in the wild because of excessive collection for the pet trade

Furniture and ornaments

Many species have been selectively collected to make furniture or ornamental items:

- ▼ a lot of furniture is made with timber from tropical rainforest trees such as mahogany, teak, and ramin;
- ▼ black piano keys were made with tropical ebony wood and the white keys were made with elephant ivory;
- ▼ jewellery has been made with shark's teeth, turtle shell, and mollusc shells;
- ▼ coral and sea shells have been collected and sold as tourist souvenirs.

Traditional medicines

The demand for traditional medicines, especially in Asia, has led to large numbers of selected species being collected. There is little scientific evidence that they are effective as medicines. Even if they were, they may become unavailable in the future as populations decline.

Many species are killed for the traditional medicine trade.

- ▼ **Tigers**: different parts are used in the belief that they cure a range of problems, for example, claws as a sedative, the tail for skin diseases, dung for alcoholism, brain for laziness, whiskers for toothache.
- ▼ **Rhinoceros:** the horn is used as a supposed cure for many medical problems from nosebleeds to smallpox.
- ▼ **Seahorses:** these are used to make medicines in the belief that they treat infertility, baldness, asthma, and arthritis.

Other products

A very fine oil was extracted from whale blubber and the spermaceti from the heads of Sperm Whales. It was used until the 1970s in the manufacture of products such as lamp oil, candles, soap, lubricating oil, cosmetics, and perfume. It has been replaced with oil from the jojoba plant.

Eradication of predators and competitors

Many species have been killed because they threaten humans or interfere with human activities. Examples include:

- ▼ animals which threaten humans, for example, sharks, poisonous snakes and crocodiles;
- ▼ pathogen vectors, for example, malaria mosquitoes, tsetse flies;
- ▼ predators of livestock, for example, wolves, puma, lions, birds of prey, herons, seals;
- ▼ agricultural pests, for example, insects, fungi, birds, molluscs;
- ▼ wild herbivores that eat crops or compete with livestock, for example, rabbits, deer;
- ▼ forestry pests, for example, wood-boring beetles, deer, squirrels, beavers.

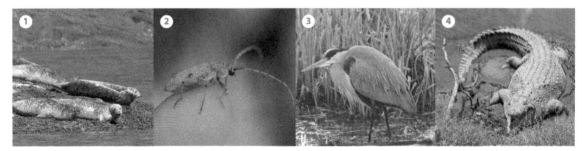

▲ *Common Seal, wood boring beetle, Grey Heron, Nile Crocodile*

Changes in abiotic factors

Human activities may alter a habitat so that it becomes unsuitable for species that are not adapted to the new conditions. The species that are most likely to be affected are those with very specialised habitat requirements. These are often species that were already rare before the habitat change took place. Although the habitat has not been destroyed, the conditions have changed so that they become outside the species' range of tolerance.

Water availability

Land drainage has affected large areas of wetland as land has been reclaimed and farmland has expanded. Over-exploitation of groundwater resources can lower the water table in the ground which may cause surface wetland habitats to dry out, making it impossible for wetland species to survive.

The water level in tropical rivers may naturally rise and fall with the wet and dry seasons. Sandbanks and river banks that are exposed during the dry season may be important nest sites for water birds, freshwater turtles, and lizards. Hydro-electric power schemes may cause sudden changes in water levels that flood the nests, killing the eggs.

▶ *Power station hot water discharge*

Dissolved oxygen

Dissolved oxygen levels in water can be reduced by hot water discharges from power stations, or by discharging organic wastes, such as sewage, which deoxygenates the water as it decomposes. A drop in dissolved oxygen levels can reduce the survival of aerobic organisms such as fish and insect larvae.

Marshland plants, such as the sundew, may be found in areas with waterlogged anaerobic soil where they are not out-competed by taller plants. Anaerobic soils have low nitrogen so large plants that have high nitrogen requirements cannot live there. Trapping and digesting insects provides the sundews with a source of nitrogen which is not present in the nutrient-deficient soil. Drainage schemes that produce more aerobic soil may allow taller competitors to colonise the area causing the sundew to die out.

Temperature

A change in temperature can affect wildlife species in many ways. The growth or survival of some species will increase but others may not be adapted to survive the change. Examples include:

- ▼ global climate change: the temperature changes will cause changes in the distribution of species as they colonise areas which become suitable, or die out in areas where they can no longer survive;
- ▼ hot effluent water: an increase in water temperature can increase the growth rates of aquatic vegetation, providing more food for aquatic animals, or it may increase the rate of decomposition causing deoxygenation.

pH

Mine drainage water and pollutant gases from burning fossil fuels, or smelting metals, can produce acidic conditions. These can denature the cell proteins of exposed tissues. Some organisms or tissues are particularly vulnerable to acidic conditions, for example, fish eggs and gills, or invertebrates with calcium-based exoskeletons such as crayfish.

Water turbidity

Activities such as ploughing, mining, or dredging may increase water turbidity. This can reduce light penetration and prevent submerged aquatic plants from photosynthesising. It can also kill filter-feeding organisms such as many bivalve molluscs whose gills become blocked.

Physical damage

A wide range of human actions can cause physical damage such as discarding litter or old fishing gear.

◀ An albatross chick that was killed by swallowing litter that its parents mistook for food

Changes in biotic factors

The survival of a species may be affected by changes in the presence and abundance of the other species in its habitat.

Pollinators

Many plants rely on pollen being transported between their flowers by insects. If the insects were to die out, then the plants would not be able to reproduce. The use of pesticides and loss of wild flowering plants has reduced populations of many insect species, including many species of bee.

Seed dispersal species

Animals that eat seeds and fruit can be vital in the successful dispersal of seeds and therefore future plant survival. Many large herbivore species are endangered, for example, elephants, rhinos, hippos, gorillas, and many monkey species. Conservation of these herbivores would help to protect the plant species that rely on them.

▶ *Seeds in the droppings of a hippopotamus*

Elephants disperse the seeds of most of the tree species where elephants are found. Unlike most large mammal herbivores, they are not ruminants so they do not repeatedly chew their food which would destroy the seeds. In addition, they are not territorial so they spread seeds over larger areas than most herbivores.

Food chain impacts

The decline in the populations of some species has been caused by the over-exploitation of their food by humans, such as puffins which have declined as sandeels have been over-fished. Over-exploitation of one species may also cause the increase of another species. For example, over-collection of turtle eggs has caused a decline in turtle numbers and therefore an increase in their food species, including jellyfish.

Jellyfish eat zooplankton so their numbers have increased due to the overfishing of competitor species which also eat zooplankton, such as sardines, herring and anchovies.

A decline in the population of sea otters on the west coast of the USA caused an increase in sea urchins that they eat. The sea urchins over-grazed the kelp seaweeds that are vital for the survival of many species including sea otters.

Introduced species

The community of species naturally found in an area will be adapted to their abiotic and biotic surroundings.

If a species is introduced, it may have adaptations that give it a greater chance of survival than the indigenous species which may then decline or die out.

Many species' introductions have had catastrophic effects on the populations of indigenous species. Populations in isolated areas, such as islands, have been very seriously affected: they have often evolved from a small number of original colonising species and may not be adapted to survive the new threats, such as mammal predators.

Introduced competitors

The grey squirrel was introduced to the UK from North America. In many areas, it has out-competed the indigenous red squirrel as it is better adapted to exploit the available food. It can digest acorns from oak trees which the red squirrel cannot. It is also larger and can compete more successfully for nest sites.

Rhododendrons were introduced to the UK from Asia because of their ornamental flowers and because they provide cover for game birds such as pheasants. They are very invasive and, being evergreen, shade the ground and prevent the regrowth of native vegetation. They also release toxins that inhibit the growth of other plants.

◀ A tanker discharging ballast water. Cargo ships often carry ballast water when there is no cargo onboard. It may be pumped onboard in one part of the ocean and introduce non-indigenous species into other areas when it is pumped overboard.

Introduced predators

The introduction of predators has reduced the populations of many wildlife species, especially in areas where the indigenous species are not adapted to survive in the presence of predators. For example:

- the range of the European Water Vole in UK rivers has been reduced by the American Mink that escaped from fur farms;
- many species in Australia are threatened by Cane Toads which were introduced from South America to control insect pests in sugar cane plantations. The toads did not control the insect pests but became serious predators of many other species;
- the ground nesting birds on many oceanic islands such as New Zealand, Australia and Hawaii are threatened by the introduction of cats, rats, pigs, and dogs;
- the introduction of cattle, sheep, pigs, goats, and rabbits has had a huge impact on the vegetation and therefore the wildlife communities that rely on it. The impact is often greatest where there are few indigenous large herbivores, for example, on oceanic islands such as Mauritius, Hawaii, and Galapagos;
- the Nile Perch was introduced into Lake Victoria to improve food supplies, but it ate the indigenous fish species such as Cichlids, many of which are now extinct.

Introduced pathogens

Humans may introduce pathogens, causing a decline in wildlife populations. The pathogens are often carried by other introduced species. When the Grey Squirrel was introduced from North America to the UK, it brought the squirrel pox virus which does not kill the Grey Squirrel but it does kill the indigenous Red Squirrel.

The White-Clawed Crayfish is indigenous to the UK but its population has declined following the introduction of several non-indigenous crayfish species such as the Signal Crayfish from North America which carries the fungal pathogen crayfish plague which kills White-Clawed Crayfish.

Many tree pathogens have been introduced into the UK. These include Dutch Elm Disease, Ash Dieback, and Sudden Oak Death. Most tree pathogens were brought into the UK on vegetation or in soil when plants were imported.

Species that hybridise

If an introduced species is very closely related to an indigenous species then cross-breeding may produce fertile hybrids. The natural gene-pool will be changed by the introduction of genes it would not naturally contain. For example, the Red Deer is indigenous to the UK but is threatened by hybridisation with the introduced Sika Deer. Also, the Wildcat population in Scotland is threatened by hybridisation with domestic cats.

Loss of species that control abiotic factors

Some species change habitats and produce abiotic features that other species need for survival. For example, African Forest Elephants create clearings and water-holes that many other species rely on for water. Beavers build dams, creating small lakes which are colonised by many aquatic species. If these species are lost then many other species may decline.

Habitat destruction

Human activities may have impacts that cause complete habitat destruction, usually due to a land-use change. These include:

- deforestation;
- ploughing of grassland;
- reservoir creation;
- mineral extraction, especially open-cast mining;
- urban expansion.

Setting conservation priorities

Wildlife conservation involves interfering in the habitats and populations of wild species in ways that are intended to be beneficial for conservation. This involves making choices and decisions that may be subjective and based on partial knowledge. The following are questions that might be asked when deciding the best strategies to conserve wildlife.

- What is the present day situation: species present, populations, and current changes abiotic factors?
- Which species should be conserved? The conservation of one species may be beneficial or harmful to other species.
- What actions need to be taken to conserve the desired species?
- Can the outcomes be accurately predicted?
- Can the impacts be monitored accurately to inform further decision making?

There are more species with declining populations than can be conserved with the level of support that is currently available. Some species/habitats/communities are perceived to be more important than others, so they may be prioritised.

The International Union for Conservation of Nature (IUCN)

The roles of the IUCN

- Coordinating global data on biodiversity conservation.
- Increasing understanding of the importance of biodiversity.
- Deploying nature-based solutions to global challenges in climate, food and sustainable development.

The IUCN categorises species according to their vulnerability to extinction. This is known as the IUCN Red List.

IUCN Red List categories

- Extinct - no known individuals remain;
- Extinct in the wild - only survive in captivity;
- Critically endangered - extremely high risk of extinction in the wild;
- Endangered - high risk of extinction in the wild;
- Vulnerable - high risk of becoming endangered;
- Near threatened - likely to become endangered in the near future;
- Least Concern – at lowest risk of becoming endangered;
- Data-deficient – insufficient information for the species to be categorised.

Selected features that may be used to categorise threatened species

IUCN category	Criteria for categorisation				
	Population decline over the previous 10 years or 3 generations	Area of habitat	Number of areas where found	Number of mature adults	Probability of extinction
Vulnerable	>40%	<2000 km²	≤10	10 000	≥ 10% in 100 years
Endangered	>60%	<500 km²	≤5	2 500	≥ 20% in 20 years or 5 generations
Critically Endangered	>80%	<10 km²	1	250	≥ 50% in 10 years or 3 generations

Selected taxa are reassessed each year and some may be categorised for the first time.

Species recategorised in 2016

The Plains Zebra has been recategorised from Least Concern to Near Threatened because of its declining population, mainly caused by habitat loss.

▲ *Plains Zebra.*   ▲ *Iberian Lynx*   ▲ *Tiger*

Species recategorised in 2015

Successful conservation of the Iberian Lynx has resulted in re-categorisation from Critically Endangered to Endangered. A captive breeding programme and the protection of two areas of suitable habitat have allowed its population to treble in 15 years..

The Tiger remains in the Endangered category, although three out of six sub-species are critically endangered. Its range continues to shrink.

The White-headed Vulture was Vulnerable, but has been re-categorised as Critically Endangered as the population has declined due to poisoning and persecution.

White Headed Vulture

Black and White Ruffed Lemur

Bearded Vulture

Fregate Island Beetle

Okapi

Kori Bustard

Species assessed in 2014

There are about 100 species of lemur, all endemic to the island of Madagascar. Of these, 22 are critically endangered and 48 are endangered. Habitat loss and hunting for bushmeat are the major threats.

The population of the Bearded Vulture or Lammergeier is increasing in Europe but declining worldwide due to poisoning, competition for food and, increasingly, collisions with power lines. It has been re-categorised from Least Concern to Near Threatened.

The Fregate Island Beetle of Fregate Island in the Indian Ocean was categorised as Threatened. A programme to eradicate rats from the island has resulted in a population increase so it has been re-categorised as Vulnerable.

Species assessed in 2013

The Okapi is only found in forests in the Democratic Republic of the Congo in Africa. Its population has declined due to hunting, habitat loss and the difficulties in carrying out conservation programmes in areas with military conflict. It has been re-categorised from Near Threatened to Endangered.

The Kori Bustard lives in sub-Saharan Africa. Its population is declining due to hunting for food and traditional medicines, habitat loss and deaths caused by collisions with power lines. It has been re-categorised from Least Concern to Near Threatened.

Selection of species for categorisation

A total of about 85,000 species have been assessed and categorised, which is a small proportion of the total number of species that exist. Because categorising a species involves a great deal of research, it is important to select species for categorisation carefully.

The criteria used to select species for categorisation include the following.

Species in habitats under particular threat

Key species in habitats that are threatened may be assessed for categorisation. Their status may indicate the status of the rest of the community of species, such as the decline of lemurs in Madagascar being used to predict the decline of many other species.

Evolutionarily unique species

Species that have a high degree of evolutionary uniqueness may be categorised, for example, if there are few closely related species. EDGE Species are 'Evolutionarily Distinct and Globally Endangered'. These species have few close relatives and are often the only surviving member of their genus and can be the last surviving genus of their evolutionary family, for example the Bactrian Camel, Pygmy Hippo, Northern Bald Ibis, Secretary Bird.

Endemic species

An endemic species is not found in any other area, so if there is a change in the threats to its survival and it dies out locally, there will be no surviving populations elsewhere. Many endemic species with small ranges are found on islands, for example, Galapagos, Seychelles, Hawaii, Madagascar. Endemic island species include Gozo Wall Lizard, Red ruffed Lemur, Aldabra Giant Tortoise.

Keystone species

A keystone species has an important role in maintaining the ecological structure of a community. Its importance is usually great compared with their low abundance or population biomass. Possible roles include the predation of potentially dominant species, provision of food, seed dispersal, or the creation of structural features of the habitat,

for example, jaguar in South America help to balance the mammalian jungle ecosystem with their consumption of 87 different species of prey. Other examples of keystone species are: African Forest Elephants, cassowaries, Grey Wolves, and beavers.

African Forest Elephants have impacts on their habitat that benefit many other species:

- they keep paths through the forest open;
- they spread the seeds of most tree species;
- they keep water holes open which provide other species with water and mineral nutrients. Many plant and animal species live in the clearings but could not live in dense forest.

Flagship species

Flagship species are species that have a high public profile. Raising support to protect flagship species may have a wide benefit for wildlife conservation in general. This may include species in the same habitat that are less likely to attract support themselves. Tigers, elephants, Giant Pandas, and Orang Utans are more likely to raise support than spiders, bats, fungi or moths which may be just as ecologically important.

Degree of population dispersal

When the global population of a species is fragmented into a number of isolated populations it is important to ensure that viable local populations are maintained. The fragmentation of habitats may not reduce the total habitat area by much but it may produce populations that will each die out because they lack sufficient resources, or have small gene pools and will suffer from inbreeding.

Where the entire population of a species is found in one area it may be vulnerable to any local change in conservation success.

Chimpanzees and gorillas are found in several countries but all Bonobos (Pygmy Chimpanzees) live in the forests of a single country.

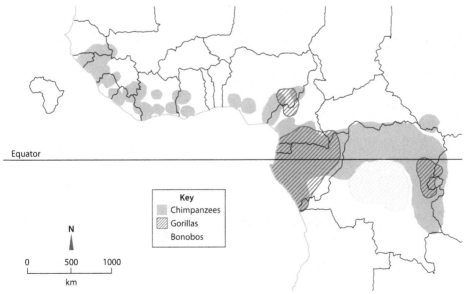

◀ *Distribution of the Great apes in Africa*

There are many different methods that can be used to conserve endangered species. Most successful conservation programmes involve a combination of methods.

Methods of conserving biodiversity

Legislation/Protocols

Laws that protect endangered species can be very valuable but they rarely protect the species effectively on their own. It can be difficult to enforce a law effectively and it may be broken through ignorance. Laws may change over time but the principles may still be relevant. There is a huge number of laws that protect wildlife but most fall into three main groups.

Legal protection of habitats and species

The Wildlife and Countryside Act (1981) is a UK law which includes much of the legislation that protects wildlife in the UK. It covers:

- designated protected areas such as Sites of Special Scientific Interest and Marine Conservation Zones;
- protection of wild birds and their nests: most birds are protected except some 'pest' species and game birds that can be legally hunted;
- protection of mammal species, for example, otters, Hazel Dormouse, Red Squirrel, badgers and their setts (tunnels);
- uprooting of wild plants: this is generally illegal;
- bats: these may not be disturbed and the woodworm treatment chemicals that are used in roofs where bats are present must not be toxic to bats.

The legal designation of protected areas can protect habitats and species in several key ways, some of which overlap:

- protection of species;
- protection of habitats;
- restrictions on activities within the protected area;
- restrictions on activities outside the protected area;
- management agreements between the landowner and the designating organisation;
- access restrictions;
- international cooperation.

Selected details of any designated areas can be used to illustrate these principles.
The following are the protected areas in the UK that are designated mainly for wildlife conservation.

- Site of Special Scientific Interest (SSSI).
- National Nature Reserve (NNR).
- Special Area of Conservation (SAC).
- Special Protection Area (SPA).
- Natura 2000 sites (SACs and SPAs).
- Ramsar Sites.
- Marine Nature Reserve (MNR).
- Local Nature Reserve (LNR).
- Marine Protected Area (MPA).
- Marine Conservation Zone (MCZ).

Trade controls

Some species are caught or killed in one country but would be sold in another country. It may be difficult to control the collection of the species but, if moving them out of the country can be stopped, there would be no point collecting them.

CITES

The main international agreement that regulates the international trade in wildlife is CITES: the Convention on International Trade in Endangered Species. Selected species are grouped in lists called appendices.

- **Appendix I:** this includes species that are threatened with extinction, so all international trade is banned except movement for conservation breeding programmes, for example, all the great apes, all the big cats, all rhinos, Blue Whale;
- **Appendix II:** this includes species that may be threatened with extinction if trade is not closely controlled. Trade is permitted from countries where the species is relatively well protected so limited exploitation does not threaten their survival, for example, Honduras Mahogany, Common Hippopotamus, Green Iguana, Great White Shark, Basking Shark, Venus Fly Trap.

Organisations which aim to achieve sustainable exploitation

A range of international organisations focus on specific wildlife groups that are exploited commercially.

International Whaling Commission (IWC)

The main aim of the IWC is to regulate and manage whaling. Populations of many whale species had been so depleted by unregulated whaling that commercial whaling was banned in 1986 until a time in the future that populations have recovered enough to be able to withstand commercial whaling.

◀ *The development of the harpoon cannon and steam-powered whaling ships by 1900 greatly increased the number of whales that were killed so many species were overfished within a few decades*

The aim of the IWC is to control whaling and ensure that exploitation is sustainable by conserving whale stocks through the following:

- total protection for certain species;
- designation of whale sanctuaries;
- setting limits on numbers and sizes of whales that can be taken;
- protection of suckling mothers and their calves;
- carrying out research into whale biology and activities that threaten whales such as ship strikes and entanglement with fishing nets.

The IWC does not ban all whaling. Whaling can take place for three reasons:

- **'Aboriginal subsistence'**: whaling is permitted for cultural groups that have traditionally hunted whales for food, for example, the Inuit (Eskimos) of Alaska have a catch quota of about 55 Bowhead Whales each year. The people of St Vincent and the Grenadines in the Caribbean can kill about two Humpback whales each year.
- **'Special Permit Whaling' or 'Scientific Whaling':** this involves the killing of whales for scientific research. Japan has used this approach to justify its whaling but in 2014 the International Court of Justice declared that Japan's whaling programme was not for research.
- Iceland and Norway use an IWC regulation to set their own quota for commercial whaling. In 2014, they killed about 800 Fin and Minke Whales.

Common Fisheries Policy of the European Union (EU CFP)

This is a series of regulations that control fishing within the territorial waters of the European Union. The aim is to ensure that fishing and aquaculture are environmentally, economically, and socially sustainable and that they provide a source of healthy food for EU citizens. Regulations change, but typically cover:

- catch quotas to limit the total mass that can be landed;
- size limits, so fewer small fish are killed and have a chance to grow;
- net mesh-size regulations that allow smaller fish to escape, survive, and have the chance to grow larger and breed;
- limits on fishing effort, such as a maximum size of fishing boat, or the number of days fishing can take place;
- a ban on the discarding of unwanted fish.

International Tropical Timber Organisation (ITTO)

The ITTO aims to encourage sustainable management of tropical forests.

In 1990, ITTO members agreed to strive for an international trade of tropical timber from sustainably managed forests by 2000, without unsustainable exploitation. However, there was little evidence of success by 2000 and this has continued to be the case.

Captive breeding programmes

For some endangered species, *in situ* conservation will not ensure their survival. Therefore *ex-situ* conservation may be required. This involves conservation away from where they would normally live. It often involves the breeding of species in captivity so that some of the young produced can be released to boost the wild population.

There are more species that need help than can be supported by *ex-situ* conservation projects. So, choices must be made about the species to be supported by these programmes.

Factors that influence decisions about captive breeding and release programmes.

- Is the wild population threatened?
- Is there a genetically diverse captive population?
- Is *in-situ* conservation being successful?
- Is keeping a captive population realistic?
- Is release into the wild likely to be successful, now or in the future?

Keeping species in captivity

Many species have such specific habitat requirements that it is difficult to keep them in captivity, for example:

- **habitat size:** some species require such large habitats that they cannot be kept in captivity. This is often the case for large animals such as whales;
- **food requirements:** some species have feeding requirements that cannot easily be provided, for example, insectivorous bats, or fish that eat plankton;
- **species interrelationships:** some species have complicated species interrelationships such as plants with symbiotic mycorrhizal root fungi relationships, plants with specific pollinators, or the Large Blue Butterfly that overwinters in ants' nests;
- **financial constraints:** keeping animals in zoos, or plants in botanic gardens, is expensive and there is not enough money available to keep all endangered species in captivity.

Captive breeding programmes

Many of the species that can be kept in captivity have not bred successfully. There are a number of factors which inhibit success.

- **Conditions for breeding:** for many species, the precise timing of breeding is vital to increase the survival chances of their young. Breeding is often triggered by stimuli such as day length, light level, temperature, amount of food or the amount of stored body fat. If these essential conditions are not known and are not provided, then they will not breed.
- **Population interactions and breeding success:** in the wild, breeding pairs of many birds may choose isolation while non-breeding individuals live elsewhere. In captivity, the mixing of breeding and non-breeding individuals may cause conflict and reduce the survival of eggs and chicks. Some species breed most successfully if breeding adults are separate from the other adults. Some species breed most successfully if there is a choice of possible partners but others pair for life.
- **Breeding habitat:** some species can only breed if they have a suitable habitat such as one that includes a suitable site for courtship display, social grouping, an area for hunting, or a nest site. For example, flamingos only breed in large groups. Mirrors around a captive population give the illusion of a larger population.
- **Gene pool size**: most captive breeding populations have small gene pools which increases the risk of inbreeding. Harmful recessive genes may be common in the population but they can only be 'expressed' and cause undesirable characteristics in the offspring if both parents carried the gene and passed it on to their offspring. Most recessive disadvantageous genes are rare so it is unusual for both parents to carry them unless they are closely related. In captive breeding programmes it is often impossible to use individuals that are not closely related. For example, the Hawaiian Goose became very rare due to hunting, habitat loss, and introduced predators. A captive breeding programme has successfully increased the wild population, but the captive population started with just seven individuals. Inbreeding produced some goslings with thin, hair-like feathers which insulate poorly so gosling survival can be low in cold weather. A 'stud book' can be used to keep records of family trees which helps to ensure breeding takes place between

▲ *Greater Flamingos at Marwell Zoo and Lake Nakuru, Kenya.*

▲ *The Hawaiian Goose.*

individuals that are as unrelated as possible. The stud book is usually managed by a zoo that specialises in keeping that particular species.

❶ *Scimitar-horned Oryx studbrook held by Marwell zoo*
❷ *Snow Leopard studbrook held by Helsinki zoo*
❸ *Partula snails studbrook held by Bristol Zoo*

▼ **Hybridisation:** a species in the wild includes individuals that naturally interbreed to produce fertile offspring. In captivity, individuals may inter-breed (hybridise) with closely related species or varieties that would not have naturally met in the wild. This can be prevented with captive animals if they can be kept apart but it is a particular problem with plants where pollen can be carried between plants by insects or the wind. The managers of early zoos did not understand the need to keep sub-species apart. The offspring produced, by breeding between populations that would not naturally have inter-bred, will have a combination of characteristics that would not be found in any individuals produced by natural breeding. These individuals probably have no conservation value. If hybridisation occurs, then the offspring will be different from the wild population and may not be as well adapted for survival. The Lion species has two distinct sub-species: the African lion and the Asiatic Lion.

Methods of increasing breeding success

Species kept in captivity do not always breed as successfully as they might in the wild so a range of techniques may be used to increase breeding success.

▲ *Hybrid lions produced by an Asiatic Lion mating with an African Lion.*

▼ **Cryopreservation:** this is the storage of eggs, semen, and embryos by freezing for future use in breeding programmes. They can be transported long distances much more easily than moving the parent animals. This allows the production of offspring without the parents having to meet. They can also be frozen and stored for use in the future, even many years after the donor individual has died.

▼ **Artificial insemination(AI):** this involves the collection of semen from a male and its insertion into a female to produce offspring. Semen can be stored for years so a male could father offspring long after he died. AI avoids many of the problems that occur in breeding programmes that involve natural mating:

- the animals may not live in the same zoo and one would need to be transported. This is expensive and may be dangerous for the animals;
- mating can be dangerous, causing injury or death, especially for large animals such as elephants and rhinos;
- potential partners may not accept each other. In the wild, males and females have space to avoid each other if they wish. Putting potential mates together can be dangerous.

Embryo transfer: some mammal captive breeding populations have very few breeding females. This slows the rate at which offspring can be produced because the duration of pregnancy can be long. However, for some species, there may be a closely related species with a larger number of females in captivity which can be used as surrogate mothers. The main stages in embryo transfer are:

◀ *This female Ocelot killed three males that were introduced into her enclosure*

- The female of an endangered species, for example Bongo antelopes, is treated with hormones so she ovulates and releases a large number of eggs.
- The eggs are washed out of the uterus and fertilised with sperm from a male Bongo.
- Each embryo is implanted into a female of a more common species, for example, Common Eland antelopes. The pregnant Elands give birth to Bongo calves.
- The female Bongo can produce many eggs on each ovulation and could do so during each oestrus cycle (every 3 weeks) rather than producing one calf per year.

❶ *Bongo*
❷ *Common Eland*

Micro-propagation of plants: this is a form of tissue culture where many clusters of cells can be produced from a single plant or tissue sample. Each cell cluster can be cultivated to produce an individual plant. In this way, many plants can be produced from a single parent plant. All the plants that are produced are genetically identical.

Cloning: this has been used with limited success in livestock breeding but not yet with wild animal species. Cloning involves the production of embryos by transferring the nucleus from a stem cell of the endangered species into an empty egg cell of a closely related species. The egg is implanted into a female of the closely-related species, eventually producing a baby animal of the endangered species.

The success rate with wildlife species so far has been very low. It is possible that deep frozen stem cells could be used to produce clones in the future even if the living population has died out.

Experiments are continuing and one day it may be possible to produce young from species that do not currently breed, for example, the Northern White Rhinoceros.

Cloning is important in some plant breeding programmes where cuttings of a mature plant can be cultivated to produce many genetically identical plants. The indigenous subspecies of the Atlantic Black Poplar in the UK is rare. Its future survival is threatened because their flowers can be pollinated by the pollen of other introduced subspecies, producing hybrid plants. To maintain the pure gene pool of the population, cloning is used to produce many young plants that are genetically identical to the non-hybrid parent plants.

❶ *Northern White Rhinoceros*
❷ *A pollarded Atlantic Black Poplar with stems that are ready to be cut and planted.*
❸ *Transplanted stems. Each will become an individual tree.*

Release programmes

The successful release of captive-bred animals into the wild requires careful planning.

Key features of successful release programmes

The number of individuals released must be sufficient to establish a viable population. Suitable release sites must be available which must provide:

▐ large enough suitable habitat;
▐ reliable food supplies;
▐ low predation risk;
▐ suitable breeding sites;
▐ water;
▐ support of the local human population;
▐ official support, for example, legal protection of the habitat and species.

Post-release support and monitoring

The survival chances of individuals bred in captivity can vary widely between species. There are different forms of release:

▐ **hard release:** this involves releasing individuals with no post-release support. It usually involves species where behaviour is controlled by instinct so that the individuals do not need to learn survival skills, for example, insects, fish, amphibians, reptiles;
▐ **soft release**: this involves post-release support such as a gradual release into larger areas and the provision of food as they learn how to find food for themselves. This is often necessary for the release of mammals and birds.

Problems faced by released individuals include:

▐ finding and recognising food;
▐ recognising poisonous foods;
▐ developing hunting skills;
▐ recognising and avoiding predators;
▐ being accepted into the social groups of the wild populations.

Captive-bred predators are often born to parents that were also born in captivity so they do not have good hunting skills to teach to their young. They are unlikely to have had the chance to learn hunting skills in captivity with live prey.

Monitoring the movements and survival of released individuals is useful in monitoring the success of the project and can help in improving future release programmes.

Species that have been bred in captivity and released successfully into the wild: Red Kites with radio tags to monitor post-release movements, European Otter, White-tailed Eagle, Scimitar-horned Oryx, Golden Lion Tamarin

Seed banks

Seed banks were set up to store the seeds of wild plants so that the species would not become globally extinct if they became extinct in the wild. If a species becomes rare in the wild, the seeds stored in the seed bank should maintain the biodiversity of the species.

Species are often selected for storage because they are already threatened in the wild, or because they are of particular importance to humans, such as the wild relatives of commercial crops.

The Millennium Seed Bank, at Wakehurst Place in Sussex, is a major centre for the conservation of plant genetic diversity. Seeds are collected from all over the world and stored under dry or refrigerated conditions. The target number of seeds for each species is 10,000 to try to ensure a diverse gene pool. To reduce the risks of a major accident, the seeds are stored underground in a reinforced vault.

❶ *The Millennium Seedbank in Sussex. (There are many other seed banks in a wide range of countries.*
❷ *Testing the viability of seeds after collection with X-ray photography*
❸ *Dry seed storage*
❹ *Germinating a sample of seeds to test the survival rate during storage*
❺ *The entrance to the Global Seed Vault. This store is underground in solid rock at -18°C on the remote island of Svalbard in the Arctic Circle*

Habitat conservation

In situ conservation is the most important method of conserving wildlife, as the wildlife species are still living where the conditions for survival are appropriate and the entire community of species are present together. Establishing a protected area, or nature reserve, makes it easier to prevent damaging influences within the area itself but it does not protect it from damaging external influences such as air pollution.

There are several general approaches to habitat conservation:

- ▼ land ownership;
- ▼ designated protected areas;
- ▼ habitat creation and management.

Land ownership

Many wildlife conservation organisations purchase areas to protect the species that already live there, or will do so once the conditions have been changed so they are suitable, for example, RSPB, National Trust, Woodland Trust.

Individual landowners may also make management decisions for the benefit of wildlife.

Designated protected areas

Designating a protected area establishes the legal status of the protection. The owners of the habitat that needs protection may not wish to manage their land for the benefit of wildlife in the same way that the statutory authorities do. Establishing a legally designated protected area should ensure that the habitat is protected.

In the UK, there are many different types of designated areas. Very few are state-owned. so they are protected by legal restrictions and management agreements.

Key features of selected designated areas in the UK

Designated area	Key feature
Sites of Special Scientific Interest (SSSIs)	Designated by UK legislation. SSSIs protect areas with the best examples of the UK's flora, fauna, geological, or physiographical features. A management plan is agreed with the owner, who must inform the governmental conservation organisation if they wish to carry out an 'OLD' – an Operation Likely to Damage. These vary between sites but often include: ploughing, use of pesticides or fertilisers, drainage, burning, or tree planting/removal.
National Nature Reserves (NNRs)	Designated by UK legislation. NNRs are the best examples of SSSIs and usually cover the best examples of complete communities of species or habitat types.
Special Areas of Conservation (SACs)	Designated under the EU Habitats Directive. Each member state in the EU must identify the habitats within its country that are of international importance, then protect them. The habitat types vary widely between different countries. Designation may also restrict activities in surrounding areas, such as drainage.
Special Protection Areas (SPAs)	Designated under the EU Birds Directive. Each member state in the EU must identify the places within its country that are of international importance for birds, then protect them. The bird species involved vary widely between different countries.
Ramsar sites	The Ramsar Convention is an intergovernmental agreement that protects wetlands. Most countries in the world are signatories. It was originally intended primarily to protect important waterfowl habitats. The Convention has broadened its scope to cover all aspects of wetland conservation and wise use, recognising wetlands as ecosystems that are extremely important for biodiversity conservation in general and for the well-being of human communities.

Note: In the UK, National Parks were primarily designated to protect the landscape and allow public access but in many other countries they are established to protect wildlife, for example, Nakuru NP, Kenya; Serengeti NP, Tanzania; Great Barrier Reef NP, Australia.

Voluntary agri-environmental schemes

Managing habitats for the benefit of wildlife can be expensive so landowners may join voluntary governmental schemes which provide the financial support needed.

Agri-environmental schemes recognise that much of the British landscape (and its wildlife habitats) was produced by farming and can only be conserved by the continuance of appropriate farming practices. Increasingly intensive farming methods, especially since the 1950s, have caused a lot of damage, often removing the habitats that were most important for wildlife such as hedgerows and hay meadows, or by using harmful pesticides. These changes took place in response to the need for increased food output to provide national food security.

In recent years, the need to conserve the farming landscape, repair damage, and enhance its wildlife value has been more fully appreciated. Many of these projects involve a lot of effort, financial investment, and possibly reduced incomes for farmers. Since the improvements they produce will benefit everyone it seems fair that some of the costs should be paid by society through central funding.

Agri-environmental schemes provide financial support to farmers to reward and encourage environmentally beneficial developments. A range of agri-environmental schemes have been used, such as Environmentally Sensitive Areas (ESA) Countryside Stewardship Scheme (CSS) Environmental Stewardship Scheme (ESS) and Countryside Stewardship (CS).

The aims of most agri-environmental schemes are to:

- ▼ conserve wildlife (biodiversity);
- ▼ maintain and enhance landscape quality and character;
- ▼ protect the historic environment;
- ▼ promote public access and understanding;
- ▼ protect natural resources.

An annual payment may be made for farming with an environmentally beneficial management plan. Points are awarded for individual features of the farm such as:

- ▼ beetle banks - to provide habitats for natural predators and reduce pesticide use;
- ▼ hedgerow, stone wall and ditch management - to maintain landscape features and wildlife habitats;
- ▼ field buffer strips - to protect rivers;
- ▼ wild bird seeds - to provide winter bird food;
- ▼ low input grasslands - to protect wildflowers;
- ▼ protected archaeological sites;
- ▼ management to reduce soil erosion - to maintain production and protect rivers;
- ▼ protection of in-field trees - as a wildlife habitat and landscape feature.

If a target points total is reached then payments are made for five years, then a new application must be made.

Higher payments may be made for organic farms or farms with extra schemes such as:

- ▼ wildflower-rich grass field margins;
- ▼ unharvested conservation field headlands for winter bird food;
- ▼ restoration of wet grassland for waders and wildfowl;
- ▼ water meadow restoration;
- ▼ maintenance or restoration of saltmarsh, sand dunes, hedgerows, moorland, traditional orchards, ponds, woodlands;
- ▼ public access.

Some management methods that gain points under the ESS:

❶ *Infilling gaps in hedgerows*
❷ *Uncultivated field margin*
❸ *Uncultivated strips along a ditch*
❹ *A scrape left for Skylark nesting*

Habitat creation and management

Management and creation of habitats is an increasingly important part of environmental management. Some habitat creation is unplanned and happens as part of other developments.

◀ *Derelict granite quarry*

Unintentional habitat creation

Human activities have always created new habitats that may be unsuitable for the species that used to live there, but are suitable for new wildlife species which may colonise the area.

Habitats that have been created as a consequence of other activities include reservoirs, flooded sand and gravel pits, roadside verges, hedgerows, ornamental gardens.

Intentional habitat creation

In-situ conservation will only be successful if there are suitable habitats for the species that will live there. These may already exist or it may be necessary to alter and manage a habitat that is currently unsuitable. This requires an understanding of the abiotic and biotic habitat features that the species require.

Many species that are not present initially will colonise as conditions become suitable. This is easiest for mobile species such as birds and many insects. If the habitat is isolated from other similar areas, then natural colonisation may be more difficult, so some species may need to be deliberately introduced by humans.

Habitats that have been created deliberately for wildlife conservation include wetlands, new woodlands, wildflower meadows and artificial coral reefs. Lakenheath and Wallasea Island RSPB reserves were both areas of arable farmland before habitat creation for wildlife began.

❶ *Lakenheath RSPB reserve: reedbeds and an aquatic biological corridor*

❷ *Wallasea Island RSPB during construction. The machinery was used to create the reserve topography of banks, lagoons, islands, and ditches*

❸ *Islands for roosting and nesting*

Habitat design

Once an area has been selected, its abiotic and biotic features can be planned to maximise its suitability for the species to be supported.

Habitat area

The habitat area must be large enough to support viable populations. The breeding population must not drop so low that the reproduction rate is too low to maintain the population and the gene pool must not be so small as to cause inbreeding.

How large this area actually is depends upon the species. In general, species that are higher up food chains have lower population densities, so a larger habitat area may be needed to support a viable population. For example, the territory of a single tiger can be upto 100 km^2, so a large area is needed to support a viable population.

An area that is too small to support populations of less abundant species, may eventually become unsuitable for other species if the absent species provided important inter-species services. For example, many rainforest monkeys eat fruit from trees. Different tree species produce fruit at different times of the year, so food will always be available as long as the forest area is large enough to have enough trees of a sufficient range of species to support the monkeys that eat their fruit. A smaller area may lack some essential trees so there would be time periods when there would not be enough food. If these periods are too long, then the monkeys may die out.

Some species benefit from small habitats. Frogs, toads, and newts breed more successfully in ponds that are too small to support the predatory fish that would eat their eggs and tadpoles.

Biological corridors

Linking isolated areas of the same habitat type allows the dispersal of young animals if there is a local breeding surplus and the mixing of different populations and gene pools which reduces the risk of inbreeding. If a species dies out in one area, then re-colonisation from other areas is possible. They can also be used to allow animals to avoid hazards when moving between habitats.

▶ A rope ladder across a road acts as a biological corridor which is used by Black Howler Monkeys which may be killed by predators such as dogs or Jaguar if they crossed at ground level

Habitat shape

The perimeter of a habitat will have a strip where the conditions are a combination of the two neighbouring habitats. Some species benefit from these conditions, for example, higher light levels at the edge of a wood, but they may not be suitable for the species that require the core habitat conditions.

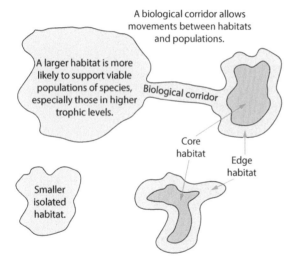

A biological corridor allows movements between habitats and populations.

A larger habitat is more likely to support viable populations of species, especially those in higher trophic levels.

Biological corridor

Core habitat

Edge habitat

Smaller isolated habitat.

▲ How habitat area, shape, and inter-connections affect the wildlife value of a habitat

Habitat diversity

Natural habitats are rarely uniform and usually have local variations in conditions, producing a greater range of possible niches. This increases biodiversity as different species colonise the areas to which each is best adapted.

Light levels

The shading effect of dense tree cover inhibits the growth of plants on the woodland floor. This can be reduced by selectively felling individual trees to create suitable conditions for smaller plants that need more light.

Water depth

Many of the plants and animals that live in aquatic habitats will colonise areas with particular water depths. The dominant plants are those that can absorb most sunlight, often by being taller. Plants with emergent vegetation above water level can only support their weight in shallow water where their roots can get a firm hold in the sediments. As the water depth increases the plant community changes as root anchorage and nutrient absorption from the sediments becomes more difficult. This explains the plant community changes that happen in a hydrosere during ecological succession as the water depth decreases. (see p xx).

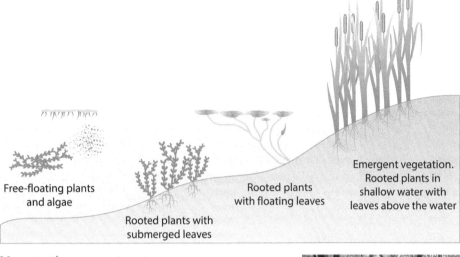

Free-floating plants and algae

Rooted plants with submerged leaves

Rooted plants with floating leaves

Emergent vegetation. Rooted plants in shallow water with leaves above the water

◀ The type of aquatic vegetation present depends upon water depth

Vegetation age structure

Some habitats are dominated by plant species with individuals that can live for a long time, such as woodlands where trees may live for hundreds of years. A natural woodland will have trees of all ages with younger trees growing to fill the clearings created by the death of older trees. In a recently planted woodland there will be few clearings until trees start to die of old age which could take over 200 years. During this time, the canopy will become very dense, light levels on the ground will drop, and biodiversity will decline, reducing the wildlife value of the woodland.

It is not possible to plant an old woodland but it is possible to create similar conditions, by selective felling to create clearings and by leaving dead wood to provide habitats for the species that would exploit old, dying, and dead trees.

◀ This single-age plantation has limited wildlife value. There is little dead wood, no clearings, and the low light levels caused by close planting means there is little undergrowth.

Provision of abiotic habitat features

The survival of a species may rely on suitable abiotic conditions. If these are provided then the biodiversity of a habitat can be increased.

Water

Providing water, such as a pond, will allow birds and mammals to drink, amphibians to breed, and provide a habitat for aquatic plants and animals.

Adult amphibians spend much of their time out of water in damp habitats but they need water for breeding

Dissolved oxygen

The lack of turbulence in slow moving rivers often produces low dissolved oxygen levels as less oxygen dissolves from the air. Making a river narrower will increase flow rates and turbulence which allows more oxygen to dissolve. This creates suitable conditions for fish such as trout and insect species such as mayfly larvae, both of which require high dissolved oxygen levels.

Temperature

Warm temperatures are needed for the development of the eggs of many species. Areas of shallow water warm up rapidly and allow the eggs of fish, newts, and frogs to develop more quickly.

Clearings where vegetation has been removed provide warmer areas of soil or sand where lizards may lay their eggs.

High light levels and low wind velocities in woodland clearings provide warm conditions for growing plants and invertebrates

Light levels

Most plants require specific light levels. Creating clearings provides suitable conditions for the plants that need higher light levels, while retaining a dense tree canopy will provide the shaded conditions needed by other species.

Light is essential for photosynthesis, so energy can be captured and converted to the chemical energy that drives metabolic processes. The pigment chlorophyll mainly absorbs red and blue wavelengths of light while most green light passes through.

Plants that live beneath the canopy vegetation in forests often have difficulty photosynthesising because the chlorophyll in the canopy has absorbed most of the blue and red light. Forest floor plants often have additional pigments such as anthocyanins and carotenoids which can absorb wavelengths of light that have passed through the chlorophyll of the canopy vegetation. These pigments also protect plants that live in bright sunlight from damaging UV light and high light levels.

pH

Many plants cannot survive in acidic soils. This may be because there are few nitrogen-fixing bacteria which make nitrates available for plant growth. Those plants that can survive the acidic conditions may have few competitors, so even small plants can survive without being overshadowed by taller plants, for example, the sundew. Many plants that live in acidic, nitrate-deficient soils capture insects which they digest to gain nitrogen nutrients.

A high or low pH can denature the proteins of the cells of exposed tissues such as lungs, gills, and root hairs. A low pH can also inhibit the production of calcium-based exoskeletons in organisms such as crustaceans.

Mineral nutrients

Some plants can live in nutrient-deficient soils where there is less competition with taller plants for factors such as light. They may not be able to compete in areas with fertile soils so the creation of a suitable habitat for these species may involve the removal of fertile topsoil or not adding fertilisers.

Salinity

Some aquatic species require water of a specific salinity. The Opossum Shrimp is normally found in inter-tidal habitats which are more saline than freshwater but not as saline as seawater. Controlling the salinity of the water can increase opossum shrimp numbers and provide food for bird species such as Dunlin and Pied Avocet.

Control of biotic habitat features

Many plants and all animals can only survive where other species they rely upon are also present. Alternatively, survival may only be possible if certain species are absent.

▲ Pied Avocet

Food

The survival of an animal species may be increased if suitable conditions are provided for its food species, for example, wildflower grasslands that support seed-eating birds.

Birds have different feeding methods to find food and avoid inter-species competition:

❶ *Dunlin eat invertebrates it finds in shallow sediments*
❷ *Honeycreepers eat nectar from flowers*
❸ *Bald Eagles eat meat from mammals and birds they catch*
❹ *Pelicans catch fish by scooping them up with a large volume of water*

Many animals have defence mechanisms against predation such as bad taste, toxins, thorns, camouflage.

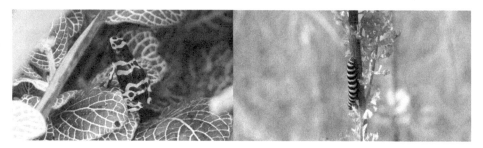

Control of predation

Control of predation will improve the survival of animals, for example, by providing island breeding sites for nesting water birds that cannot be reached by terrestrial predators such as foxes. If predators cannot be excluded, they may be trapped and removed or culled.

Introduced mammal predators are often a problem on islands which have no indigenous mammal predators, where colonies of ground-nesting birds became established. Eradication programmes have been carried out on many islands. For example, the eradication of rats in the Scilly Isles where 3000 rats were killed (see the images below). Some of the islands are now free of rats and the breeding success of birds such as the Manx Shearwater and Storm Petrel have increased significantly.

Eradication of rats on St Agnes and Gugh, Scilly Isles (2013).
Images show poisoned bait and a baited tube placed on a path used by rats.

Control of competitors

The survival of a species may be increased if competitor species are controlled. For example, removing invasive rhododendron bushes allows wildflowers to grow because they are not outcompeted for light.

Pollination

Many flowering plants need insects to pollinate their flowers so they can produce seeds. They attract pollinators such as bees, hover flies, wasps and butterflies using attractive flowers that produce sugar-rich nectar. It may be necessary to have a range of other flowering plant species present with different flowering times so that the insects have food available all through the seasons that they are active.

Seed dispersal

Some animal species are important to plants for the dispersal of their seeds, such as hippopotamus, forest elephants, seed-eating birds, many species of monkeys.

▲ *Manx Shearwaters*

Control of pathogens

Disease is a density-dependent factor which can maintain the health of the surviving population by removing the weakest individuals. However, introduced diseases can wipe out indigenous species that have no resistance to them.

Species re-introductions

Some habitats have been changed by human activities but still retain many of their original features. It may be possible to restore the habitat by re-creating more natural conditions. Many species will colonise these habitats naturally, especially the more mobile species such as flying insects and birds. Other species that are less mobile may fail to colonise and may have to be re-introduced. It is particularly important to re-introduce any absent keystone species.

- **Re-wilding in the Yellowstone National Park, USA**: the Gray Wolf was the top predator in the Yellowstone National Park in the Rocky Mountains, USA, but they were exterminated by 1926. This caused changes in the populations of other species. Wolves have been reintroduced since 1995. This has caused big ecological changes:
    - deer populations have declined, so fewer young trees are killed;
    - having more trees has allowed beaver populations to increase;
    - the dams that beavers create have increased the area of wetland habitats;
    - wetland species have become more common: birds, fish, invertebrates etc.

  Overall, biodiversity has increased. However, the wolves have caused some problems for nearby livestock farmers.
- **Re-wilding in Scotland**: most of Scotland used to be covered in a mixed forest including pine, oak, birch, and rowan trees. These were largely cleared for fuel and replaced with moorland grazed by sheep and deer.

  The removal of the grazing animals and reafforestation will allow the recovery of populations of species such as the Capercaillie. European Beavers have been reintroduced and there are proposals to reintroduce Eurasian Lynx and Grey Wolves, although these are very controversial.

Other species that have been successfully reintroduced to some areas in the UK include the Red Kite, White-tailed Eagle, Eurasian Otter, Common Crane, Great Bustard, and the Large Blue Butterfly.

A habitat may develop a much higher biodiversity if a variety of species is introduced, such as planting mixed-species woodlands rather than a plantation of a single tree species. The abiotic factors which affect survival may be altered by the other species living in the same habitat, for example, in a forest:

- tall foliage may cause reduced light levels due to shading;
- transpiration increases the humidity;
- vegetation acts as a windbreak and reduces wind velocity;
- decomposition of dead vegetation increases nutrient availability.

Control of ecological succession – plagioclimax maintenance

Successful conservation of wildlife habitats does not just involve establishing a suitable habitat area then protecting it from damaging external influences. The natural changes that take place during ecological succession may reduce its value for the species that are present during any individual stage of succession. (For more details of ecological succession, See page 73.)

In the UK, there are very few habitats that are completely natural because most areas have been changed by human activities. Sometimes the activities that have produced a semi-natural habitat have continued for such a long time that the habitat produced has become so familiar that it may be thought to be natural. A wide variety of wildlife species may have colonised the habitat creating a semi-natural habitat of great conservation value.

In many areas, the activities that disturbed the climax community are carried out regularly so a new community of species develops. This is called a plagioclimax community. Many plagioclimax communities are important for humans, for example, grazed farmland, heathland, and coppiced woodland. They are maintained as plagioclimaxes for human use but they are also colonised by wildlife species, for example, the wildflowers that live in hay meadows.

❶ *Machair grassland*

❷ *Grazing marsh in The Broads - traditional and modern methods of cutting reedbeds*

The traditional human activities that produced plagioclimaxes may change, which could move the conditions outside the range of tolerance of the wildlife species living there.

Conservation programmes that aim to protect species living in plagioclimax communities often involve continuing the activities that traditionally maintained the plagioclimax. This often involves a particular style of farming, for example:

⚐ hay meadows on Machair grassland on the Outer Hebrides in Scotland;

⚐ maintaining grazing marshes in The Broads National Park.

Activities that continue in maintained plagioclimax environments

⚐ **Grazing**: this prevents the establishment of taller plants and maintains a grassland plagioclimax. Conservation grazing is often used to maintain habitats such as chalk grassland and flower-rich meadows.

Trampling by livestock produces bare ground which is important for the germination of wildflower seeds and to produce the warmer clearings needed by some invertebrates and reptiles. Animal dung produces small areas with higher nutrient levels which may support different plant species and many invertebrates. Different grazing species are used for the maintenance of different plagioclimax habitats:

- sheep eat shorter grasses. Some breeds eat bushes and can be used to control invasive scrub;
- ponies selectively eat grass and usually avoid flowering plants but they will eat invasive bracken which is avoided by most grazing animals;
- cattle are good for removing long, rough grass.

⚐ **Mowing**: this removes the same vegetation that would be removed by grazing herbivores but it also removes the thorny, stinging, or bad-tasting plants that herbivores may have avoided.

▶ **Burning**: this can be used to remove vegetation that would not be eaten by grazing animals, for example, mature heather bushes and young trees on heathland. It creates the open, unshaded areas needed for the growth of young heather plants that will re-establish the heathland. Heather seeds lie dormant in the soil until they are stimulated to germinate by the heat of the fire.

▶ **Coppicing: t**rees are cut to ground level every 3 – 30 years depending on the intended use of the harvested branches. In many areas that were traditionally coppiced, about 0.5 ha was cleared each year with a rotational cycle of 8 years. So, a coppiced woodland would be a patchwork of areas of woodland of different ages, each being suitable for its own community of wildlife species.

▶ **Pollarding**: this is similar to coppicing but with branches cut above the height at which deer or livestock could eat the re-growing branches.

◀ *Heather re-sprouting after burning*

Population control

It may be necessary to actively control the populations of selected species either by increasing or reducing them, depending on which species are desirable. The release of captive-bred individuals will boost the wild population and help to support the population if the population size is low, the breeding rate is low, or the mortality rate is high.

The population of undesirable species may be controlled to reduce predation or competition. The animals may be culled, or trapped and removed.

Restoration and maintenance of a valuable wildlife habitat often involves the removal of unwanted species. Some undesirable species may be a part of a natural ecological succession. Others may be invasive introduced species.

Conifer plantations are removed from the New Forest to re-establish heathland for Sand Lizards and Smooth Snakes

❶ *Sand Lizard*
❷ *Rhododendrons have been removed to prevent shading of indigenous plants*
❸ *Many deer species, such as Muntjac Deer, are culled to reduce the habitat damage they cause*

Selected habitats

All threatened habitats have their own unique features, importance, and threats. The following habitats have been selected to illustrate important ecological principles or aspects of conservation.

Temperate broadleaf woodland

Most temperate broadleaf woodland is found in the northern hemisphere, in Europe, eastern North America, and East Asia. Most trees in temperate broadleaf woodlands are deciduous trees that lose all their leaves each year.

A wide range of tree species live in temperate broadleaf woodlands. The dominant tree species depend upon the soil conditions, for example, the dominant tree species in British broadleaf woodlands are:

- beech – on moist soils, for example, clay;
- ash – on alkaline soils, for example, limestone;
- oak – wide range of tolerance.

Ecological features

- Temperate broadleaf woodlands do not have major temperature extremes.
- There is no pronounced dry season – water is available all year.
- The soils are usually deep and fertile. The trees play an important part in the soil formation with dead organic matter and its retention by vegetation cover and root binding.
- The tree canopy layer is present from spring until autumn, so the growth of plants under the canopy is more difficult because they are shaded during the time when the temperatures are best for growth. Many woodland floor plants overcome this by growing early in spring before the trees have produced leaves, for example, British Bluebells, snowdrops, Lesser Celandine.
- The lack of available food during the winter causes many animals to become less active, store food, hibernate, or migrate.

Importance of broadleaf woodland

High biodiversity

Having a high biodiversity creates a higher ecological stability. No species are completely dominant so a change in the population of one species will have a relatively small impact on the overall community of species.

Woodland resources

Temperate broadleaf woodland was historically important for a wide range of resources. Wood was used for:

- building construction – timber frames, wattle and daub panels;
- fencing;
- tools;
- carts;
- wood fuel;
- charcoal for metal smelting.

The woodlands also provided a food resource from the animals and plants found there, for example, deer, wild boar, fruit, nuts, herbs.

Forest resources are no longer widely exploited in the UK except timber from commercial plantations.

Recreation

Many woodlands are important for public recreation: walking, camping, cycling, picnics etc.

The hydrological cycle

All trees play a role in the hydrological cycle through interception, evapotranspiration, and the control of water in the soil.

Carbon sequestration

All plants absorb carbon dioxide during photosynthesis but most release it again during respiration and the decay of their vegetation. Plants with woody tissue can build up a store of carbon in the cellulose and lignin that forms wood, so woodlands are large reservoirs of stored carbon which reduces atmospheric carbon dioxide concentrations.

Threats

- **Woodland clearance:** as societies have developed and populations have grown, natural woodland habitats have been cleared to provide space for new land uses:
  - farmland;
  - plantations of single species or non-indigenous species;
  - urban developments;
  - transportation infrastructure, for example, new roads;
  - mineral extraction.
- **Habitat fragmentation:** woodland clearance may leave remaining areas that are isolated from each other. If animals cannot move between these areas, then each separate population becomes more vulnerable to extinction.

Conservation efforts

Different woodland management techniques create woodlands of different wildlife value.

Woodland management

- **Historical methods**
  - 'Wildwood': areas with virtually no interference, for example, hunting forests.
  - Mature 'standard' trees: for example, oak for timber-framed houses, furniture, and ships.
  - Coppiced woodland: for example, hazel for fencing, wall panels, oak for charcoal, pit props and tannins for leather tanning.
  - Pollarding: similar to coppicing but cutting was carried out at a greater height to reduce the problem of animals eating the re-growing branches.

These methods often created woodlands with high habitat diversity, high biodiversity and high wildlife value.

- **Modern methods**
  - Monoculture plantations of single-age trees which have low wildlife value.
  - New woodland areas around field margins.
  - Community forests planted for recreational and amenity use.
- **Conservation management**
  - Coppicing to create wildlife habitats.
  - Creation of woodland clearings to increase habitat diversity.
  - Planting of mixed-species woodlands to increase biodiversity.

▲ *Ancient woodland indicator species: Common Bluebells and ferns*

Legal protection of ancient woodlands

An 'ancient woodland' in the UK is defined as one that existed before 1600. Few woodlands were deliberately planted before 1600 so a wood that is over 400 years old is likely to have developed naturally a long time ago.

An ancient woodland usually has a very high biodiversity because there has been a long time-period for species to colonise. Some species of wild plant colonise woodlands very slowly, so the presence of many such species is evidence that the woodland is ancient.

Designated protected areas

▼ Sherwood Forest National Nature Reserve.

▼ Epping Forest SAC.

▼ There are many woodland SSSIs.

▼ Many UK National Parks have areas of deciduous woodland.

The 2012 National Planning Policy Framework states that '…planning permission should be refused for development resulting in the loss or deterioration of irreplaceable habitats, including ancient woodland and the loss of aged or veteran trees found outside ancient woodland, unless the need for, and benefits of, the development in that location clearly outweigh the loss'.

Although ancient woodlands may be generally protected, overgrazing by deer or deliberate clearance of ground vegetation may prevent regeneration by young trees so the woodland may gradually become degraded and lose some of its wildlife value.

Planting of new woodlands

Large areas of new woodland have been planted in the UK over the past 30 years, usually on small areas of farmland. These have often included a mix of indigenous tree species that are likely to have an increasing wildlife value as the woodlands mature. They are especially valuable if they join existing areas of woodland, or habitats such as hedgerows, which can act as biological corridors linking small fragmented areas of woodland.

Tropical rainforest

Tropical rainforests are the most biodiverse terrestrial ecosystems. They have not been fully researched but the relative ease with which new species can be discovered suggests that over half of all terrestrial species live in tropical rainforests, although the rainforests only cover about ten per cent of the Earth's land area.

Ecological features

The tropical climate has been relatively stable over long time periods, compared with regions further away from the equator. This has given rainforest species a long time to evolve and become adapted to local abiotic and biotic factors. This has produced a huge number of different species, although many are relatively rare and may have small ranges. Being adapted to relatively stable conditions can make species vulnerable to extinction as a small change in environmental conditions may move them outside their range of tolerance.

High light levels allow photosynthesis rates to be high, providing a lot of food energy to support a rich food web.

Constant warm temperatures and regular high rainfall allow plants to grow throughout the year without the seasonal changes that occur in higher latitudes. This ensures reliable food supplies are available to animals throughout the year. Populations rarely have the seasonal fluctuations found in higher latitudes and there is no need to hibernate or migrate to more favourable areas. Migratory species found in tropical rainforests have normally come from other areas that have fluctuating conditions and have migrated to the rainforests because they are so stable.

Because the abiotic conditions have been relatively stable for a long time and do not fluctuate seasonally, there is probably little need for most species to evolve further and become better adapted to abiotic factors. The main survival pressure is produced by biotic factors: getting food, avoiding being eaten, and evolving better inter-species relationships.

Although there are high light levels, there is also a lot of competition for light. Plants that have evolved to grow a tall trunk will have better access to light but must invest a lot of energy over a long time to produce the wood that forms the trunk. Smaller plants may need to evolve methods of utilising lower light levels, such as denser chlorophyll or additional pigments to absorb wavelengths of light that pass through the leaves of taller plants. Plants that are epiphytes and live on higher branches of trees have greater access to light without being tall but may have less reliable water and nutrient supplies.

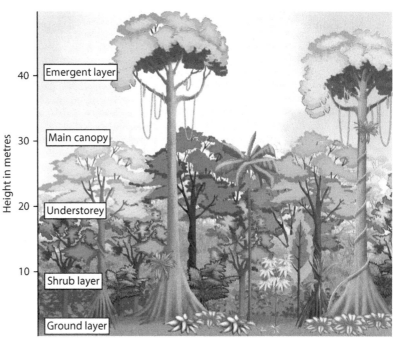

▲ *Stratification in tropical rainforest*

With no distinct seasons, different plant species do not have to flower or produce seeds and fruit at the same times as each other. So plants have less competition for the services of animals to pollinate flowers or spread seeds. Food in the form of nectar, seeds, or fruit is available to animals throughout the year, which increases animal survival.

Most trees are deciduous and shed their leaves every year but different species do so at different times of year. So animals that feed on vegetation do not have long periods when there is no food, as is the case in temperate broadleaf woodlands.

Very high biodiversity

High biodiversity on its own does not make an area important but it does increase the chances of finding species that are useful to humans, for example, new food species, medical discoveries, biomimetic applications.

Because there are no cold winters to kill off herbivores, plants need to protect themselves from being eaten. This is often done by producing toxic chemicals such as alkaloids that may have medicinal value for humans. Animals also produce medicinally valuable chemicals to avoid predation, especially those that cannot protect themselves with teeth or claws, or those that use venom to catch prey. So, taxa such as frogs and reptiles are much more likely to produce medicinally useful chemicals than mammals or birds.

Forest resources

Rainforests are important to the people that live in or near the forests. As long-distance transport became easier, forest resources also became important in other areas such as Europe.

Resources gained from forests

Resource	Uses
Timber	House construction, furniture, tools
Fibres	Cotton Hemp – rope Raffia – rope, baskets Wood cellulose -rayon
Resins, oils, and waxes	Rubber – latex gloves, vehicle tyres Carnuba wax – floor and car polish, confectionary coating Palm oil – processed foods, cooking oil, biofuels
Food	Chocolate from cacao, Pineapples, lemons, Brazil nuts, vanilla, coffee, bananas, oranges, Spices – pepper, turmeric, cinnamon Bushmeat New food species Genetic resources for crop breeding
Medicines	Cinchona trees produce quinine which is used to prevent malaria Mexican wild yams produce diosgenin, used to make medicines such as cortisone to treat arthritis and asthma Curare lianas produce d-turbocuarine, used to treat multiple sclerosis and Parkinson's disease and used in anaesthesia Venom of the Fer-de-Lance snake, used to develop the medicine Captopril that reduces blood pressure

Climate maintenance

▶ *A house in Central America made with timber from the local rainforest*

Tropical rainforests are very important for increasing downwind rainfall. Over half the rainfall in the Amazon rainforest results from transpiration elsewhere in the forest rather than coming directly from the evaporation of seawater.

As with temperate broadleaf woodland and all trees, carbon sequestration by photosynthesis stores large amounts of carbon in tropical rainforests which helps to reduce the natural greenhouse effect.

Soil maintenance

The warm, moist conditions make dead vegetation decay very rapidly so nutrients can be re-absorbed by trees very quickly. Because of this, soils in tropical rainforests are often very shallow. The vegetation cover and tree roots are important in preventing the soil that is present from being eroded, as the foliage protects the soil from heavy rain and the roots hold the soil together. Forest clearance can lead to serious soil erosion.

Threats

A wide range of human activities threaten tropical rainforests. Some take place in the forest area itself but some threats originate elsewhere such as atmospheric pollution.

Fuelwood collection

Wood is the most important domestic fuel in rural areas of LEDCs. The rate of wood collection is usually faster than the rate of re-planting and natural re-growth.

Timber harvesting

Timber from tropical rainforests is harvested for use in two main ways:

- ▼ use in the country of origin for house construction and furniture;
- ▼ export to MEDCs for use in products such as furniture, doors, windows, decking, and plywood.

Clearance for alternative land uses

Large areas of rainforest are cleared for other uses, mainly agriculture.

- ▼ **Subsistence agriculture:** 'slash and burn' or 'shifting field' agriculture has been carried out in rainforests for hundreds of years and generally caused few environmental problems. Small clearings were made by felling trees to create an area that could be farmed by a family. These would be farmed for a few years then abandoned as soil nutrients were depleted and forest regrowth reclaimed the clearing. The family would make a new clearing elsewhere. This type of agriculture is sustainable as long as there is enough time for the forest to recolonise the cleared area and for the soil fertility to recover before it is cleared again. If the human population density is too high, then the time gap between an area being abandoned and cleared again will be too short. The forest would not have recolonised fully and the soil would not have regained its fertility. The family could not farm the area for as long as previously. If this continues then the forest will be degraded and soil fertility will decline.
- ▼ **Commercial agriculture**: as human populations grow, the demand for farmland increases and habitats such as rainforests may be cleared. Rainforest clearance for cash crops and cattle ranching is often unsustainable, as the poor tropical soils may become infertile and fail to provide high yields indefinitely. If the land is abandoned, it may be difficult for the forest to re-colonise if there are no surviving forest areas nearby from

which species could recolonise. Large areas of rainforest have been cleared for commercial cultivation of cash crops, mainly for export, for example, palm oil plantations in South East Asia, soya bean production in Brazil, and coffee plantations in Vietnam.

▸ **Mineral extraction:** there are many valuable deposits of metal minerals present under tropical rainforests, including aluminium, iron, gold, silver, and copper. Extraction results in habitat loss and can cause water pollution when the mineral is processed, such as discharges of turbid drainage water, cyanide, and mercury.

▸ **Reservoirs:** new hydroelectric power schemes can flood large areas of forest and create a barrier to mobile species such as migratory fish and river dolphins. The reservoir of the Tucurui HEP scheme in Brazil covers an area of 2850 km². The decomposition of dead organic matter in deep, static, reservoir water can produce acidic, deoxygenated water that may be harmful to aquatic life downstream. The flow of water out of the reservoir may be controlled to generate electricity to match demand but fluctuating river levels downstream can affect wildlife See p204, Hydro Electric Power.

▸ **Climate change**: the temperature rise caused by climate change may directly affect the survival of some species. Temperature change will also affect wind and precipitation patterns. Droughts in tropical rainforests caused by climate change will increase the number of forest fires and the area the fires cover. Fires are also likely to last longer, causing more severe damage. A short fire may just burn off dead vegetation and leaf litter, but a long fire may boil tree sap and kill the trees.

The populations of many frogs and toads in cloud rainforest are declining, in countries such as Costa Rica. Rising temperatures are reducing condensation and clouds are forming higher up the mountains. This reduces the area of habitat that is sufficiently humid for them to survive.

Epiphytic plants such as orchids and air plants absorb water from the bark surface of the trees they live on. Their populations decline if the air is less humid.

Some computer climate models predict that some rainforest areas will be replaced by savannah grassland.

▸ **Tourism:** as with any developments, an expansion of tourism facilities can threaten habitats and wildlife. Ecotourism is an increasingly important way of generating income without having to destroy the forest. However, in some countries the large numbers of visitors can cause damage as has been found in Costa Rica and Malaysia.

Conservation efforts

Many protected areas have been established to conserve tropical rainforest.

▸ **Cameroon**: the Korup National Park in Cameroon, Africa, was set up in 1986 and protects 1,260 km² of tropical rainforest. It is one of the least disturbed rainforests in Africa and retains very high biodiversity, including many species that are of importance to humans. There are over 600 tree species, 1000 butterfly species, and 160 mammal species, many of which are endemic. The plant *Ancistrocladus korupensis* was discovered in the Korup and has been found nowhere else. It produces alkaloid chemicals that are of medicinal value, including Michellamine B, which is being researched as a treatment for HIV, and Korupensamine E, a new antimalarial drug.

- **Brazil**: in 2014 the new Alto Maues reserve was established to protect 6,680 km² of rainforest. It is home to over 600 species of birds and at least 13 species of primates.

  In 2002, the Tumucumaque National Park was established to protect 39,000 km² of rainforest: nearly twice the area of Wales. This makes it the largest rainforest reserve in the world. It is next to a rainforest reserve in French Guiana, giving a total protected area of 59,000 km².

- **Belize**: the Rio Bravo Conservation and Management Area in Belize, Central America, covers 100,000 hectares of rainforest and associated habitats. First established in 1988, it has been funded by conservation charities in the USA and Europe, with donations from companies such as Coca Cola and electricity companies in the USA and Canada. Money is also raised through ecotourism projects.

  Sustainable exploitation of high value timber from trees such as the mahogany also helps to pay for forest conservation. This is done by selective logging which does not cause long-term damage to the forest See p386 The RBCMA (rainforest reserve).

Debt for nature swaps

Many countries that have threatened rainforests are in debt to other countries, with little realistic chance of being able to pay it all back. The country that lent the money may be prepared to cancel the debt in return for a partial repayment or a guarantee that an area of the rainforest will be protected.

The USA has cancelled debts of $24m owed by Guatemala and $21m owed by Brazil. Sometimes an intermediary organisation such as a conservation charity may negotiate to pay off part of a debt in return for the balance of the debt being cancelled. The country that has had its debt cancelled agrees to conserve a wildlife habitat. The WWF has organized debt for nature swaps in this way to protect rainforests in Costa Rica and the Philippines.

Tropical coral reefs

A combination of specific conditions and species' adaptations have produced the most biodiverse marine biome.

Ecological features

The water in tropical seas is often deficient in nutrients so biological productivity may be low. However, the animals that form coral reefs have inter-species relationships that use nutrients very efficiently and allow a high biomass of life to thrive. Corals belong to the phylum cnidaria which is made up of over 10,000 species including the jellyfish.

▼ *Coral polyp nutrition*

Coral nutrition

Coral nutrition comes from:

- **Cilia:** these are finger-like projections on the coral polyp tentacles which trap planktonic items floating past the polyp which are then passed down to the stomach where they are digested.

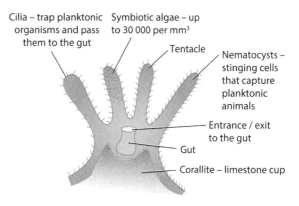

Cilia – trap planktonic organisms and pass them to the gut

Symbiotic algae – up to 30 000 per mm³

Tentacle

Nematocysts – stinging cells that capture planktonic animals

Entrance / exit to the gut

Gut

Corallite – limestone cup

- ▶ **Nematocysts:** these are stinging cells that harpoon planktonic organisms floating past the polyp. These are then carried by the cilia to the stomach.
- ▶ **Symbiotic algae:** zooxanthellae are photosynthetic algae that live inside coral polyp cells. They absorb sunlight and provide food energy for themselves and the coral polyps. The polyps and algae have an efficient method of recycling nutrients. Carbon dioxide and excretory waste products produced by the polyp are absorbed directly by the algae for photosynthesis and growth. The algae produce oxygen and glucose which the coral polyps need. Coral polyps gain over ninety-five per cent of their food energy from this symbiotic relationship. In return, the algae have a protected habitat and a supply of the nutrients they need.

  Much of the carbon dioxide produced by the respiration of the polyps is used by the algae for photosynthesis. Surplus carbon dioxide is incorporated into calcium carbonate that forms coral. Other wastes from the polyps provide the nutrients needed by the algae which they may not have been able to absorb from the nutrient-deficient seawater.

Reef building corals

Many species of corals secrete a limestone base which is continually added to, building up into a reef. Other cnidarians such as sea fans and soft corals do not produce a hard skeleton so they do not add to the reef.

❶ *Brain coral*
❷ *Stag horn coral*
❸ *Coral reefs support very biodiverse communities of other species*

The physical structure of the reefs also provides many places for animals to live, as well as being a rich source of food that supports a complex food web.

Abiotic conditions

Tropical coral reefs are only found where there are very specific abiotic conditions, which makes them vulnerable to environmental change.

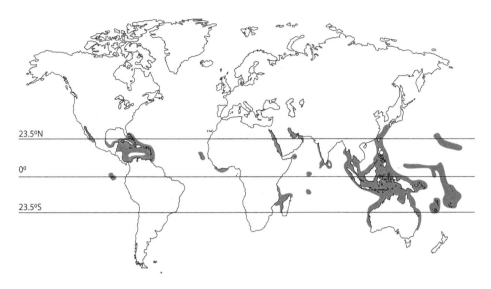

◀ *The global distribution of tropical warm water coral reefs*

Conditions critical to coral survival

Critical conditions	Impact on Coral reefs
Light	The symbiotic algae within the coral polyps require bright sunlight. In the tropics, there is bright sunlight in shallow water for about 12 hours almost every day.
Temperature	The temperature must be warm and constant, in the range 25-29°C.
Immersion	Polyps must be covered in water almost all the time to prevent them drying out. They cannot live in deep water because not enough light would reach them for algal photosynthesis. Many coral reefs are found where the tidal range is small so they can live near the water surface without being uncovered at low tide.
Turbidity	The seawater must have very low turbidity. Turbid water reduces light penetration so photosynthesis would be reduced. Suspended solids carried by the water could also settle on the reef, sticking to the cilia and blocking the entrance to the stomach. The survival of coral reefs often relies on mangrove forests and seagrass beds that trap the eroded soil washed off the land and prevent it settling on the reefs.
Salinity	Coral polyps do not have the ability to regulate water concentrations within their cells. If the salinity of the water changed outside the narrow range of tolerance of the corals, the cells would be killed by osmosis with water flowing into or out of the cells.

Importance of tropical coral reefs

Although coral reefs only cover about 1 per cent of the area of the oceans they are ecologically very important, supporting over a quarter of all marine species. They provide valuable resources and help to resist damaging environmental changes.

▸ **Fisheries**: coral reefs support many species that are exploited for food, including fish, crustaceans such as lobsters and molluscs such as conch.

▸ **Medicinal discoveries**: many species that live on coral reefs do not have spines, teeth or a hard shell to protect themselves. Instead, they may produce toxic chemicals which may be useful as medicines when used in carefully controlled amounts.

Medical discoveries sourced from Coral reefs

Source	Medicinal use
Chemicals in sponges from a coral reef in the Caribbean Sea	Antiviral drug AZT: used to treat HIV/AIDS. Ara-C is used to treat leukaemia.
Chemicals in a sea hare (mollusc) on coral reefs in the Indian Ocean	Dolastatin 10: inhibits cell division; has been tested as a treatment for cancer and malaria.
Secosteroids - enzymes used by corals to protect themselves from disease	Secosteroids: used to treat asthma, arthritis and other inflammatory disorders.
Bugula neritina (a Bryozoan colonial marine animal)	Compound bryostatin 1: used to treat a range of cancers including cancers of the lung and prostate gland. It is used in combination with other medicines such as vincristine (extracted from the tropical plant: the Rosy Periwinkle). Bryostatin 1 also improves memory and is being researched as a treatment for Alzheimer's disease.
Species of sea squirt	Trabectedin is used to treat the cancer soft-tissue sarcoma. It was discovered in a sea squirt but is now manufactured from a similar chemical produced by a bacterium.
Coral	Used to make bone grafts for patients with diseases that cause bone deterioration.

- **Climate control**: reef-forming corals deposit a skeleton of coral with each polyp sitting in a coral cup. Coral is made mainly of the mineral calcite, which is made of calcium carbonate, with some magnesium carbonate. Each carbonate molecule requires the absorption of a molecule of carbon dioxide, so growing coral reefs are an important carbon sink, helping to resist climate change.
- **Erosion protection**: Many tropical islands are formed by fragments of coral, producing low-lying sand islands. Coral reefs absorb the energy of waves that would otherwise have eroded or washed away these islands. The irregular shapes and complex structure of the coral dissipate the energy of the waves effectively. Fragments of the coral form sand which helps to build up shores.
- **Tourism**: coastal areas and islands with coral reefs are popular tourist destinations for ecotourism activities such as scuba diving and snorkeling, as well as simple relaxation in pleasant surroundings.

Threats

- **Physical damage:** hard objects can kill polyps as they are pushed against the hard limestone beneath the living cells. Litter such as floating bottles, lost fishing gear, boat anchors, and careless divers can all damage reefs. Damage is also caused by extraction of coral for land reclamation and construction.
- **Collection of ornaments and souvenirs**: many species from coral reefs are collected to be sold as ornaments such as mollusc shells, hard corals, and sea fans. Trade in about 2000 species of coral is restricted by CITES Appendix II.

❶ *Sea fan ornament*
❷ *Shark necklace*

▌ **Sedimentation:** turbid water carried by rivers or sediments disturbed by coastal developments can cover and kill corals.

▌ **Pollution:** a wide range of pollutants can harm coral reefs. Large oil spills can cover coral reefs. Even at lower concentrations oil is toxic to corals. Nutrients such as nitrates and phosphates from agricultural runoff and sewage effluents can stimulate the growth of algae that cover corals. The shading caused by the algae reduces the growth of the symbiotic algae within the polyps and prevents the release of eggs when the corals reproduce.

Ocean acidification is caused by increased carbon dioxide concentrations in the atmosphere. More carbon dioxide dissolves in the oceans producing carbonic acid which makes the oceans more acidic, it is therefore difficult for the coral polyps to produce their coral skeleton.

▌ **Coral bleaching:** this occurs when the symbiotic algae within the coral polyps are expelled. Bleached corals look pale, hence the term 'bleaching'. This can be caused by a variety of natural and anthropogenic factors. One natural factor is the raised light levels caused by increased solar activity, but many human activities can cause bleaching including:

- increased water temperatures caused by global climate change;
- low oxygen levels due to high zooplankton activity caused by overfishing of their fish predators;
- pollution, including sewage, pesticides, cyanide and sunscreen products;
- bleached coral polyps, which are not dead and may regain algae in the future grow very slowly and are less able to recover from damage.

▼ *Red Lionfish*

▌ **Fishing:** this is not always damaging but if the catch rate is excessive then over-fishing can reduce fish populations and affect other inter-dependent species. The Crown of Thorns Starfish is a predator of coral polyps in the Indian and Pacific oceans. They are eaten by Giant Triton molluscs. Overfishing of the Giant Triton on Australian coral reefs allowed Crown of Thorns Starfish populations to rise, leading to the destruction of large areas of coral reef by the starfish. See page 341, The environmental impacts of fishing

▲ *Seagrass bed*

▼ **Introduced species**: non-indigenous species have been introduced in several ways:
- from ballast water discharged from ships;
- escaped fish and crustaceans from fish farms;
- accidental and intentional releases from aquaria.

The Red Lionfish was accidentally introduced to the Caribbean in the 1990s. They are indigenous to the Indian and Pacific Oceans but have few predators in the Caribbean Sea so they have spread rapidly. They are general predators and have reduced the populations of many indigenous fish species.

▼ **Coastal developments:** the expansion of coastal towns, the construction of tourist resorts, ports and marinas can destroy coral reefs directly and increase turbidity causing damage to reefs near the developments.

▼ **Loss of associated habitats:** mangroves and seagrass beds help to trap suspended sediments and reduce water turbidity. They also provide nursery grounds for many of the fish species that live as adults on coral reefs. If the mangroves and seagrass beds are damaged, then the coral reefs nearby become damaged too.

Conservation efforts

▼ **Marine protected areas**: many countries are trying to protect their coral reefs by designating Marine Protected Areas or National Parks, for example, the Great Barrier Reef National Park in Australia, Barrier Reef Marine Protected Area, Belize, and the Chagos Archipelago. A range of management practices can be used to protect the reefs.
- Fixed mooring buoys can be installed so boats do not need to use their anchors.
- Divers, snorkelers, and swimmers can be taught not to touch the coral or kick up sediments onto the coral.
- Fishing may be controlled or banned with the establishment of No-Take Zones. These may actually increase long-term catches as the protected breeding populations may produce more offspring that can move out and colonise other areas.
- Sustainable development of ecotourism and fishing can ensure the local economy is protected.
- Environmental protection in other areas can benefit coral reefs, such as protecting mangroves and seagrass beds, controlling soil erosion, controlling pollution, and controlling developments such as ports and tourist resorts.

▼ **Control of fishing:** fishing for some species that have been over-exploited may be banned so their populations can recover. Control methods include:
- the length of the fishing seasons being restricted;
- placing a minimum catchable size to prevent the capture of small fish, so they have a chance to grow larger and breed
- imposing a maximum catchable size to protect large individuals that are likely to produce many young;
- restrictions placed on damaging fishing methods such as dynamite fishing, trawling, or fishing with nets with a small mesh;
- No Take Zones (NTZ) may be established where fishing is banned. This allow a larger population of breeding adults to develop. The surplus young that are produced will spread out and colonise areas where fishing is permitted, increasing overall catches. Large NTZs, Chagos Archipelago, Indian Ocean; Great Barrier Reef, Australia. Small NTZs, Lundy Island, UK; Lamlash Bay, Isle of Arran, UK

- **Control of tourism:** recreational activities may be restricted to minimize the damage that may be caused. For example:
  - turtle nesting beaches may be protected to reduce disturbance;
  - spear fishing may be banned;
  - permanent mooring buoys may be installed so visiting boats do not need to use anchors;
  - the collection of souvenirs may be banned, for example, corals, mollusc shells.

- **Sustainable exploitation:** exploitation may be permitted but it may be restricted to ensure it is sustainable, for example, in Belize the removal of soft coral sea fans is regulated by CITES Appendix II.

- **Reef creation:** artificial reefs have been created from concrete structures such as 'reef balls' or by sinking structures that were made for other purposes such as old ships and oil rigs. In the Gulf of Mexico, several old warships and over 400 old oil rigs have been used to create artificial reefs.

▲ *A Jack up oil rig*

Deep water coral reefs

These are coral reefs that are found in water where sunlight does not reach them. They are also called cold water coral reefs. Neither name is perfect as some are found in shallow water while others are found where the water is relatively warm. The common feature is the lack of sunlight to support photosynthetic algae within the coral polyps.

Ecological features

The coral polyps that form deep water coral reefs do not have the symbiotic photosynthetic algae that are found in tropical coral reefs so they have much less food energy available and grow much more slowly than shallow-water tropical coral reefs.

The slow rate of deep water coral growth means that reefs recover much more slowly from damage than tropical coral reefs in shallow water.

▲ *Deep water coral reef in the Bering Deep, near Alaska Source: NOAA*

Importance of deep water coral reefs

Deep water coral reefs have only been discovered since the 1970s, with many being found since 2010, so there has been little time for research into their importance, their ecological roles, or the resources they may contain. Deep water coral reefs often support a large biomass of fish but these are often slow-growing species with a low reproductive rate so it is easy to over-exploit the populations. The Roundnose Grenadier, Blue Whiting, and Orange Roughy are deep water species that have been commercially fished.

The Orange Roughy was not exploited on a large commercial scale until 1980 but, by 1990, the global catch was declining because the population had been over-exploited. Fishing of some populations has been banned in an attempt to let them recover.

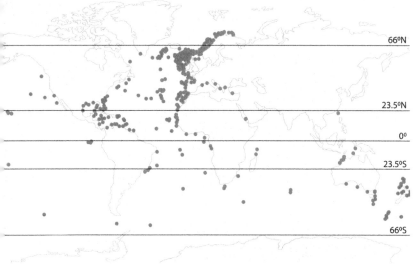

▲ *The global distribution of deep water coral reefs*

Threats

Deep water trawling has over-exploited fish populations, killed a lot of by-catch species, and damaged the deep water reefs that support the fish. The slow rate of coral reef growth means it will take many hundreds of years for the damage to be repaired.

The expansion of oil and gas exploration in deep water is a future threat, as more accessible supplies of oil and gas on land and in shallower water are depleted.

Increased releases of carbon dioxide are gradually causing the acidification of oceans. This may eventually threaten the survival of deep water corals.

Conservation efforts

Protected areas have been established to stop damaging activities, such as trawling, for example, Darwin Mounds SAC off the NW coast of Scotland and Oculina Bank off the coast of Florida.

Oceanic islands

These are islands that are sufficiently isolated from major land masses so it is difficult for species to colonise. This often produces unusual communities of species.

Ecological features

⚐ **Isolation and biodiversity**: most oceanic islands were formed by volcanic eruptions or the build-up of sand from nearby coral reefs. Their isolated positions make it difficult for most continental species to colonise. Marine species and seabirds can colonise relatively easily as can plants with floating seeds. Some species may have colonised by chance such as tortoises carried on drifting logs, or terrestrial birds carried by strong winds.

The species that succeed in colonising will gradually evolve to occupy the available ecological niches. Evolution has produced unique species on different islands because the conditions that affected selection pressure, and the characteristics that provide survival advantage, are different on different islands.

The biodiversity of isolated islands may be low because they are difficult to colonise, so some taxa may be absent or have few original colonists, such as mammals, land birds, reptiles, amphibia, and land plants. The local evolutionary processes may produce many endemic species with small ranges and small populations that make them vulnerable to extinction.

⚐ **Lack of mammal predators**: it is difficult for mammals to colonise isolated islands. Seals and bats may do so but not terrestrial mammals. Some larger islands still have mammal species from when they were attached to larger continents but they have evolved into unique species, for example, the marsupials of Australia or the lemurs of Madagascar.

2

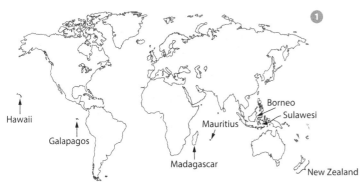

❶ *Selected islands with large numbers of endemic species*
❷ *Puffin nest colony*

Importance of oceanic islands

The high proportion of endemic species increases the possibility of the discovery of unique medicines or features that could be used in biomimetics.

Threats

- ⚑ **Exploitation of species**: some island species were heavily exploited in the past, usually for food, for example, the Dodo, giant tortoises, and marine turtles.

- ⚑ **Introduced species**: the lack of mammal predators meant that the indigenous species were not adapted. to survive the arrival of predatory species such as rats from shipwrecks, or cats that were introduced as pets. Introduced herbivores such as goats and rabbits often destroy the indigenous plant communities. The lack of predators allowed herbivore populations to become very large.

   Introduced plants may have colonised and out-competed the indigenous vegetation. Pathogens may have been introduced that affect the indigenous species. Avian malaria was introduced to Hawaii which has killed off many bird species. Above 1500m malaria rarely occurs because it is too cold, but as global warming cause temperatures to rise, avian malaria spreads to higher altitudes and the range of indigenous bird species is reducing.

- ⚑ **Habitat change/destruction**: urban, agricultural and tourist developments have caused habitat destruction. Sea level rise is also a threat.

Conservation efforts

These usually involve attempts to stop or reverse the damaging effects of human actions. The biggest single action that has conserved endemic species has been the eradication of introduced species such as rats, goats, cats, and rabbits. Introduced species have been successfully eradicated from nearly 1000 islands.

Species eradications

Islands	Introduced species controlled
Ramsay Island (Wales, UK)	Rats
Lewis and Harris (Scotland, UK)	Weasel
South Georgia (British Overseas Territory, South Atlantic)	Rats
Flatey (Iceland)	Rats, House Mouse
Diego Garcia (British Indian Ocean Territory)	Cat
Hawaii - several islands (USA)	Rats

Mangroves

Mangroves are coastal forests that grow in saline, oxygen-deficient soils, usually in tropical areas. They provide a range of important resources and ecological services.

Ecological features

Mangroves are tropical forests dominated by halophytic trees that live in inter-tidal areas with saline water. They are adapted to survive conditions that are saline, anaerobic and stormy. Inter-tidal habitats also have extremes in conditions such as temperatures and the availability of water.

❶ Mangroves
❷ Birds nesting in mangroves
❸ Mangroves cleared for urban development
❹ Coastal development on an area of mangroves

Importance of mangroves

- **Biodiversity:** mangroves provide a habitat for a wide variety of species, including crabs, lobsters, shrimps, sponges, fish, molluscs, reptiles, and birds.
- **Coastal erosion protection:** the vegetation and prop roots of mangroves absorb the energy of waves, reducing the impact of storms and hurricanes on more vulnerable coastal areas behind the mangroves. The 2004 tsunami that caused devastation in South East Asia did least damage where communities still had intact mangroves.
- **Fisheries:** mangroves provide important nursery grounds for fish that spend their adult lives in the open sea or on coral reefs. The dense roots protect the young fish from larger predators.
- **Protection of coral reefs:** reefs are damaged by suspended solids carried by rivers that then sink onto the coral polyps and kill them. River water that flows through mangroves slows down and the suspended solids are deposited before they reach the reefs. The mangroves also absorb nutrients from farmland which then can't cause the growth of algae on the coral reef which would threaten the survival of the coral polyps.

▼ **Resources:** mangroves provide timber for construction and fuel.

▼ **Medicinal resources:** many mangrove plants have been used in traditional herbal medicines. The extracts of the leaves of some mangrove trees are being researched as antimicrobial medicines to treat antibiotic-resistant bacteria such as MRSA. A cyanobacteria from Caribbean mangroves is used to treat small-cell lung cancer.

Threats

Although mangroves are often important to local communities, the growth of human populations and the expansion of economic developments such as aquaculture, urban developments, and ports cause large-scale mangrove destruction.

Conservation efforts

In regions where protection of mangroves is seen as important surviving mangroves may be designated as protected areas. Seventy-five per cent of the mangroves of Sri Lanka have been lost but the remaining areas were legally protected in 2015.

In areas where mangroves have been lost, natural recolonisation or replanting by people may take place. Natural regeneration can be very quick because mangrove trees produce seeds that germinate before they fall off the parent tree, into the sea where they are carried by water currents. If the sprouted shoot touches the sand, then roots are produced which anchor the young plant to the seabed.

Antarctica

Antarctica is an unusual area with extreme and fluctuating abiotic conditions. These have produced a unique community of species.

Ecological features

Antarctica is the only polar land mass and is the last pristine continent; it has unique features and is vital in maintaining conditions across the Earth. These factors have driven the campaign to preserve it. It is a large continent surrounded by an ocean, while the Arctic is an ocean surrounded by land. Antarctica's unique features:

▼ its large landmass – almost 60 times the size of the UK;

▼ ice and snow, upto 4.8km deep, cover ninety-eight per cent of its surface;

▼ at an average temperature of -49C it is the coldest continent on Earth;

▼ it has low precipitation with snow falling mainly near the coast and has Earth's largest desert;

▼ high average altitude;

▼ little terrestrial life including no permanent human inhabitants;

▼ abundant marine life in the surrounding sea;

▼ high levels of marine nutrients in the surface water are brought up from the seabed by upwelling currents. These nutrients support a rich food web;

▼ large seasonal variations in ice cover as the seasonal changes in temperature cause sea ice to freeze or melt;

▼ extreme seasonal changes, especially light levels with 24-hour daylight in the summer and 24-hour darkness in the winter. The summer sunlight and high nutrient levels produce a rich phytoplankton bloom that supports the rest of the foodweb.

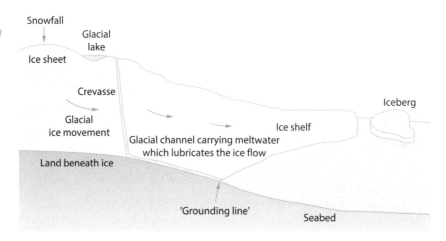

▶ *The movement of ice from the land into the sea from Antarctica*

Snowfall

Glacial lake

Ice sheet

Crevasse

Iceberg

Glacial ice movement

Ice shelf

Glacial channel carrying meltwater which lubricates the ice flow

Land beneath ice

'Grounding line'

Seabed

❶ *Adelie Penguins*
❷ *Elephant seal pup*
❸ *Krill*
❹ *Chinstrap Penguin*

Few terrestrial plants or animals can survive its harsh climate with its low air temperatures and long Antarctic winter. The sea is warmer than the land, with temperatures ranging from -1.8°C to +3.5°C. Most of the animals found in Antarctica get their food from the sea, for example, penguins, seals, and albatrosses.

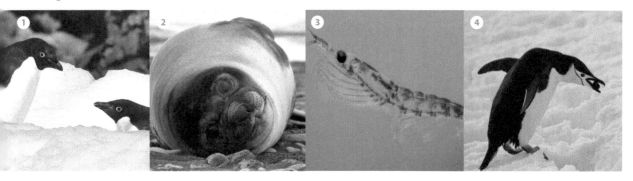

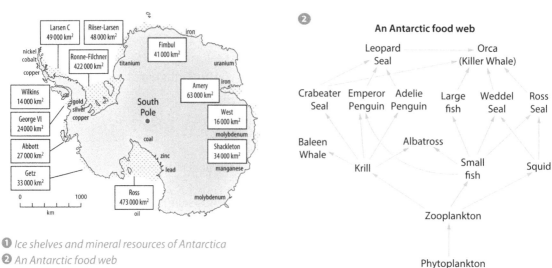

Larsen C 49 000 km²
Riiser-Larsen 48 000 km²
iron
nickel
cobalt
copper
Ronne-Filchner 422 000 km²
titanium
Fimbul 41 000 km²
uranium
Wilkins 14 000 km²
gold silver copper
South Pole
Amery 63 000 km²
iron
George VI 24 000 km²
West 16 000 km²
molybdenum
coal
Abbott 27 000 km²
zinc
Shackleton 34 000 km²
lead
manganese
Getz 33 000 km²
0   1000
km
Ross 473 000 km²
molybdenum
oil

❷ **An Antarctic food web**

Leopard Seal → Orca (Killer Whale)

Crabeater Seal   Emperor Penguin   Adelie Penguin   Large fish   Weddel Seal   Ross Seal

Baleen Whale   Albatross

Krill   Small fish   Squid

Zooplankton

Phytoplankton

❶ *Ice shelves and mineral resources of Antarctica*
❷ *An Antarctic food web*

A lot of the krill rely on the sea ice because they shelter from predators in cracks under the ice where they feed on algae.

Importance of Antarctica

Antarctica is important in providing a range of ecological services, resources, and opportunities for human activities.

Impact of Antarctica on the Earth

Key contributions	Impact on the Earth
Control of natural cycles	The ice on land is a huge store of water with 70 per cent of the Earth's fresh water present as ice on Antarctica. This long-term storage of water has kept global sea levels relatively low. Ice has a high albedo so most sunlight is reflected away, reducing its warming effect. If the area of ice was reduced, then temperatures would rise. Much of the carbon present in the algae that are eaten by krill, sinks to the seabed in krill faeces. This carbon sequestration helps to reduce carbon dioxide concentrations in the atmosphere.
Resources	Harvested biological resources include krill and three fish species. Exploitation of the mineral resources of Antarctica is currently illegal but it is known that there are reserves of gold, silver, nickel, titanium, uranium, coal, oil, and other potentially exploitable resources.
Research	Antarctica is a unique location for scientific research. It is the most isolated place on Earth so human influences are small. It is a good place for astronomical research as there is little pollution interference from light, infra-red, or radio waves. There is also little cloud cover to block observations. The climate is relatively stable and predictable so it is a good place for climate research. The unique wildlife makes it an important place for ecological research.

❶ *A scientific research station in Antarctica*

❷ *Taking an ice core for analysis of past climates*

Threats

▼ **Global climate change:** the rises in temperature and sea level caused by global climate change are having significant impacts, especially around the coast and on the Antarctic peninsula which extends further north than the rest of the Antarctic land mass. Although the rise in global temperatures caused by climate change is unlikely to melt much of the ice in Antarctica because it is so cold, if any ice did melt it is likely it would affect the remaining ice significantly. Glaciers could move more rapidly towards the ocean caused by lubrication from released meltwater. At the same time, ice shelves in the coastal waters which block the seaward movement of glaciers could break up as the seas heat up, enabling the glaciers to move towards the sea more easily. The sea level rise may also cause ice shelves to lift off the seabed on which they were grounded. They may then break up into icebergs and float away, removing the barrier to land ice behind which could then flow towards the sea.

Despite the rising temperature of the air and sea around Antarctica, the area of sea ice that forms each winter shows an upward trend. The exact causes for this are not fully understood but there are several possible explanations:

• stronger winds may be spreading the ice further;

- warmer air can hold more water vapour which may cause more snow to fall. This increased snow and the slush ice on which it falls may freeze together to form ice;
- ice on land that melts and flows into the sea may produce a layer of floating fresh water which freezes more easily than sea water.

The long-term trend may be for a reduction in the extent of sea ice. This would affect the marine food web as the decline in the populations of algae and krill that live under the sea ice would affect the species that rely on them for food.

The ice on land in Antarctica has a mean thickness of 1,800m, so there will be no significant reduction in the area of land ice for a very long time even if melting increases. However, sea ice is only one to two metres thick, so warming could cause a reduction in sea ice area. This would reduce the albedo of the ocean and allow further warming as more sunlight is absorbed.

- **Ozone depletion:** raised UV levels caused by ozone depletion has had little impact on the organisms that live on land because there are few of them and the animals that are present often have thick feathers or fur. Planktonic organisms in surface waters are more vulnerable to raised levels of UV, for example, algae, krill, and the larvae of fish and sea urchins.
- **Tourism:** unregulated tourism could threaten Antarctic wildlife through disturbance and the introduction of non-indigenous species and pathogens from humans. Pollution caused by fuel, sewage, and wastes could also increase. The number of tourists visiting Antarctica is increasing rapidly although there have been proposals for a cap on numbers. Most people visit by ship as there is no tourist accommodation on Antarctica. Most tourists visit a small number of landing sites which reduces the wider impact but increases the dangers for these sites.

  Disposal of wastes, oil spills, and the disturbance of wildlife are all potential problems. There are also concerns that pathogens may spread from humans to wildlife.
- **Scientific research**: research in itself is not a threat to Antarctica but carrying it out increases the risk of impacts such as pollution events and wildlife disturbance. Strict regulations are in place to minimize the impacts.
- **Overfishing:** the sea around Antarctica has many species that have been over-exploited in the past, leading to dramatically reduced populations, for example, some whale species and fur seals. Current fishing for krill threatens the species that feed on it including whales, albatrosses, and penguins. Overfishing of Patagonian Toothfish threatens the food supply of Sperm Whales and Elephant Seals. Longlining for toothfish also threaten albatrosses as they can be caught on the hooks and drown.

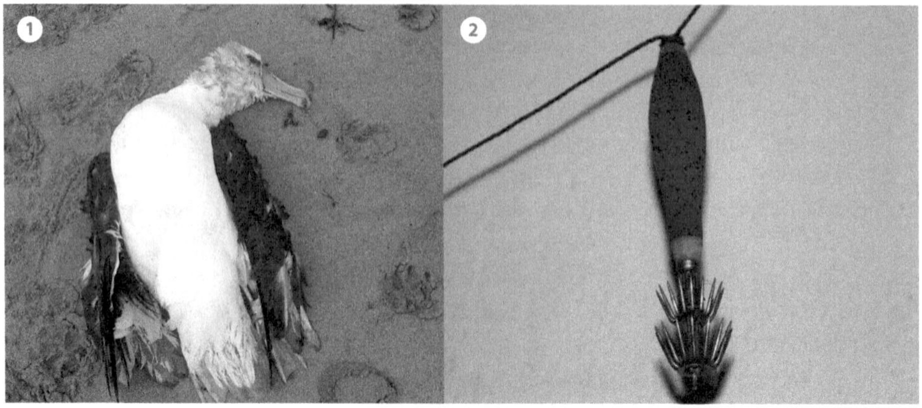

❶ *A dead albatross*
❷ *A long-line lure*

- **Future mineral exploitation:** Antarctica has deposits of minerals such as coal, oil, iron, copper, chromium, and platinum. The pressure to exploit these will increase as reserves elsewhere are depleted. Although mineral exploitation is currently banned, Antarctica has deposits of many minerals that are becoming scarce elsewhere in the world. The legal protection and difficulties of operating in such an extreme environment mean that mining is unlikely in the foreseeable future.

Conservation efforts

- **The Antarctic Treaty (1959):** this was set up to protect Antarctica and has been signed by 52 countries, including all the countries active in the area.
- **Conservation of living organisms:** fishing is regulated by the Commission for the Conservation of Antarctic Marine Living Resources (CCAMLS). Krill and some fish species are exploited but fisheries are closed if populations become over-exploited. No mammal species can be exploited commercially.
- **Control of tourism**: the impact of tourism is controlled by:
  - having no holiday accommodation on land so wastes are kept on the tourist cruise ships;
  - allowing only one cruise ship at any site at one time, with a maximum of 100 visitors ashore;
  - tourists having to be accompanied by trained guides;
  - requiring tourists to stay at least five metres from wildlife and leave no litter;
  - wearing protective clothing to prevent the introduction of pathogens and non-indigenous species; the protective clothing is cleaned before another site is visited.
- **Waste management:** this is managed by:
  - controlling and removing wastes;
  - ensuring that the only long-term residents on Antarctica are research scientists and support staff;
  - any waste materials that are produced being removed, for example, fuel containers, batteries, toxic wastes, plastics, used lubricating oil;
  - ensuring that sewage is only discharged into the sea where currents will disperse and dilute it so that microbes in the sea can break it down;
  - the removal of wastes produced before the introduction of these regulations, unless it would cause more environmental damage to do so.
- **No military activities:** none are allowed (except when supporting scientific research) and no nuclear explosions are permitted nor the dumping of radioactive waste.
- **No resource exploitation:** no commercial mineral exploitation is allowed.

Key principles

- Wildlife species provide a wide range of ecological services that help to maintain a stable biosphere.
- The resources provided by wildlife species are important in supporting human lifestyles.
- Many human activities threaten wildlife species and habitats.
- A range of different strategies can be used to conserve biodiversity.
- The study of selected important ecosystems helps in understanding the importance of biodiversity and how it can be conserved.

Life processes in the biosphere

Chapter topics
▼ Adaptation to the environment
▼ Ecological succession
▼ Species diversity and ecological stability
▼ Ecological terminology

Adaptation to the environment

All organisms must be adapted to the range of abiotic and biotic conditions that exist in their habitat if they are to survive. Species become better adapted through processes that involve the production of new characteristics by random mutations, followed by natural selection, which gives an increased chance of survival to better adapted individuals. This is the process of evolution.

Organisms that are poorly adapted may die if the environmental factors are unsuitable, or if other species are better adapted.

There is a range of tolerance within which organisms can survive. This means that for any specific condition or factor most organisms survive within a relatively narrow range. A population with a large gene pool is more likely to survive environmental changes more effectively as some individuals will be adapted to new conditions. Although the non-adapted individuals would die, the survivors would be able to breed and rebuild the population because their offspring will be adapted to surviving the new conditions.

❶ *How the range of tolerance affects survival*
❷ *Having a wide range of tolerance increases the chance of surviving environmental change*

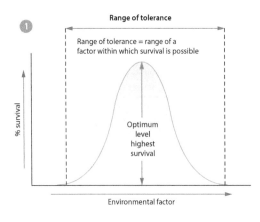

❶ Range of tolerance

Range of tolerance = range of a factor within which survival is possible

% survival

Optimum level highest survival

Environmental factor

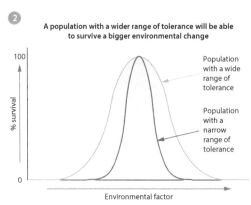

❷ A population with a wider range of tolerance will be able to survive a bigger environmental change

100

% survival

Population with a wide range of tolerance

Population with a narrow range of tolerance

0

Environmental factor

For environmental scientists, an understanding of adaptation is not just a matter of interest in knowledge of the species. An understanding of a species' adaptations helps in understanding

its habitat requirements which is important during decision-making in planning conservation management. It helps when deciding how to manage the environment and how to provide conditions that increase the chances of survival.

These decisions will often involve small beneficial changes to a specific condition, where a species was close to one extreme of its range of tolerance and where changing conditions threatened to make the conditions unsuitable for survival.

Abiotic factors

The survival and distribution of species is mainly controlled by abiotic factors.

Genetic diversity within the gene pool often means that survival declines when conditions become less suitable and fewer individuals within the population are still within their individual ranges of tolerance.

Important abiotic factors that affect species distribution include:

- light;
- water;
- pH;
- mineral nutrients.

If the abiotic conditions are within the range of tolerance of a species, then it must also be adapted to the inter-species relationships involved with biotic factors.

Biotic factors

The survival of a particular species may depend upon the presence or absence of other species.

Important biotic factors that affect species distribution are:

- food supply;
- seed dispersal;
- pollination;
- disease.

Ecological succession

All species have a stage in their life cycle when movement to colonise new habitats can take place. This is essential to avoid extinction as changing conditions make the current location unsuitable for survival.

The period when survival in an area is possible may last a long time, or it may be very short. In all cases, it is important to be able to move, colonise, grow, breed, then colonise and populate other areas.

When a species colonises an area, it will change the habitat, which may make it suitable for other species to colonise that could not have survived there before.

The full range of processes and stages in these changes can best be seen in a newly created habitat which currently has no life, for example, a new pond, or bare rock exposed by a retreating ice sheet a landslide, or created by a volcanic eruption.

The stages in the sequence of events that follows are called seres. Each sere has a prefix named after the starting conditions:

- water: hydrosere;
- bare rock: lithosere;
- sand: psammosere.

The process of changes in a sere is called ecological succession and includes the following stages.

- The first living organisms to colonise must be adapted to abiotic conditions which are more extreme than later on when the habitat will support a higher biomass, for example, less shelter from strong winds, brighter sunlight, or more extreme temperatures.
- The first organisms to colonise are called 'pioneer species'.

- As time passes and populations increase, the pioneer species change the habitat and make it suitable for species that were not able to survive before. The new colonisers may out-compete the pioneer species which become less dominant and may eventually die out.
- These new colonisers also change the conditions, making the habitat suitable for colonisation by more new species.
- As the changing abiotic conditions become less extreme the adaptations that are needed for survival are increasingly based on biotic factors and inter-species relationships.
- The sequence of new species colonising, thriving, then dying out, continues until a final community of species develops which remains dominant as long as the climate does not change. This is called the climax community. The species that make up the community are controlled by the climate, so it is often called the climatic climax community.

How abiotic and biotic conditions change during ecological succession

Conditions	Changes during ecological succession
Abiotic conditions	
Temperature extremes	High to low
Water availability	Variable to reliable
Light levels	High to lower (if shaded by taller plants)
Nutrient availability	Low to high
Rates of change	Rapid to slow
Biotic conditions	
Main pollination method	Wind pollination to insect pollination
Main seed dispersal method	Wind dispersal to animal dispersal
Importance of inter-species relationships	Low to high
Biomass	Low to high
Biodiversity	Low to high

❶ *The general relationship between temperature, precipitation and the major biome groups*

❷ *The development of a climatic climax community. Ecological succession in the UK*

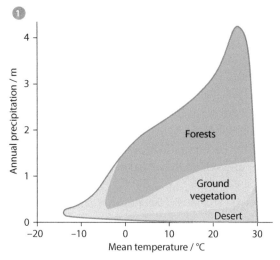

❶

Rainfall and temperature are critical determinants of a biome. For example, areas which have water available throughout the year typically develop into woodland. The type of woodland that develops is controlled by the temperature, for example, tropical rainforest develops when temperatures are higher, temperate deciduous woodland at moderate temperatures, and boreal conifer forest in cooler environments.

Areas where rainfall varies from season to season usually become grassland, for example, tropical savannah and temperate grassland.

❷

Hydrosere
Water

Sediments build up – mineral particles, organic matter

Psammosere
Sand
Increased organic matter, nutrients, water content

Conditions in all three areas become similar– soil builds up, providing support nutrients and water supplies needed to support woodland

Climatic climax community.

Broadleaf deciduous woodland

The starting point of ecological succession is controlled by local events such as flooding, the build up of sand, landslides etc. The climax community is controlled by the climate, especially temperature and water availability.

Lithosere
Rock

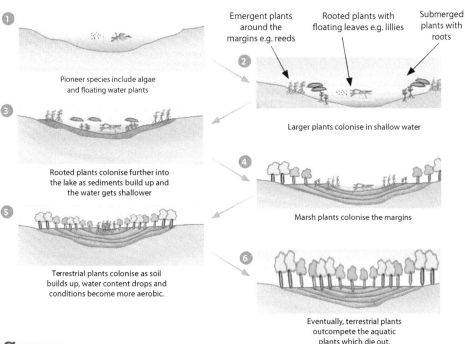

① Pioneer species include algae and floating water plants

Emergent plants around the margins e.g. reeds

Rooted plants with floating leaves e.g. lillies

Submerged plants with roots

② Larger plants colonise in shallow water

③ Rooted plants colonise further into the lake as sediments build up and the water gets shallower

④ Marsh plants colonise the margins

⑤ Terrestrial plants colonise as soil builds up, water content drops and conditions become more aerobic.

⑥ Eventually, terrestrial plants outcompete the aquatic plants which die out.

◀ *The stages in a hydrosere*

Seres

A sere is the sequence of stages in ecological succession during which an uncolonised habitat develops into the climax community. Seres are often named after the conditions at the beginning of succession.

Hydrosere

When an area of freshwater is created it is usually quickly colonised by single-celled algae from the soil. Birds, such as herons and ducks, and flying insects, such as water beetles and pond skaters, can bring in spores and seeds of algae, diatoms, and plants. The lake edges start to be colonised by rooting plants such as reeds, lilies, and reedmace. However, the open water may be too deep for such plants so only floating plants live there. The more the area is colonised by plants the more food and shelter there is so more animals that arrive can survive.

As plants grow and die, the lake gradually fills in with dead organic matter as well as soil and sediments carried in from the surrounding area. As the water becomes shallower, conditions continually change until rooted plants can survive. Emergent plants, that have their leaves above the water, shade the submerged plants which gradually die out.

As sediments fill the lake and open water recedes, aquatic species progressively disappear. As soil accumulates and develops to the extent that it can support the weight of much bigger plants, trees that can survive in waterlogged soil, such as willow and alder, start to colonise the area.

As transpiration by trees removes water and more sediments accumulate the soil becomes drier. Trees such as oak will be able to colonise. These larger trees create a denser canopy, providing shade which inhibits the growth of smaller plants.

Eventually, the community is dominated by the largest trees, with other plants and animals living in, on, or under them. Few of the original species involved in the early stages of the ecosystem's development are still present.

① *A sequence of plant groups colonise aquatic habitats as the water depth reduces*

② *A lake that has been almost filled with sediments and dead organic matter*

Lithosere

The development of a community of species on bare rock, created by a cliff fall, the retreat of a glacier, or a volcanic eruption is called a lithosere. The initial abiotic conditions are very harsh and unsuitable for most organisms. Temperatures are extreme, water availability is severely limited and there is no soil. Simple autotrophs such as lichens and algae are the first to colonise the area. Conditions improve as dead organic matter and rock fragments gradually accumulate. Mosses colonise and a thin layer of soil starts to build up. Grasses and ferns then colonise. As the layers of soil form and plants get larger, the abiotic factors become less extreme. The conditions are never as hot or cold, or wet or dry, as they were at the beginning of the community's development and the development of the soil makes plant nutrients more available. Seedlings of less hardy plants can survive under the shade of the larger plants. Once pollinating insects become established flowering plants colonise and survive as pollination takes place.

▲ Plants colonising a volcanic lava flow

Once the soil is deep enough and the edaphic factors (soil factors) are suitable, trees can colonise. The first tree species to establish usually have wind-blown seeds, such as birch trees, while the seeds of later species are dispersed by animals, for example, beech and oak trees.

In the early stages of development, a hydrosere and a lithosere are very different from each other. This is due to their different original conditions. However, as succession occurs these differences are reduced and the final communities are very similar to each other because they are controlled by the climate of the region which is the same for both communities.

Psammosere

A psammosere involves ecological succession that starts on sand. Plant nutrients are not readily available, drainage is rapid so water supplies are poor and moving sand makes it difficult for plants to establish a good root hold without being covered and killed.

As plants succeed in colonising, the sand is stabilised, nutrient supplies increase, organic matter builds up, and water becomes more available.

Eventually, the sequence of changes in the community of species will establish the same climatic community that would have been produced by a hydrosere or lithosere.

▲ Marram grass colonising a sand dune

Conservation of plagioclimax communities

In many areas, the human activity that deflects the climax community occurs regularly, so the natural climax community does not have time to reform and a new community of species develops. This is called a plagioclimax. A long-term balance between succession and human activities that maintain many plagioclimax communities produce habitats that don't appear to change, for example, grassland, lowland heathland, and moorland.

Conservation of climax communities such as natural rainforest, coral reefs, mangroves and Antarctica typically takes the approach of minimal human impact. However, in the UK, conservation management of plagioclimax communities is usually through maintenance of the traditional activities that created them.

Plagioclimaxes in the UK and their management

Habitat	Approaches used to manage the plagioclimax
Lowland heathland	Grazing or burning
Hay meadow	Mowing
Wet meadow	Grazing
Upland moorland	Grazing or burning
Arable field	Ploughing
Garden lawn	Mowing
Coppiced woodland	Felling at intervals of 8 to 20 years
Reedbeds	Mowing or cutting

If the human activity that produced a plagioclimax stops, then secondary succession will eventually re-establish the climax community. So, if the conservation of species that live in a plagioclimax community is the main conservation priority then the activities that produced the plagioclimax must be maintained.

Secondary succession

Many human activities that disturb climax communities, such as tree felling, ploughing, and burning, recreate the conditions that were suitable for the species that colonised the area earlier in the sequence of ecological succession. These species recolonise the area. If the habitat is left alone, succession will continue to change and will eventually re-create the climax community. This is secondary succession. This takes place more rapidly than primary succession because the soil does not have to develop and many of the seeds will already be present so there are fewer delays caused by the time taken for species to colonise.

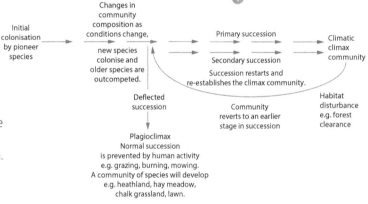

Species diversity and ecological stability

In extreme environments that are dominated by abiotic factors and where populations are likely to fluctuate dramatically, species diversity is often low. Where few food species are available, a change in the availability of one food species will have a big impact on the number of predators. This will then impact the availability of the food species, creating cycles of population rise and fall.

Less abiotically extreme environments usually have higher biodiversity. These become more stable ecosystems in which populations are dominated by biotic factors. Examples include tropical rainforests and coral reefs.

The level of diversity can be quantified using several different calculations. One common way to measure biodiversity is Simpson's Diversity Index.

❶ *Primary succession, secondary succession, and plagioclimaxes*

❷ *Woodland colonisation of a grassland where grazing has stopped*

Simpson's Diversity Index formula

$$D = \frac{N(N-1)}{\sum n(n-1)}$$

where:

N = Total number of organisms (all species)

n = Total number of organisms of an individual species

∑ = Sum of

The higher the value of D, the higher the biodiversity. See page 402, Chapter 15 Research methods.

Estimating the total number of species

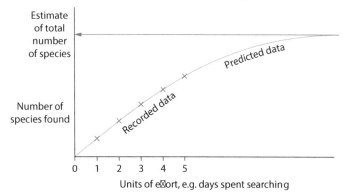

▲ *Total number of species in an area can be estimated from the changing rate of discovery of new species*

As we have not yet discovered all the different species that exist it is not easy to estimate how many there are. However, the past rate of discovery can be used as the basis for estimating the number. The gradual reduction in the rate of finding new species can be used to estimate the total number of species that have not yet been discovered and therefore the total number of species that exist. New species are currently being discovered at a rate of about 20,000 per year. Current estimates for the total number of species vary from 5 to 100 million. Only two million species have so far been named.

Some ecosystems are so inaccessible, for example, the deep-sea floor and the canopy of tropical rainforests, that they have yet to be fully researched.

Population dynamics

Population dynamics involves the processes that can cause populations to change in size and structure.

Population regulation

The number of individuals of a species that live in an area is controlled by the balance of factors which tend to increase or reduce the population.

The population will increase if the reproduction rate is high and the death rate is low.

The population will decline if the reproduction rate is low and the death rate is high.

Successful wildlife conservation will maximise the factors that increase the population while minimising the factors that reduce it.

The environmental factors that affect the death rate can be controlled by good environmental management.

Birth rate

The maximum birth rate (natality rate) is determined by the natural ability of the species to reproduce. Evolution has produced birth rates for each species that are appropriate for the death rate. Species with lower chances of survival have higher birth rates.

Death rate

The death rate is controlled by environmental factors such as disease, drought, predation and shortage of food.

r-selected species

These are species that can respond rapidly to low survival rates. They reach sexual maturity quickly, produce many young and can disperse widely.

r-selected species include mice, locusts and greenfly.

r-selected species:

❶ *locust*
❷ *spider*
❸ *rowan*
❹ *rabbit.*

k-selected species

These are species that recover slowly from a decline in population. They usually reach sexual maturity at an older age, produce few young, but often live for a long time. An increase in the death rate caused by a change in the habitat or by human exploitation may cause a population crash. The low reproduction rate of k-selected species may make it impossible to replace the losses.

k-selected species include whales, elephants, rhinos.

k-related species:

▲ *Southern White Rhinos*   ▲ *African Bush Elephant*   ▲ *Whitetip Reef Shark*

An understanding of population dynamics is important in monitoring the survival of a species, its breeding success and to assess Maximum Sustainable Yield (MSY). The MSY of a population is an estimate of the greatest exploitation that is possible without causing unsustainable long-term population decline.

To forecast a change in the size of the population the following variables are required:

- current population;
- numbers of births and deaths;
- number of individuals immigrating and emigrating.

Population = starting population + births + immigrants – deaths - emigrants

Factors affecting mortality rates

Density independent factors: these include factors where the population density has no effect on the chances of survival of an individual, for example, drought, flood, volcanic eruption.

Density dependent factors: these include factors where the chances of an individual surviving depend on the population density of the species. Survival chances are usually higher when the population density is low and lower when the population density is high. For example:

- Food supply:

  Intra-species competition for food is greatest when the population density is high.
- Disease:

  Diseases spread more easily between individuals when they are close together.

As the population density increases the density dependent factors become more important until the combined mortality rate, caused by density dependent factors plus density independent factors, forms a long-term balance with the birth rate.

Carrying capacity

The carrying capacity is the greatest population that an area can support indefinitely without damaging or over-exploiting the environment. The mortality rate in a population changes if the population size is above or below the carrying capacity, so that the population size changes back to the carrying capacity.

Predator-prey population relationships

Predator and prey populations are closely related. When the prey population rises there is a lot of food for the predators, so their population rises. The high predator population causes the prey population to decline. The low prey population creates a food shortage for the predators so their population declines. The low predator population then allows the prey population to rise again.

Artificial population control

Intervention to artificially control the population through culling may be required to enable the species or habitats to survive where natural control mechanisms no longer regulate the population.

This is often necessary if:

▸ the breeding rate of an endangered species is low, so a captive breeding and release programme is needed to maintain or increase the population;

▸ a non-indigenous species is introduced which reduces the populations of indigenous species because it is a predator, competitor, or pathogen;

▸ an indigenous predator has been removed so its prey species becomes over-populated and needs to be culled to avoid the ecological damage it may cause by its impact on other species. For example, as wolves in Scotland have been exterminated their prey species, Red Deer, must be culled to prevent their population rising too high which would lead to over-grazing.

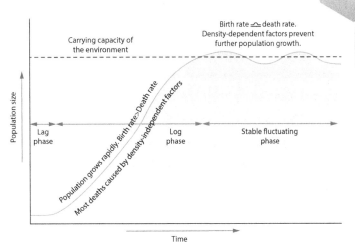

▲ *A sigmoidal population growth curve*

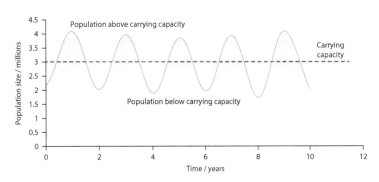

▲ *How homeostatic population regulation controls the population around the carrying capacity*

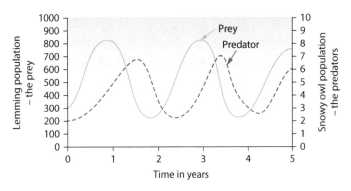

▲ *The relationship between predator and prey populations*

Ecological terminology

Organisms and environments can be categorized in many ways that help the understanding of their ecological roles and interrelationships.

Taxonomy

Taxonomy is the science of grouping organisms according to the similarities in their features. Any taxonomic group is called a taxon.

The grouping of organisms into most taxa is subjective and opinions can change as new information becomes available. For example, the African elephant is now considered to be two distinct species:

- African Bush Elephant (*Loxodonta africana*);
- African Forest Elephant (*Loxodonta cyclotis*).

Species is the only 'real' taxon. Although our understanding is not always good enough to accurately distinguish between very closely related species.

Species

A species is a group of closely related organisms that resemble each other more than members of other groups. They form a reproductively isolated group that naturally breed with each other to produce fertile offspring. Most species could not produce fertile offspring with other species:

- differences in behaviour would prevent individuals from attempting to mate;
- anatomical differences make mating impossible;
- even if mating was possible, differences in numbers or shape of chromosomes may make fertilisation or cell division impossible.

Very closely related species may be biologically capable of producing fertile offspring but do not naturally do so. However, in captivity, where they are not isolated and natural behavioural patterns break down, they may mate and produce fertile offspring, for example, some duck species, or one humped and two humped camels (Arabian and Bactrian camels).

Naming species

Species are given Latin names which are used by ecologists in all countries to avoid confusion that could be caused by the use of names in different languages or the use of local names.

The first part of the species name relates to the genus: a group of the most closely related species, for example, *Passer* - 20 closely related sparrow species.

Note: The genus name always has an upper case letter, while the species name has a lower case letter.

The second part of the name is added to identify an individual species within the genus, for example, *Passer domesticus* - the House Sparrow of Europe, Asia, and North Africa.

The common names of all taxa have lower case letters but some authorities use upper case letters for species names.

This approach is taken in this book. So rhinoceros refers to several species: lower case r. The Black Rhinoceros is a species: upper case B, R.

Evolution

Evolution is the process that changes the gene pool of a species, in some cases separating gene pools which eventually become two or more species. It is driven by the increased chance of survival, produced by being better adapted to the local conditions than other members of the species. The characteristics that provide survival advantage can vary in different areas. Over time, evolution may produce isolated populations that are sufficiently different from other populations that they no longer interbreed. They are closely related but are different species.

Although these different species may still be genetically similar, they are reproductively separated by behavioural or geographical isolation. In the wild they do not interbreed and further evolution will eventually make interbreeding impossible.

Habitat

A habitat is an area or location where a species or community of species lives, for example, moles live in the soil within a grassland, Blue Tits living in the foliage of trees in a woodland, and Stag beetles live in the trunks of oak trees.

Ecological niche

The ecological niche of a species is the role that it plays in its habitat. This includes the way it uses environmental resources and its relationship to other species, such as pollination or seed dispersal. For example, the Tawny Owl is a nocturnal carnivore, nesting in holes in hollow trees, feeding on small mammals and birds.

Within a single habitat, two species cannot occupy exactly the same niche because one would be better adapted than the other. The less well adapted would not be able to compete and would die out.

▶ *Tawny Owl*

Population

A population includes all the individuals of a single species that live in a particular area, for example, all the English Oak trees in a deciduous woodland or all the Common Carp in a lake.

Community of species

A community of species includes all the members of all the species that live in an area, for example, the combination of all the populations of all the species in an area such as all the species of plants, bacteria, fungi, protista, archaea, and animals.

Ecosystem

An ecosystem is the combination of the biotic and abiotic features of an area. It includes the community of species, their inter-relations with each other and their relationship with the physical environment such as energy, water, and nutrients. They are usually relatively self-contained with few movements of organisms in or out of the ecosystem.

Examples include tropical rainforest, estuary, savannah grassland, coral reef.

Biome

A biome is a large geographical region with specific climatic conditions within which a characteristic community of species lives. It includes all the areas where the community is found, for example, tropical rainforests, mangroves, savannah grassland, and tundra.

Biomes are usually named after the most obvious organisms, often the characteristic vegetation.

▼ World map of terrestrial biomes

The distribution of biomes is controlled by climatic factors such as temperature, light levels, water availability, and seasonal fluctuations in these.

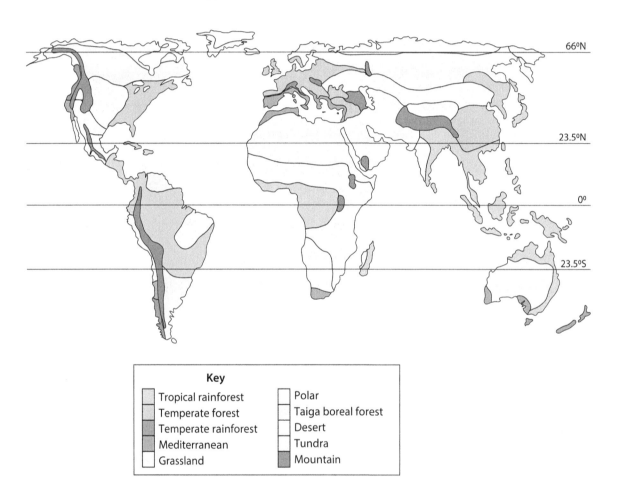

66°N

23.5°N

0°

23.5°S

Key

	Tropical rainforest		Polar
	Temperate forest		Taiga boreal forest
	Temperate rainforest		Desert
	Mediterranean		Tundra
	Grassland		Mountain

Possible confusion between ecosystems and biomes

A biome includes all the areas covered by the same community of species, for example, all tropical rainforests or all tropical coral reefs.

Ecosystems often have the same names as biomes but each isolated area is a different ecosystem, for example, separate tropical coral reefs, or areas of savannah grassland.

All coral reef ecosystems belong to the same coral reef biome and all tropical rainforest ecosystems belong to the same tropical rainforest biome.

Biosphere

The biosphere is all of planet Earth that is inhabited by living organisms including the land surface, soil, water, and atmosphere.

Key principles

- ⚑ The conservation of wildlife is not just an aesthetic or ethical issue. It is vital for our survival.
- ⚑ All species have inter-species relationships for ecological services such as food, mineral nutrients, habitat provision, pollination, and seed dispersal.
- ⚑ Humans gain a wide range of benefits from other species by exploiting them for resources and applying the knowledge we can gain by studying them.
- ⚑ Human activities threaten the survival of other species in a variety of deliberate and accidental ways.
- ⚑ The conservation of biodiversity can be achieved using a variety of strategies, including:
  - legal protection;
  - captive breeding and release programmes;
  - the management of existing habitats;
  - the creation of new habitats.

The Atmosphere

Chapter topics
▼ How the atmosphere supports life on Earth
▼ The structure of the atmosphere
▼ Energy processes in the atmosphere
▼ Global climate change
▼ Ozone depletion

The atmosphere is a thin layer of gases surrounding the Earth, held in place by gravity.

The atmosphere is essential to life on Earth as it provides vital life support systems such as protection from solar radiation, gas resources and aiding the transport of energy and water around the globe.

Composition of the atmosphere

The atmosphere is composed of Nitrogen, Oxygen, Carbon dioxide, Rare and other gases. The table shows the proportions of each.

Composition of the atmosphere, values are rounded so do not total 100%

Gas	Proportion of dry air/ %
Nitrogen	78
Oxygen	21
Carbon dioxide	0.04
Rare gases (combined)	1
Ozone	0.000007

Natural processes are in a state of balance which maintains the average composition of the atmosphere so that it only changes over very long timescales. This is known as a **dynamic equilibrium**. Photosynthesis and aerobic respiration are particularly important processes. Although they roughly balance each other, the rates at which they occur vary over different timescales so the concentration of each gas fluctuates around a mean concentration.

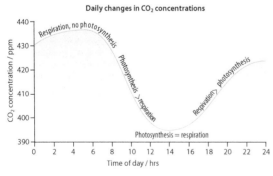

Daily fluctuations in CO$_2$ concentrations

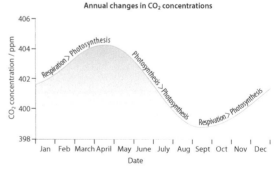

Annual fluctuations in CO$_2$ concentrations

Many of the processes that affect the atmosphere are interconnected. So, if one process is changed it can cause changes in other processes. This is important because it means

that human actions can trigger a sequence of events where a human action changes one process which causes other processes to alter as a direct result of the first change. There is a lot that is yet to be discovered and understood about how atmospheric processes work so it is not possible to accurately predict the impact of a human activity on specific atmospheric processes.

How the atmosphere supports life

Gases for natural processes

The atmosphere contains carbon, oxygen, hydrogen and nitrogen. These are needed to make the biological molecules used by living organisms. They are extracted from the atmosphere as N_2, O_2, CO_2 and H_2O. Carbohydrates, lipids and proteins all contain carbon, oxygen and hydrogen. Proteins also contain nitrogen.

Absorption of electromagnetic radiation from the Sun

Much of the biologically damaging radiation in the 'Solar Wind' is prevented from reaching Earth by the upper atmosphere. Most of the ultraviolet light that passes through the upper atmosphere is prevented from reaching the Earth's surface by the various forms of oxygen present in the stratosphere.

The element oxygen is present in the atmosphere in three forms with one, two, or three atoms (O, O_2 and O_3) known as **monatomic**, **diatomic** and **triatomic oxygen**. Together the three form a dispersed layer in the stratosphere called the ozone layer, or ozonosphere. These gases absorb ultraviolet light, producing a dynamic equilibrium of chemical reactions which form and destroy ozone.

Delaying the escape of infrared energy

Much of the incoming visible light is absorbed, converted to heat, and re-emitted as infrared energy. Naturally occurring atmospheric gases absorb this infrared energy, convert it to heat and increase the temperature of the atmosphere. This raises the temperature of the Earth in two ways:

▼ the warm atmosphere emits infrared energy which is absorbed by the Earth's surface;

▼ the warm atmosphere reduces heat loss by conduction from land and the oceans.

Heat distribution

Most of the energy from the Sun, absorbed at the Earth's surface, is absorbed in tropical regions. The warm surface heats the atmosphere above and this heat is distributed to higher latitudes by warm winds, such as the south-westerly winds that bring heat energy to the UK from the Caribbean Sea.

Ocean currents

Winds blowing over the oceans create currents that distribute heat by carrying warm water from tropical areas to higher latitudes, such as the North Atlantic Conveyor. These currents can also distribute dissolved nutrients.

Transport of water vapour

Winds transport water vapour to areas that would otherwise get little or no precipitation.

Atmospheric pressure

Atmospheric pressure controls the ease with which water molecules can evaporate and escape from the water surface. If atmospheric pressure was much lower there would be no liquid water on Earth.

Gases for human exploitation

Humans extract a variety of industrially important gases from the atmosphere including nitrogen, oxygen, carbon dioxide, and inert gases such as argon, neon, krypton, and xenon.

The structure of the atmosphere

Altitude affects the composition and physical features of the atmosphere resulting in a series of layers, of which the troposphere and the stratosphere are the most significant. It is these layers that are affected by human activities.

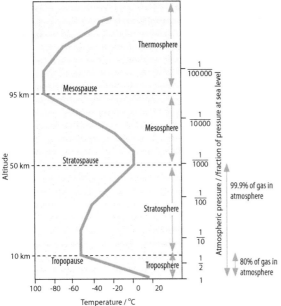

◀ *The structure of the atmosphere.*

Energy processes in the atmosphere

The solar energy arriving at Earth and the energy being radiated to space are generally in in a state of dynamic equilibrium. The wavelengths of electromagnetic radiation arriving are mainly ultraviolet, visible light, and near infrared. The wavelengths of radiation leaving Earth mainly involve long wavelength far infrared radiation. This energy, and the processes it drives, controls factors such as the climate, ocean currents, the hydrological cycle and therefore the distribution of species. Any human activities that affect the movement of energy could affect any of these factors and thus the survival of living organisms.

▶ *The energy budget of the atmosphere*

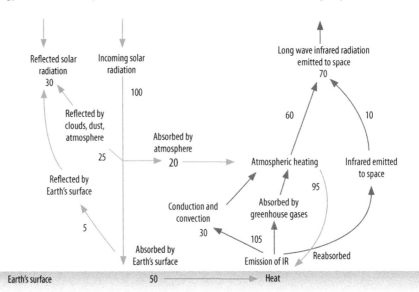

Global climate change

Global climate change involves changes to the composition of the atmosphere that alter energy processes, the climate and the physical and biological processes they control. Changes resulting from human activity are known as anthropogenic changes.

The natural greenhouse effect

Natural atmospheric greenhouse effect describes the atmospheric processes that warm the troposphere. Visible light passes through the atmosphere easily and is absorbed by the Earth's surface which warms up. The warm Earth's surface emits infrared radiation which cannot pass through the atmosphere as easily as visible light because it is absorbed by gases in the atmosphere: the 'greenhouse gases'. Greenhouse gases are any gases that are better at absorbing infrared than the average for the atmosphere. The most important natural greenhouse gases are carbon dioxide and water vapour.

If there was no natural greenhouse effect, the mean temperature of the Earth's surface would be 33°C colder than it actually is.

The Enhanced Greenhouse Effect and global climate change

Human activities are increasing the concentration of the greenhouse gases that absorb infrared radiation and warm the atmosphere. Some are gases that naturally occur in the atmosphere while others are only released by human activities.

The major anthropogenic sources of greenhouse gases

Greenhouse gas	Human activities which increase atmospheric concentration	Relative effects (per molecule)
Carbon dioxide	Combustion of fossil fuels and wood, ploughing of soils, drainage of marshes and bogs	1
Methane	Anaerobic respiration by microbes in padi fields, landfill sites, and the intestines of livestock. Methane is produced during the formation of fossil fuels and released by the ventilation of coalmines, leaks from natural gas fields and pipelines.	25
Oxides of nitrogen	Oxygen and nitrogen from the air react at high temperatures in locations such as vehicle engines and power stations. They are then released into the atmosphere in exhaust gases. Fertiliser use can increase NOx emissions, including nitrous oxide.	160 (nitrous oxide)
Chlorofluorocarbons (CFCs)	CFCs were used as aerosol propellants, fire extinguishers, refrigerants, solvents, and in expanded foam plastics.	25000 (typical value)
Tropospheric ozone	Produced by the photochemical breakdown of NO_2 and subsequent reactions with oxygen.	2000

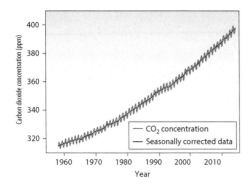

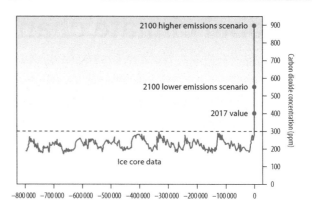

▲ Atmospheric CO_2 concentrations measured on Mauna Loa, Hawaii

▲ Long term atmospheric CO_2 concentrations

Consequences of Global Climate Change

The relatively small temperature increases involved in climate change may have a range of direct and indirect impacts on the abiotic and biotic conditions on Earth.

Ecological changes

Global Climate Change may result in changes in species survival caused by altered abiotic factors such as temperature and water availability.

- ▶ Species may be affected directly by the temperature, by changes to other species they rely on, or by changes to natural processes that affect them.
- ▶ Temperature rise may cause plants to grow faster. This could provide more food for herbivores such as butterfly and moth caterpillars. Many plants produce toxins that build up in their leaves to protect them from being eaten. If plant growth begins earlier in the year, then the toxins may build up sooner which could kill the caterpillars.
- ▶ Precipitation changes may cause wetland habitats to enlarge or shrink.
- ▶ Oak trees have deep roots and will be able to survive droughts better than beech trees that have shallower roots.
- ▶ Dormouse hibernation may be disturbed by warmer winters, causing them to use up stored fat. They may starve before the Spring when they could start feeding again.

▲ The leaves of this beech tree are dying during a drought

▲ Hazel Dormouse survival is better if winters are not too warm

▼ The timing of ecological events such as flowering, migration and nesting may change. Survival of interdependent species may be reduced, for example, if pollinating insects emerge earlier or later than normal and are not present when flowers are produced.

▼ The distribution of species may change as conditions change and they colonise areas that have become suitable. For some species this may not be possible:

- they may colonise new areas more slowly than they disappear from their old range. This is very likely for species that grow slowly such as trees;

- suitable new areas may not be available;

- human land use may block movement;

- species live in inter-dependent communities of species. All the species will not be able to move at the same speed.

❶ Sundews can only live in marshy areas where larger competitor plants do not grow

❷ The area inhabited by frogs can be reduced if the climate becomes drier

The species most likely to be affected are those that are closest to the edge of their range of tolerance.

Some species may be unaffected by changes in the physical environment, but other species they rely on may be. There could be a change in food supply, predation, disease, or the survival of pollinators, or seed-dispersal species.

Bats in the UK

Climate change may affect bats in the UK in positive and negative ways. Warmer, shorter winters may increase survival during hibernation. Warmer weather may increase the populations of food species, especially night-flying insects. Wetter, stormier weather may reduce the time for which bats can feed, which may reduce survival.

❶ Many plants are dependent on the insects that pollinate their flowers
❷ Triton molluscs are becoming more common in the seas around the UK as the water becomes warmer
❸ In warmer weather caterpillars may be more active and cause more damage to plants, but the plants may also be able to grow faster and produce more toxins to protect themselves.
❹ As temperatures rise, mosquitoes are colonising areas that were previously too cold. This also extends the range of diseases carried by mosquitos, such as malaria.

The population of a species may decline in one area, leading to local extinction, but survival may improve in other areas, possibly leading to the colonisation of new areas and an increase in its range. Colonisation is only possible if suitable new areas exist and there is a biological corridor linking the areas. Birds and flying insects can often colonise new areas quite easily but many plants and less mobile animals cannot.

As conditions for survival change, small populations may become isolated from the rest of the population, for example, as sea levels rise and create islands, or as temperatures rise and isolated populations retreat upwards to cooler mountainous areas.

There may be little or no population movements between these isolated populations which can cause several problems that threaten future survival:

- ▼ the gene pool would be divided into several smaller gene pools which makes inbreeding more likely;
- ▼ it may not be possible for surplus individuals from other areas to repopulate an area where the local population has died out.
- ▼ although the overall population may be large enough to be viable, the individual smaller populations may not be.

The increase in the concentration of greenhouse gases is predicted to have significant impacts on the abiotic conditions on Earth and therefore the survival of species.

The simplest effect is the absorption of more of the infrared energy emitted by the Earth's surface which is converted to heat so the atmosphere becomes warmer. The actual temperature rise may be quite small but even a small change can affect many other processes which could have big impacts on life on Earth. The mean global temperature rise over the past 100 years is only about 1°C but a further rise of 2°C is predicted to have very serious consequences.

Changes in climatic processes

The retention of more heat energy in the atmosphere produces changes in atmospheric pressure and the evaporation of water that produce new weather patterns.

Wind pattern changes

Jet streams are strong winds that blow from west to east along a meandering path in the upper troposphere. They are caused by the difference in temperature and density between two air masses such as the warm air in mid latitudes (30 – 60° N or S) and the cold air in polar regions. Winds blow to equalise the pressure differences, but they do not blow in a straight line from high pressure areas to low pressure areas because the rotation of the Earth creates a Coriolis force which causes winds to blow in a spiral fashion.

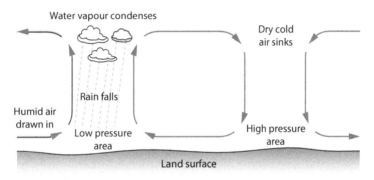

◀ *The distribution of precipitation is controlled by high and low pressure systems*

The jet streams control the movements of air bodies that create rain such as the cyclonic storms that are carried across the Atlantic to the UK.

Polar regions are warming faster than areas nearer the equator, so the temperature differences that create the jet streams are getting smaller. The jet streams in the Northern Hemisphere are moving nearer to the pole, are moving more slowly and are following a more meandering path. The waves created by the meandering path are called Rossby waves and can carry unusually cold air southwards or warm air northwards. The slower movement can cause weather systems to remain over an area, creating longer, more intense weather such as prolonged droughts or increased rainfall leading to floods.

Changes in rainfall

Increased temperatures cause more evaporation, which eventually causes more precipitation, in the same area or elsewhere.

With higher temperatures, the air may have to move further towards a cold area before the water vapour cools enough to condense and fall as rain or snow.

Changes in wind direction and velocity may also affect precipitation by carrying the humid air to new areas causing increased rainfall in one area but reduced rainfall in another.

Changes in the cryosphere

Warmer temperatures can have a direct effect on the ice on Earth as it is likely to melt more rapidly, but increased evaporation may increase precipitation, including snowfall. Areas which are extremely cold may have very low snowfall because precipitation falls before it gets there. Higher temperatures may allow more precipitation to reach such areas.

Reductions in the amount and duration of snow cover

Higher temperatures reduce the amount of ice and snow, and the length of time it remains on the ground before it melts. Less snow or ice cover reduces the albedo of the Earth's surface so less sunlight is reflected away and more is absorbed. This causes further heating.

Changes in the extent and speed of movement of land ice

Snow that falls on land may collect, become compacted into ice which then flows gradually downhill when the mass has built up sufficiently, forming a glacier. As the moving ice reaches lower altitudes, it warms up and melts. It may reach the sea before it melts and produce icebergs as the glacier breaks up, or it may melt before it reaches the sea and add to river flow.

Warmer temperatures may cause the front end of the glacier to melt faster than it is moving forward so the ice front retreats up the valley.

◀ *Arctic glaciers are shrinking as temperatures rise*

Meltwater from the surface of the glacier may flow down through cracks in the ice to the bottom of the glacier where it can lubricate the ice as it slides over the rock, causing it to move more quickly.

If the increased speed due to the lubricated movement is greater than the faster melting, then the glacier front may move further down the valley. Although it is extending further, the total volume of ice in the glacier may fall if there is no increase in snowfall where the glacier is formed.

So, retreating and extending glaciers can both be evidence of warming temperatures.

Categories of ice formations

Ice formation	description
Ice sheet	Ice covering an area over 50 000 km2. Only two ice sheets exists, on Greenland and Antarctica
Ice cap	Ice covering an area less than 50 000 km2. The ice is thick enough to have its own topography.
Ice field	Ice covering an area less than 50 000 km2. The topography of the ice follows the underlying land.
Glacier	A large body of dense ice moving over the land under its own weight.
Ice shelf	A floating mass of ice attached to ice on land. Ice shelves are formed when glacial ice flows off the land onto the sea.
Iceberg	A large piece of ice floating in the sea that broke off a glacier or ice shelf.
Sea ice	Relatively thin ice that forms on the sea as water freezes. It forms from sea water, but the ice crystalises as fresh water.

For more information on Antarctica see page 67.

Loss of ice shelves

As land ice flows into the sea it floats and breaks off to form icebergs. As sea levels rise, the land ice does not need to move so far before it floats off into the sea. Some ice sheets that are grounded on the seabed may float and break up earlier as sea levels rise and the ice breaks off earlier.

Ice shelves that break up do not directly cause a rise in sea level because they are floating and have already displaced sea water, however ice sheets that are grounded on the seabed block the forward movement of ice on land. Once the ice shelf has broken up, the glaciers or ice sheet behind may flow more rapidly towards the sea.

The ice sheet of West Antarctica is largely held back by ice shelves, so it is more vulnerable to rises in temperature and sea level than the East Antarctic ice sheet which is more completely on the land with few ice shelves.

▲ *Land ice that flows in the sea as icebergs are contributing to rising sea levels*

Changes in ice thickness and area

During the Arctic and Antarctic winters the area of ice that forms on the sea surface increases as temperatures drop. The area of ice that forms declines as temperatures rise. This is relatively thin ice that forms as ice crystalises in the sea. The area of sea ice that forms around Antarctica each winter has increased in recent years, possibly due to increased freshwater flowing off the land, floating on the denser sea water then freezing.

The area of ice has a big impact on future temperatures. Ice has a high albedo and reflects most sunlight. If the ice melts then more sunlight would be absorbed, causing a further increase in temperature and even more ice melting.

Ice lakes

The water produced by melting ice can collect on the surface of glaciers producing ice lakes. If the front ice wall of the lake melts then the water may be released, rushing down the valley below causing sudden flooding. As glaciers melt more rapidly, such events may become more common. This is a serious threat in the Himalayas where there are large human populations living in the valleys downstream of glacial lakes.

Ice and snow-fed rivers

Warmer conditions may reduce snowfall and increase rainfall. This can affect river flow patterns. Rainwater tends to flow into rivers soon after it has fallen. In some areas snow may build up during cold weather then melt gradually during warmer weather. So, rivers fed by meltwater may have a more even flow than if they were fed directly by rainwater. In other areas, precipitation falling as snow may reduce river flow as the snow accumulates but may cause a big increase in river flow if the climate suddenly warms such as during a spring thaw.

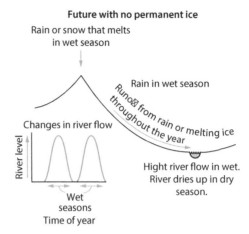

'Normal' situation with permanent ice

Snow in wet season

Ice + Glaciers

Snow added to ice

Rain in wet season

Runoff from rain or melting ice throughout the year

Changes in river flow

River level

Wet seasons
Time of year

River level fluctuates but river never dries up

Future with no permanent ice

Rain or snow that melts in wet season

Rain in wet season

Runoff from rain or melting ice throughout the year

Changes in river flow

River level

Wet seasons
Time of year

Hight river flow in wet. River dries up in dry season.

▲ *The impact of ice melting on rivers downstream and the people living there.*

▲ *A snow-fed river in South America*

▲ *The glaciers on Mount Kenya are shrinking rapidly and will probably disappear by 2050.*

Sea level rise

Rising temperatures cause an increase in sea level for two reasons:

▼ **Thermal expansion of seawater:** the warmer atmosphere heats the seawater which therefore expands, causing the sea level to rise. However, such changes will take a very long time as there is an enormous quantity of water in the oceans and water has a high specific heat capacity. Only the water at the surface is warmed by direct contact with the atmosphere, so cold deep water can only heat up when the slow ocean currents bring it to the surface.

▼ **Melting land ice:** as the Earth warms up ice will melt. Ice that is floating on the sea surface does not cause sea level to rise when it melts as it contracts during melting and occupies the same volume as the volume of the ice that was below water level. Ice that is on land, however, will cause sea level to rise as the water flowing into the sea increases its volume.

Changes in ocean currents

Ocean currents are important in distributing heat around the planet. They can have a big influence on the climate on land as water warms or cools the coastal land areas and the atmosphere. Ocean currents are a complex system, largely driven by processes that occur in the atmosphere, for example:

▼ winds cause surface water to move;

▼ evaporation caused by warming causes water to flow in to replace the water that has evaporated;

▼ heating or cooling changes the density of surface water which affects the ease with which surface water sinks;

▼ changes in salinity caused by evaporation, or inflow of freshwater from melted land ice, affect water density.

The North Atlantic Conveyor (the 'Gulf Stream')

The North Atlantic Conveyor involves the movement of layers of surface and deep water in the North Atlantic Ocean which distribute heat energy and control the climate.

The natural North Atlantic Conveyor

Warm water from the tropical Atlantic Ocean travels north-eastwards towards North West Europe. Two processes drive this movement:

- ▶ friction with the prevailing winds blowing over the ocean surface from the South West to the North East causes surface water to flow in the same direction;
- ▶ water in the North East Atlantic sinks as it cools and becomes denser, drawing water in to replace it.

The UK is warmed by the North Atlantic Conveyor (Gulf Stream) which brings water from tropical regions. This prevents the cold weather found in regions of the same latitude, for example, Moscow, or Churchill, Canada where polar bears are found.

Changes in the North Atlantic Conveyor caused by global climate change

Higher atmospheric temperatures cause land ice on Greenland to melt and flow into the sea. It dilutes the seawater causing the salt concentration to go down. This less saline water is less dense than normal seawater so it is less likely to sink. This reduces the flow rate of the water current which could cause NW Europe to become colder.

▼ *The North Atlantic Conveyor*

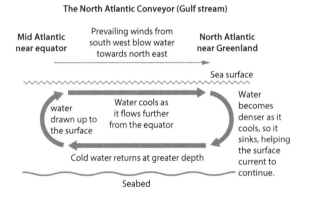

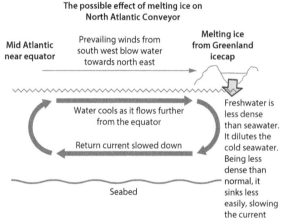

El Niño and La Niña or ENSO (El Niño Southern Oscillation)

El Niño

El Niño is the name given to a sequence of events which occur naturally, typically every 2 to 7 years, although, they seem to be happening more frequently. These changes in wind patterns may be partly a result of global climate change. The name comes from Spanish and means the Christ child. It has been used to name these events as they often start around Christmas time.

In normal conditions, reliable 'trade winds' blow westwards across the Pacific Ocean near the equator which moves a surface ocean current in the same direction. This causes deep cold water to be drawn upwards near the coast of South America. This water from the deep ocean is rich in nutrients and causes large algal blooms near the sea surface. These blooms feed a rich food web, including important commercial fisheries which provide food for the human population. The current continues to move west becoming warmer as it travels. It eventually moves south along the east coast of Australia as a warm current.

Ocean currents in the Pacific Ocean and El Niño

Normal year

warm water

cold current

Trade winds blow westwards

Strong ocean current

Water warms up and is carried west

cold current

desert

rain

warm water

El Niño year

Wind direction reversed

Current reversed

colder water

warmer water, increased evaporation

drought

rain and floods

▲ *The wind patterns and ocean currents in the Pacific Ocean during normal and El Niño years*

This current also affects rainfall patterns. The water temperature is a major determinant of where the rain will fall. If the current is cold at the coast then any water-bearing winds heading over the sea towards the land will be cooled down. This may cause the water vapour to cool, condense, and fall as rain before it reaches the land.

If there is a warm coastal current then winds blowing towards land are likely to retain water vapour and may allow it to reach the land where it can fall as rain.

In some years, the winds that create the surface currents change direction so that the ocean current slows or reverses. This stops the nutrient upwelling off South America so the rich food web collapses. The temperature drop in the western Pacific and the temperature increase in the eastern Pacific cause changes in the amount and distribution of precipitation. Rainfall in eastern Australia is reduced while coastal parts of South America that are normally deserts may have heavy rains and floods.

Global impacts of El Niño events

Because the world's wind systems are interconnected, El Nino events are associated with unusual weather elsewhere in the world such as:

▼ droughts in NE Africa, S Africa, and China;

▼ fewer hurricanes in the North Atlantic;

▼ fewer tropical cyclones in Japan

The exact causes of El Niño events are not fully understood but they seem to be occurring more frequently, possibly due to human impacts on the atmosphere.

Historical disasters that may have been made worse by El Niño events

Date	Event
4000 yrs ago	The collapse of the civilization of Ur in the Middle East caused by droughts during a series of El Niño years
Mid 7th century	Floods that caused the collapse of the Moche civilization in Peru, South America
1588	Storms that sank many ships of the Spanish Armada
1789-93	Storms and crop losses that increased the discontent that led to the French revolution
1812	The cold winter weather that stopped Napoleon's advance on Moscow
1942	The cold winter weather that stopped Hitler's advance on Moscow
1912	The southward movement of icebergs from Greenland that led to the sinking of the Titanic

La Niña

A La Niña event occurs when the winds blow more strongly in the normal direction, so water currents speed up and temperature differences between the western and eastern Pacific are increased.

There is limited scientific agreement on the link between human activities and changes in the ENSO, but If human activities are involved, then future global weather patterns may become less predictable.

Impacts of climate change on human society

Health

Temperatures in some parts of the world are at the upper end of the range of tolerance for humans. If climate change raises temperatures then a heat wave is more likely to cause health problems.

Urban area often have raised temperatures from the 'heat island' effect of heat emissions and light absorption by dark surfaces. This makes the impact of heatwaves even more severe.

People with existing health problems such as heart or respiratory disease may be more vulnerable to extreme temperatures.

Disease vectors may change their distribution as temperatures rise, for example, the mosquitoes that spread malaria.

Food poisoning may become more common as pathogens grow more rapidly on unrefrigerated food.

Water supplies

Changes in evaporation, precipitation, and river flow may create water supply problems ranging from droughts to floods.

▲ A lake in East Africa that dried out during a period of low rainfall

Food supplies

Changes in temperature and water availability may change the crop species that can be grown. Reduced water availability may make crop irrigation more important. Warmer winters may allow more pest insects to survive, causing more pest damage in the following growing season.

Impacts on infrastructure

Changes in temperatures and precipitation patterns will have impacts on how societies operate. If the changes are rapid or involve sudden extreme events then they would cause greater problems.

▼ **Road heat stress :** high temperatures cause melting of the tar that holds stone chippings together on road surfaces, causing roads to deform. Some roads will need to be re-laid using tarmac with a higher melting point.

▼ **Track buckling:** high temperatures can cause rail track to expand and buckle. Before being laid, track is stretched or heated to reach the length it would expand to at a particular temperature (27°C in the UK). Temperatures below this could not cause buckling, but temperatures much above this temperature could. Rising temperatures may require the track to be re-laid with pre-stretching for a higher temperature.

- ▼ **Drainage:** Higher rainfall or periods of sudden heavy rain will increase flooding risks.
- ▼ **Landslides:** Heavy rain can waterlog the ground and lubricate soil and rock particles, making landslides more likely especially on deforested hillsides.
- ▼ **Bridge damage:** High river flow after heavy rain can put pressure on bridge supports, especially if objects such as tree trunks hit the bridge or block the arches. This is most common with old bridges with thick structures and narrow arches.

▲ *A house destroyed by a landslide following heavy rain*

Difficulties in monitoring and predicting climate change

Climate change is a complex issue, involving many interconnected natural systems. Although general trends can be predicted, it is more difficult to predict individual changes, with accurate details of when and where they will occur. There is very little disagreement within the scientific community that the climate is changing and that human actions are a major cause of these changes.

Changes may occur over different scales of time and space. Since climates and many natural processes often fluctuate, it can be difficult to be sure that individual events are part of a longer-term trend.

Time scales
- ▼ Short term, for example, a sudden storm or a wetter winter.
- ▼ Long term, for example, a trend of winters with increasing rainfall.

Spatial scales
- ▼ Local, for example, a sudden slow-moving storm causing local flooding.
- ▼ Regional, for example, an area with increased rainfall due to increased evaporation or changed wind direction.
- ▼ Global, for example, increased global temperatures due to increased infrared absorption.

Particular changes may occur in different locations or at different times. If one area receives less rainfall then another area may receive more. If the landmass of Britain heats up then there may be lower rainfall in summer as the water vapour would not condense. However, in winter it could be cold enough for condensation and higher evaporation rates over the ocean could mean that more rain would fall. So, there are no straightforward answers to the question, 'Will it rain more in Britain?'

Interconnected systems

We do not fully understanding the natural processes that control the atmosphere, biosphere, and hydrosphere or the interconnections that exist between them.

Interactions between these systems operating over different scales make it much more difficult to accurately monitor changes and predict how their effects may combine. For example, in the UK, the following may all occur, but over different time scales.

▼ Changes in the jet stream may raise temperatures.

▼ A slowing of the North Atlantic Conveyor may lower temperatures.

▼ The underlying trend of increasing greenhouse gases may raise temperatures.

Natural fluctuations

The global climate has never been constant. All climatic factors fluctuate because they are influenced by variability in solar output, the Earth's orbit and changes in the Earth's surface caused by previous climate variability. These natural changes can hide or exaggerate anthropogenic changes.

The potential changes already discussed could occur naturally so it is difficult to determine whether an event is caused by human actions or not. An individual storm, or even several, does not indicate a trend. The change may be the frequency with which events such as floods, storms or droughts occur and often this can only be assessed years later when the trend becomes clear.

Time delay between cause and effect

There is often a time delay between a cause and an effect , for example, the atmosphere may warm up quite quickly, but it could be a very long time before the world's oceans reach the same temperature, because the volume of the oceans is so great and water has a very high heat capacity.

Data collection

To identify trends, reliable data are needed, collected over long time periods.

Historic data

Historic data collected in the past on atmospheric composition, temperature and weather patterns may be unreliable due to the lack of sophisticated equipment, or a lack of data collection on a global scale. Temperature records collected in towns may show warming that is caused by an increase in the heat-island effect as the town grows rather than as a result of a global temperature rise.

Proxy data

Proxy data involves making an estimate about one factor that can't be measured by using a related factor which can be measured or estimated, for example:

▼ dendrochronology: the width of a tree ring shows the growth rate and may indicate the temperature at the time it was laid down. The ages of tree rings can be estimated easily.

▼ some coral species produce large coral heads with annual growth rings which can be used to estimate past temperatures in the sea.

▼ pollen grains can become preserved in lake sediments. The presence of pollen of particular species indicates the climate that was present when it was produced. The date when the pollen was produced can be determined using radio-carbon dating of organic material in the sediments.

▲ *Tree growth rings indicate rates of growth in each year the tree was aliv*

▲ *Taking a core sample from a coral head*

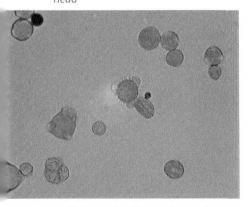

▲ *Pollen grains that can be used to deduce the climate*

Ice core data

Over 40 ice cores have been drilled to gain information about the historical atmosphere, mainly in Antarctica and Greenland. Annual accumulations of snow build up into ice layers, so deeper ice layers are older. Data on ice up to 800 000 years old has been collected from the 3200m core from Dome Concordia in Antarctica.

Air bubbles trapped in ice provide information on the atmosphere when the bubble became trapped, such as the carbon dioxide concentration and the ratio of oxygen isotopes which gives information on the temperature when the gas was trapped.

The layers are clearest in shallower ice. Compaction caused by pressure can make deeper layers less distinct but radio-isotope analysis can also be used to estimate the age of the ice. Layers of volcanic ash can be used to compare ice cores and identify layers of similar age.

Satellite data

Sensors carried by satellites are used to collect data on factors such as wind velocity, ocean currents, temperature, wave height, ice cover, ice thickness and vegetation cover.

Low Earth Orbit (LEO) satellites in polar orbit at altitudes of about 800km collect detailed information of the whole of the Earth's surface. Each orbit lasts about 1 ½ hours and successive orbits overfly different areas so the whole of the Earth's surface can be surveyed over about 15 days.

Satellites in geostationary orbit provide less detailed information from a constant position 36 000km above the equator. Many are used to monitor the weather and climatic conditions.

Monitoring ocean currents

Surface currents can be monitored using satellites or buoys and floats at the water surface.

Deeper currents can also be monitored. Argo floats, can be programmed to sink to a particular depth for specific durations, such as 10 days after which they surface, transmit the data then submerge for another 10 days. Data are collected on factors such as temperature and salinity. The sequence of position plots show the direction and speed of the current.

Computer models

The understanding of climate systems continues to grow and is helped by computer modelling which allows interconnections and their consequences to be estimated more accurately.

A computer model can be tested by feeding in data for a particular year, such as 1900, and seeing whether the model can predict the outcome for a later year, like 2000. If the prediction was similar to the real outcome then the model can be trusted, with caution. The model can be continually modified using more data collected and by analyzing differences between the predicted and real outcomes.

Feedback mechanisms and tipping points

A change in one environmental factor may cause other factors to change. These may have an impact on the original change, either increasing or reducing it.

- ▼ Negative feedback mechanisms reduce the size of the original change.
- ▼ Positive feedback mechanisms increase the size of the original change.

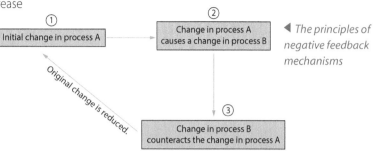

◀ The principles of negative feedback mechanisms

Negative feedback mechanisms

A negative feedback mechanism takes place when an environmental change causes other changes which decrease the rate of the initial change or the level of its impact. This reduces its effect and helps to re-establish the original equilibrium. For example:

- ▼ **Increased low-level cloud:** higher temperatures increase evaporation, which leads to increased condensation and produces more clouds. Clouds have a higher albedo than most of the Earth's surface, so more sunlight is reflected away and the amount of warming is reduced.

▲ Low level cloud density is greater when evaporation rates are high

- ▼ **Increased photosynthesis:** higher temperatures increase the rate of photosynthesis which removes more carbon dioxide from the atmosphere. If this carbon dioxide is stored in woody tissue then carbon dioxide levels in the atmosphere will rise less and warming will be reduced.

Positive feedback mechanisms

A positive feedback mechanism takes place when an environmental change causes other changes which increase the rate of the initial change or the level of its impact and thus increases the effect of the original change.

This sequence of changes either increases temperatures directly or increases the concentrations of gases which will cause further temperature rise. The following are examples of positive feedback mechanisms.

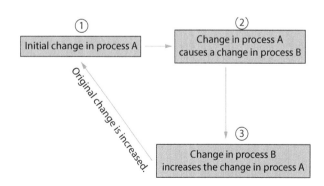

▲ The principles of positive feedback mechanisms

- **Soil decomposition:** the rate of decomposition of dead organic matter in soil is largely controlled by the temperature and in cooler areas organic matter can build up over time. If the temperature rises, the rate of decay may increase and aerobic decomposition by microorganisms will release more carbon dioxide, maybe for very long periods of time until the organic matter level has dropped to a new equilibrium level.
- **Melting permafrost:** land areas in Arctic and Antarctic regions may have soil that is waterlogged but permanently frozen. This frozen soil includes dead organic matter that decomposed slowly under anaerobic conditions, releasing methane gas which was trapped by the permafrost. Warming can cause the frozen soil to defrost, releasing the methane gas, which is a powerful greenhouse gas and causes further warming.
- **Ocean acidification:** nearly half the carbon dioxide released into the atmosphere since the industrial revolution has dissolved in the oceans, producing carbonic acid and making the oceans more acidic. Ocean acidification reduces coral survival and therefore reduces carbon sequestration as less carbon dioxide is stored as calcium carbonate in the coral.
- **Ice and snow melting:** ice and snow have a high albedo so most of the incoming sunlight is reflected and not absorbed. If warming reduces the area of snow or ice then more sunlight may be absorbed, causing further warming.
- **Release of methane hydrate:** dead organic matter in deep sea sediments has decomposed to produce methane gas. Under high pressures and low temperatures it forms solid methane hydrate in the sediments. If deep seawater temperatures rise then methane hydrate may melt, releasing methane gas into the atmosphere. This would cause further temperature rise.
- **Increased forest and peat fires:** many peat bogs have waterlogged soils where dead organic matter builds up to form peat. As these areas warm up and dry out, peat fires become more frequent so carbon dioxide is released and less carbon will be present in the remaining peat. Drier conditions would also cause forest fires to be more extensive and last longer, releasing more carbon dioxide into the atmosphere.
- **Increased water vapour:** warmer temperatures caused by carbon dioxide and other anthropogenic greenhouse gases increase the rate of evaporation. Although there will be an increase in the rate of precipitation, warmer air can hold more water vapour. Water vapour is a powerful greenhouse gas and higher levels cause further warming.

Tipping points

Tipping points is the concept that human actions that cause climate change may cause changes in natural processes that themselves cause climate change to the extent that the original human actions are no longer needed for climate change to continue increasing. In this situation, stopping the original human activity would not stop climate change.

If climate change is to be controlled, it is vital that this is done before tipping points are reached.

Examples of natural processes that may become unstoppable if temperatures rise too much:
- Faster soil decomposition
- Release of CO_2 by increased forest and peat fires
- Snow on land melting, caused by increasing temperatures reduces the Earth's albedo so more sunlight is absorbed, raising temperatures further and causing more snow to melt.

Control of global climate change

The response to anthropogenic climate change may involve the control of greenhouse gases and changes to society that would minimise the severity of the impacts.

Control of greenhouse gases

Methods to control greenhouse gas levels

Greenhouse gas	Control Method
Carbon dioxide See page 225, Energy conservation	• Reduction in fossil fuel use, for example, through energy conservation • Use of energy resources with low carbon emissions • Carbon sequestration, for example, by planting more trees or storage of carbon dioxide from power stations in underground geological structures.
Methane	• Reduction in landfill waste, for example, through increased recycling, reducing packaging, reducing food waste. • Reduced livestock production • Improved recovery of gas from coal mines and gas and oil facilities
Oxides of nitrogen See page 253, Control of oxides of nitrogen	• Reduced use of internal combustion engines, for example, more use of public transport • Catalytic converters in vehicle exhausts so that harmful gases are removed and converted into nitrogen and oxygen. Carbon monoxide and hydrocarbons are broken down and converted into carbon dioxide and water. • Addition of urea to power station effluents or diesel engine exhausts to reduce NOx concentration and convert exhaust gases into nitrogen and steam

Chlorofluorocarbons
See page 111, Restoration of the ozone layer
	• Use of alternative materials in manufacture and in appliance operation, for example:
	  • butane or propane in aerosol cans
	  • hydroflourocarbons (HFCs) and hydrochlorofluorocarbons (HCFCs) in refrigerators
	  • alcohols as solvents for cleaning electronic equipment
	• Use of alternative operational processes
	  • trigger and pump action sprays cleaners instead of aerosol cans
	  • - stick and roll-on deodorants instead of aerosols

Tropospheric ozone	Controls and processes which reduce NOx emissions also reduce the formation of ozone in the troposphere

Carbon storage

▼ **Carbon sequestration:** planting more trees would sequester carbon in wood through photosynthesis.

▼ **Carbon Capture and Storage (CCS):** a developmental technology that may remove carbon dioxide produced by industrial processes such as fossil fuel power stations. The main stages in CCS are:

1. Capture of the CO_2 or removal of carbon from the fuel.
2. Transport by road tanker, ship, or pipeline.
3. CO_2 storage in depleted oilfields, gas fields, aquifers, or its use in secondary oil recovery.

Geoengineering

This involves largely untried technologies that might control natural processes to reduce the anthropogenic greenhouse effect, examples include:

▼ painting roofs white to increase their albedo and reflect more sunlight;
▼ adding nutrients to the sea to stimulate plankton growth. The shells of the dead animals would take carbon to the sea bed;
▼ putting solar shades in orbit to reduce sunlight reaching the Earth.

Some of these strategies could have unpredictable consequences that could cause environmental damage.

Adapting to climate change

The severity of the impacts of climate change may be reduced by preparing to cope with the predicted changes.

Flood control

Flooding caused by rising water levels can be reduced by building higher river banks or coastal defences. If water levels in the river rise above the level of the surrounding land, it would be necessary to pump rainwater from the land up into the river or sea.

❶ A river bank being raised to reduce flood risks
❷ A barrier to prevent flooding of a coastal town by exceptionally high tides
❸ A temporary flood barrier being used after heavy rain to prevent river flooding

▲ The Thames barrier

▲ A flood barrier to protect a house from river flooding

Coastal erosion control

As sea level rises, coastal erosion rates rise as waves strike the upper shore for longer in each tidal cycle. A variety of sea walls and wave screens are used to protect coasts.

Managed retreat

Some areas of land are so important that flood control measures must be used, even if they are expensive. In other areas, the cost of flood prevention may be greater than the value of what needs protection, or it may be ineffective. These areas may be abandoned as water levels rise or land becomes eroded.

▶ *A coastal erosion control scheme*

Urban drainage control

More sudden or increased rainfall may cause flooding when river levels rise too high. A range of techniques may reduce flooding.

Permeable urban surfaces

Replacing impermeable concrete and tarmac with permeable ones, such as gravel or soil, reduces flooding in the urban area. Slowing runoff also reduces extremes in river flow and helps prevent flooding downstream.

River flow management

Tributaries flowing into a river will increase the river water level. Retaining the water in the tributary or slowing the flow of the water from the land may reduce flooding around the main river.

▶ *Houses in Happisburgh, Norfolk have been abandoned as the coast has been eroded*

❶ *This dam is used to regulate river flow downstream after heavy rain to prevent flooding of houses near the river.*

❷ *Plantations can be planted to slow the flow of water into reservoirs and rivers after heavy rain.*

Runoff from rural land into rivers after rain can be delayed by constructing low soil dams or increasing afforestation. Larger dams can be used to regulate river flow, storing water in times of heavy flow and releasing it to maintain river flow in dry weather.

Maintaining flood plains and woodland to delay runoff into rivers also helps reduce flooding.

Raised buildings

Raising buildings on stilts protects against flooding up to the height of the stilts.

Floating houses

In low lying areas where flooding is common, constructing houses on tethered floating platforms would protect them from flooding, for example, in the Netherlands and the river deltas of Bangladesh and India.

Ozone depletion

The element oxygen is present in the atmosphere in three forms with one, two or three atoms. O, O_2, and O_3 are present in the stratosphere in a dynamic equilibrium of chemical reactions caused by the absorption of ultraviolet light.

Importance of stratospheric ozone

Formation of ozone

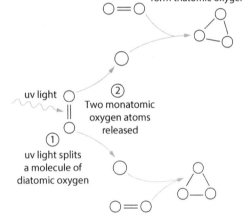

Ozone concentrations in the stratosphere are as high as 10 parts per million. It is located approximately 20-50 kilometres above the Earth's surface. It is important because it prevents most of the high-energy ultraviolet solar radiation from reaching the Earth's surface. Ultraviolet light is short wavelength electromagnetic energy with wavelengths between 10 and 400nm. UV can be categorized by its wavelength.

The UV light considered in studying ozone depletion is UVB.

Type of UV light	Wavelength range	Characteristics
UV A	320 - 400nm	Not absorbed by ozone or diatomic oxygen
UV B	280 - 320nm	Almost fully absorbed by ozone
UV C	<280nm	Completely absorbed by ozone and diatomic oxygen (O2)

The effects of UVB light on living organisms

If UVB is not absorbed in the atmosphere then it will reach the Earth's surface and may be absorbed by living cells. The energy of the UVB is absorbed and some is converted to chemical energy as it breaks up biological molecules causing skin damage, DNA damage, skin cancer, cataracts, leaf tissue damage and reduced photosynthesis and damage to marine organisms such as algae, corals, and planktonic organisms.

Destruction of ozone

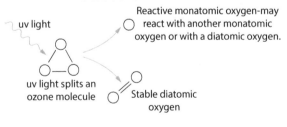

▲ *The role of UV light in the formation and destruction of stratospheric ozone*

Chlorofluorocarbons (CFCs)

CFCs were developed in the 1920s for use in air conditioning units, refrigerators, as aerosol propellants and as solvents for cleaning electrical equipment. Their properties made them ideal for these uses.

▼ Boiling points close enough to ambient temperatures that the gases can be liquefied with easily achievable pressures. So, aerosol cans did not need to be very strong and compressors in fridges and AC units did not have to be very powerful.

▼ Ability to dissolve grease and oils but not damage electrical components.

▼ CFCs are not flammable.

▼ Most are non-toxic.

❶ This can contained pure CFCs (trade-name: Freon) which was used as a solvent to clean computer circuit boards

❷ When the can was made in 1980 the can was labelled 'Environmentally safe propellant'. This meant that the CFCs were non-toxic to the user. The environmental harm caused by CFCs was not fully understood in 1980

The Rowland-Molina hypothesis

In 1974, two American research scientists suggested that the chemical properties of chlorofluorocarbons (CFCs) could lead to ozone depletion in the stratosphere. Their theory was based on the chemical behaviour of CFCs.

▼ **Persistence of CFCs:** CFCs are chemically stable so they remain in the atmosphere long enough to be carried up to the stratosphere.

▼ **Dissociation by UV and the release of chlorine:** although CFCs are stable in the troposphere, in the stratosphere they are exposed to higher levels of UV. They absorb the UV which breaks carbon to chlorine bonds and releases chlorine free radicals.

▼ **Reaction of chlorine and oxygen:** chlorine reacts with monatomic oxygen, therefore preventing its reaction with O_2 to form O_3. Further reactions prevent the formation of more ozone molecules.

▼ **Other halogens:** bromine and iodine can cause similar reactions.

Evidence for ozone depletion

Measuring ozone

The actual concentration of ozone is not used as a measure of ozone depletion because the atmosphere at the altitude of the ozone in the stratosphere is not normally sampled and concentrations vary at different altitudes. Ozone is measured in Dobson Units (DU) which estimates the total thickness of all the ozone in the atmosphere as if it existed as a layer of pure ozone at sea level. 100 DU is equivalent to a 1mm thick ozone layer. Normal ozone levels are about 300 DU. Ozone depletion can be mild or severe. An 'ozone hole' refers to levels below 220 DU, a level that had not been recorded before pollution by CFCs and other ozone-depleting substances (ODSs) had occurred.

Ground-based data collection

The first evidence of ozone depletion was collected by the British Antarctic Survey at Halley Station in Antarctica. The detection of higher levels of UV at ground level was evidence of ozone loss in the stratosphere.

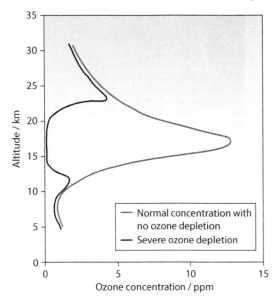

▲ The effect of ozone depletion on ozone concentration over Antarctica

Satellite surveys

Satellites orbit the Earth at greater altitudes than the stratosphere so UV passing downwards through the stratosphere cannot be measured. However, readings of UV light reflected by the Earth were higher than expected, suggesting ozone levels were reduced.

Air samples from the stratosphere

Ground-based and satellite surveys showed high UV levels as evidence of ozone depletion but could not confirm the cause, or detect any changes in the chemistry of the stratosphere. Air samples collected by helium balloons and high-flying research aircraft confirmed the chemicals that were causing depletion, especially chlorine and chlorine monoxide.

Variability in ozone levels

The concentration of ozone varies between different areas, at different times, and at different altitudes.

Ozone depletion is most severe at altitudes of 12 to 24 km where UV light splits ozone molecules, releasing monatomic oxygen that can react with chlorine, preventing the reformation of ozone.

The worst ozone depletion occurs over Antarctica where levels have sometimes dropped below 100DU. Ozone depletion over the Arctic is less severe and, globally, a drop in ozone levels of about 4% has occurred.

The severity of ozone depletion varies at different times of the year. Over Antarctica, the ozone hole is most severe between September and December, when levels start to recover.

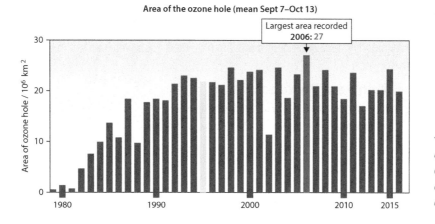

Area of the ozone hole (mean Sept 7–Oct 13)

Largest area recorded
2006: 27

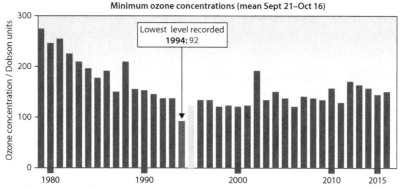

◀ *Changes in the area of the Antarctic ozone hole and the degree of ozone depletion*

Minimum ozone concentrations (mean Sept 21–Oct 16)

Lowest level recorded
1994: 92

The effect of ozone depletion on ozone concentration over Antarctica.
Source: NASA

Ozone depletion over Antarctica

The atmospheric conditions over Antarctica are unique and make ozone depletion much more severe. Stratospheric temperatures over Antarctic are lower than anywhere else on Earth, allowing the formation of stratospheric clouds and ice crystals. These provide surfaces on which chemical reactions take place, producing chlorine molecules (Cl_2) from the chlorine released from CFCs.

Winds around Antarctica rotate to create a 'polar vortex', with little mixing between the air over Antarctica and the rest of the atmosphere. This maintains low temperatures and produces higher concentrations of the chlorine that forms on the ice crystals.

It is completely dark in the Antarctic winter. When spring arrives, sunlight splits the chlorine molecules which produce the chlorine free radicals that cause ozone depletion.

Restoration of the ozone layer

International concern about ozone depletion led to international agreements to control the problem.

The Vienna Convention for the Protection of the Ozone Layer (1985)

This produced an agreement between every country in the UN to protect the ozone layer but included no legally binding goals. Such binding goals were laid out in the Montreal Protocol.

The Montreal Protocol

The main aspects of the Montreal Protocol are that:

- ▼ the manufacture and use of CFCs and other ozone-depleting substances (ODSs) was phased out and then banned;
- ▼ the use of HCFCs will be phased out by 2030;
- ▼ essential uses of some ODSs are still permitted, for example, halon fire extinguishers in aircraft;
- ▼ a fund is available to help countries implement the Montreal Protocol.

How the Montreal Protocol has been implemented

1. Use of alternative processes

- ▼ Pump action sprays are now used, for example, for domestic cleaning products.
- ▼ Stick or roll-on deodorants.

2. Use of alternative materials

- ▼ Hydrochlorofluorocarbons (HCFCs) were introduced to replace CFCs for refrigeration and air conditioning units. They are less chemically stable than CFCs so most would break down in the troposphere and would not reach the stratosphere where they could cause ozone depletion.
- ▼ Hydrofluorocarbons (HFCs) have replaced HCFCs for many uses. They contain no chlorine and do not cause ozone depletion but they are more expensive do not work as well as CFCs and are greenhouse gases..
- ▼ CFCs as aerosol propellants have been replaced by hydrocarbons such as propane and butane. Unlike CFCs these are flammable and pose a fire risk.
- ▼ CFCs in foam plastics have been replaced with HCFCs then with HFCs. HFCs are being replaced with other gases such as carbon dioxide and nitrogen.
- ▼ CFCs in asthma inhalers have been replaced with hydrofluoroalkanes (HFAs).
- ▼ A range of alternatives are used to replace CFC solvents, depending on what is being cleaned. These include alcohols, HCFCs, CO2 pellet blasting, and ultrasound cleaning.
- ▼ Safe disposal of waste CFCs. Waste CFCs from old fridges and air conditioning units are drained and incinerated. The CFCs are broken down into carbon dioxide and acidic gases (HCl, HF) that can be neutralized with crushed lime.

Evaluation of the effectiveness of ozone restoration methods

Although emissions of many ODSs have been controlled, the story of ozone depletion is not over. It will be many years before the pollutants produced by human activities have stopped causing ozone depletion but the severity of ozone depletion is reducing.

The success of the Montreal Protocol had several causes:

- international recognition of the serious consequences of ozone depletion;
- agreement between nearly every country that action must be taken;
- the development of alternative processes and processes so the use of most ODSs was no longer necessary.

Some ODSs have not been banned, for example, dichloromethane. Research continues into their impacts. Their continued use may delay the restoration of the ozone layer.

▼ NOAA Images: Changes in ozone depletion over Antarctica 1979 - 2016

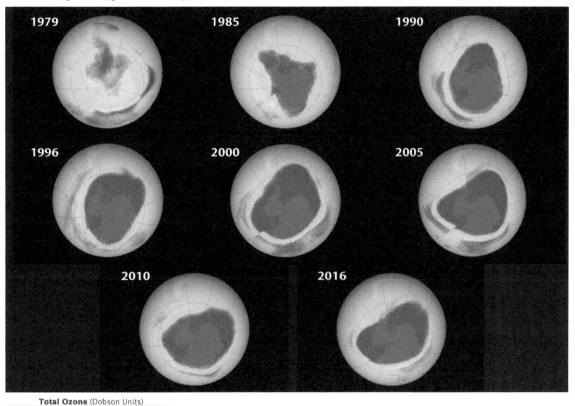

Total Ozone (Dobson Units)
0   100   200   300   400   500   600   700

Key principles

- The atmosphere plays important roles in many natural processes that are important for life on Earth.
- The troposphere and stratosphere have different roles in supporting life.
- The gases of the atmosphere control the atmospheric processes which control the climate.
- An increase in atmospheric temperatures affects a wide variety of natural processes, both directly and indirectly.
- The interconnections between natural processes and the impacts of negative and positive feedback mechanisms make accurate predictions of climate change difficult.
- Reducing anthropogenic releases of greenhouse gases requires major lifestyle changes.
- The control of ozone depletion has been a success story of scientific research, analysis, the development of solutions, and their effective implementation with global political support.

The Hydrosphere

▼ Global demand for water
▼ The natural hydrological cycle
▼ Human impacts on the hydrological cycle
▼ Exploitation of new water sources
▼ Sustainable management of water sources

Water is a renewable resource that is essential for all living organisms. Human society has only been able to develop easily where water is available.

Although water is an abundant renewable resource, it is often unevenly distributed and human activities affect the quantity and quality of the water that is available.

Developing strategies to ensure adequate future supplies of water requires an understanding of human uses of water, how these are changing, the natural processes that cycle water in the environment and how human activities affect these.

Human uses of water

Use	% of total	Selected major activities
Agriculture	70	Irrigation
Industry	22	Cooling Heating Washing Solvent
Domestic uses	8	Flushing toilets Washing clothes, dishes Hygiene

Global demand for water

The global demand for water is increasing for a range of reasons.

▼ **Increase in population:** the population may grow because the birth rate is higher than the death rate or because of immigration from other countries or other regions within the same country.

▼ **Increase in per-capita use with increased affluence:** in the poorest communities where there is no piped supply, domestic water use may be limited to the amount that can be carried from the source such as the nearest river or well. As piped water becomes available and people become increasingly affluent, they use more for washing and buy more appliances that use water such as washing machines, dishwashers and swimming pools. Although modern appliances may be designed to use less water, there is still a link between affluence and water consumption.

▶ **Increased irrigation of farmland:** subsistence agriculture usually relies on the water that is naturally available, adapting the type of farming if water is a problem, for example, nomadic herding rather than arable farming. As commercial agriculture expands, the increased income allows money to be invested in irrigation schemes. Irrigation water may be pumped from aquifers and rivers or from water stored in reservoirs. Irrigation now uses more water than all other human uses combined.

▶ **Industrialisation:** different industries have different water requirements. Heavy industry, such as the chemical and steel industries or paper making, use much more water than lighter manufacturing industries. The service industries use very little water apart from the water used by the workers for domestic uses.

The natural hydrological cycle

Water is an abundant renewable resource with a variety of natural processes that combine to form the hydrological cycle. The amounts of water in each reservoir remain constant over long time periods because the processes are in a state of dynamic equilibrium and processes cancel each other.

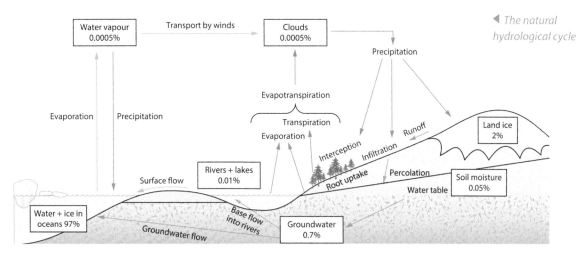

◀ *The natural hydrological cycle*

▲ *Processes, precipitation, interception, infiltration, percolation, groundwater flow, runoff, evaporation, transpiration, river channel discharge*

	Quantity of water /% of total (rounded values)	Residence time (typical values)
Oceans	97	Up to 4000 years
Land ice	2	20-100 years
Groundwater	0.7	100-10 000 years
Lakes and rivers	0.01	2 months – 100 years
Soil moisture	0.005	2 months
Atmosphere	0.001	10 days
Living organisms	0.00004	1 week

The importance of a reservoir of water cannot be predicted from its quantity. Some reservoirs are abundant but are transferred slowly, for example, groundwater, others have a small total quantity but are transferred quickly, for example, atmospheric water.

Residence times, transfers rates and water volume are connected and one value can be calculated if the other two are known.

Residence Time = Volume of water in the reservoir/mean transfer rate

Human impacts on the hydrological cycle

Human activities alter the transfer rates in the hydrological cycle, upsetting the dynamic equilibria that existed. This changes the amounts of water present in the different reservoirs on global, regional, and local scales.

The extent and direction of the changes may be different in different areas, for example, one area having declining rainfall while another area may have increasing rainfall.

The rates of change can vary, for example, some glaciers are shrinking rapidly while others are changing slowly. Changes to large reservoirs such as the oceans or land ice are often less obvious than changes to small reservoirs such as the atmosphere, rivers, or soil moisture.

The main impact of the industrial and domestic use of water is on water quality through the release of pollutants. Their impact on the hydrological cycle tends to be local and is most obvious where large urban centres have developed in areas with restricted water supplies.

Deforestation

Vegetation intercepts rainfall which may evaporate before it reaches the ground. Trees also return a lot of water from the soil to the atmosphere by transpiration. The loss of trees can cause a significant reduction in precipitation in downwind areas as more of the water infiltrates the ground, or runs off into rivers.

Agriculture

Soil can be compacted by the use of heavy farm machinery or by livestock trampling. Water does not infiltrate easily into compacted soil so soil moisture levels drop and runoff increases.

Crop irrigation increases evaporation rates.

The loss of soil biota such as worms reduces infiltration, increases surface runoff and reduces water retention by the soil. See page 330, Changes in the hydrological cycle (agriculture).

Urban development

Urban areas often have impermeable surfaces such as concrete and tarmac. This reduces infiltration while increasing the rate of runoff. Rapid runoff from large urban areas can increase river flooding downstream.

Global climate change

Higher global temperatures affect rates of melting, evaporation and condensation as well as wind patterns. These combine to alter the type, amount, timing and location of precipitation.

More rapid melting of snow and ice is caused by the warming associated with global climate change. Snow fall in cold weather and its later melting in warm weather reduces extremes in river flow, so the loss of ice may increase flooding after heavy rain and low river flow during periods of low rainfall.

Changes in evaporation, temperature and wind velocity/direction will change the timing, type and amount of precipitation.

Water abstraction

Rivers and reservoirs

Some abstraction of river water has little impact on the river as the used water is cleaned and returned to the river. However, rivers have often been used to carry away wastes. Some abstractive uses do not return the water to the river which reduces downstream flow, for example, agricultural irrigation.

Environmental effects of reservoirs

Construction of a dam and reservoir creation alters the environment of the reservoir site itself and the surrounding area.

- **Habitat change:** flooding the reservoir obviously destroys the previous habitats but it also creates new and valuable ones. Wetlands are uncommon habitats in most regions so the reservoir may be more valuable than what has been lost.
- **Wildlife barriers:** the dam and reservoir act as a barrier to wildlife that migrates along the river such as salmon and sturgeon. Free movement along the river is an important part of recolonising areas that have become vacant in bad years. The dam may prevent this.
- **River regime downstream of dams:** the reservoir may be used to provide water in two different ways.

  Water may be used to regulate the river flow, holding water back during times of surplus to ensure adequate river flow in times of shortage. This reduces the risk of flooding downstream but also reduces periods of lower flow which are important for some species such as river turtles that lay their eggs in sandbanks. Periods of rapid flow are also important to wash away sediments from gravel river beds in which salmon and trout lay their eggs.

  The changes in flow fluctuations can change river erosion and sedimentation and therefore the development of meanders.
- **Sedimentation:** the sediments that are carried into the reservoir will settle there and not be carried further downstream. In the past, they may have been important to fertilise the floodplain downstream. They may also have built up river banks and coastlines and counteracted erosion.
- **Microclimates:** the large body of water may change the local climate. The high heat capacity of water helps to reduce temperature fluctuations. It will be warmer in winter and cooler in summer.

Water provides less friction than land, so windspeeds will be higher.

Greater evaporation from the reservoir surface may increase humidity, cloud cover, and precipitation downwind of the reservoir.

Over-exploited rivers

▶ **Rivers flowing into the Aral Sea:** the Syr Darya and Amu Darya rivers flow through central Asia to the Aral Sea, which used to be the fourth largest lake in the world. Since the 1960s, huge irrigation schemes in part of the Soviet Union (now part of Kazakhstan) used river water to irrigate cotton and rice crops. River flow into the Aral Sea declined, sometimes to zero. The area of the lake was reduced by 90% and pollution by pesticides, fertilisers, and industrial waste caused serious problems.

There are still disagreements between the countries that share the rivers: conflict between Kazakhstan, Uzbekistan, Turkmenistan, Tajikistan, and Krygystan. Abstraction for irrigation reduces downstream flow. Flow through HEP dams in the summer may be reduced to store water for winter generation but this reduces the availability of summer irrigation water downstream.

▶ **River Nile:** the Nile is the longest river in the world, flowing through ten countries including Egypt, Sudan, and Ethiopia. There is a long history of disagreements between countries over direct water abstraction for irrigation and the construction of dams to regulate flow, provide water, and generate electricity. As populations grow and these countries develop economically the demand for water will increase and the risk of conflict may grow.

▶ **Rivers of Tibet:** Tibet used to be an independent country but was incorporated into China in 1950. The Tibetan plateau is the source of many of Asia's major rivers, with more than 1500 million people depending on water from the Indus, Ganges, Brahmaputra, Yangtze, Mekong, Salween, and Yellow rivers. Growing populations and increased demand for agriculture and industry may lead to water shortages and conflict between countries. This problem of water shortages may be made worse by seasonal fluctuation in river flow caused by climate change. The melting of glaciers in the Himalayas maintain river flow during dry seasons but receding glaciers may produce less reliable river flow in the future.

▶ *The major rivers of Asia that have their sources in Tibet*

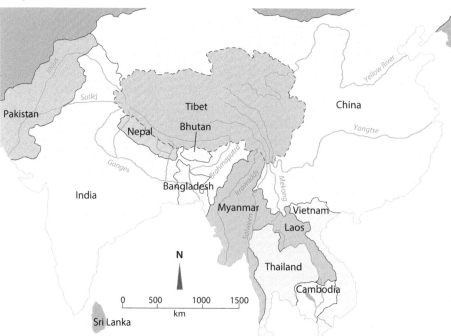

Other over-exploited rivers

River	Countries affected
Colorado	USA, Mexico
Murray-Darling	Australia
Yellow River	China
Indus	Pakistan
Euphrates and Tigris	Turkey, Iraq, Syria
Jordan	Israel, Lebanon, Jordan, Palestine

The abstraction of river water often reduces downstream flow. This affects the river and any lakes that it feeds. Some rivers completely cease to flow.

Aquifers

Features of aquifers

An aquifer is a body of rock that holds water which is exploited as a resource. For a rock to form an aquifer it must have certain features.

- **Porosity:** this is a measure of the proportion of a rock's volume that is space and could therefore hold water. Chalk, limestone and sandstone are porous rocks that can form aquifers.
- **Permeability:** this is a measure of the ease with which fluids may flow through a rock because of the interconnections between the spaces and their size. Some materials such as clay are porous but the pores are too small for water to flow through easily.
- **Associated geological structures:** the rock below the water-bearing rock must be impermeable to prevent the escape of the water. Granite and clay are suitable impermeable rocks. Some of the rock above must be permeable to allow recharge of the aquifer.

▲ *A lake that dried up following over-exploitation*

Aquifer recharge

The natural amount of water in an aquifer is in a state of dynamic equilibrium of the natural inflow or recharge of water into the aquifer and the water that flows out of the aquifer. If abstraction of water by humans is greater than the rate of recharge then the volume of water in the aquifer will decline. It may be a long time before the decline in the aquifer becomes obvious because the original stored volume may have been very large. The reduction of water in the aquifer can have serious consequences.

Most aquifer recharge takes place as precipitation landing on the ground surface infiltrates and percolates through soil and rock to the aquifer. Water abstraction from aquifers that are recharged by surface water can be sustainable as long as it does not exceed the recharge rate.

Some aquifers were recharged during the last ice age 10-20,000 years ago when the global climate was wetter. Many of these are not currently being recharged so their exploitation will eventually lead to shortages. Some contain huge volumes of water and will last a long time, but relying on this water for long-term supplies is dangerous because supplies are not sustainable.

Ancient aquifer water is often saline and can cause soil salinization as irrigation water evaporates, leaving the salt behind. This can cause osmotic dehydration and the death of crops.

Over-exploited aquifers

▛ **Changes in surface hydrology**: many rivers, lakes and marshes are fed by groundwater flowing out of aquifers. If the groundwater is overexploited then the water table may be lowered, reducing or stopping the outflow of water into the wetland, causing it to dry up.

▛ **Ecological impacts:** if the water table is lowered then plants with a higher water requirement will die or become less abundant as they fail to compete with plants that have a lower requirement for water.

Aquatic or semi-aquatic animals will die if wetlands dry out. Other species may be affected, even though they do not rely on the water directly, because they depended for food on the species that needed the water.

▛ **Salt water incursion:** in coastal areas the water table may be slightly higher than sea level. As rainwater percolates down to the aquifer, water flows sideways and out into the sea. This seawards flow of freshwater prevents seawater from flowing into the aquifer under the land surface. If the aquifer is overexploited then seawater from the sea, or in the rock under the sea, flows sideways into the aquifer to replace the freshwater. The salt makes the aquifer water unsuitable for irrigation as it could kill the crops by osmotic dehydration.

◀ *A groundwater-fed river that dried up when the water table dropped*

▛ **Subsidence:** water that is no longer present in the interstitial spaces in the rock cannot provide support for the rock particles so they will be compacted by the weight of material above. This will cause subsidence at the surface which can cause serious damage to buildings and pipelines.

▛ **Reduced supplies:** if the extraction rate exceeds the recharge rate then the volume of water available for abstraction will be reduced. The unsustainable use of aquifer water may have carried on for many years before problems became obvious, so the human activities that relied on it may suddenly have to stop. Nearly half the world's population live in countries that are over-exploiting their aquifers.

▶ *Aquifer depletion caused the subsidence that damaged this building in Mexico City*

Monitoring aquifer depletion

Aquifer water levels can be monitored by checking the level of the water table in wells or boreholes but this is very slow and difficult to coordinate on a large scale.

NASA operates two GRACE satellites (GRACE = Gravity Recovery And Climate Experiment). Their orbit is affected by the force of gravity which is influenced by the mass of water in aquifers below their flight path. The entire Earth is surveyed every 30 days.

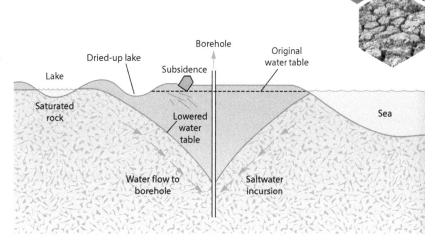

▲ *The effects of aquifer depletion*

Examples of over-exploited aquifers

▼ **High Plains Aquifer:** the High Plains Aquifer in the USA includes the Ogollala Aquifer. It extends over 450,000km² in mid-west states. This is one of the most important agricultural regions of the world and food production relies on irrigation with aquifer water. The water in the aquifer is largely paleowater (fossil water) which recharged the aquifer during or before the last ice age. Long-term abstraction rates for agriculture are greater than current recharge rates.

▼ **North China Plain:** the North China Plain is the largest agricultural region in China with fertile soil but few rivers, so groundwater is used for irrigation. The growing demand for irrigation water and the demands of the growing population have caused the water table of the aquifer to decline by around one metre per year. Measures are being introduced to try to reduce water use:

- low-pressure irrigation pipes are being used to reduce leaks:
- the most important crops are wheat and maize, however, the growth of crops that require less water has been proposed;
- consumers are being charged for the volume of water they use to encourage water conservation.
- Large scale afforestation projects have been developed to sequester carbon as a method of tackling climate change and to reduce soil erosion but transpiration by the trees reduces soil moisture levels.
- There are plans to transfer water 450 km from the Yangtze River to the area.

▼ **Malta:** Malta has an annual precipitation rate of 550mm but the evapotranspiration rate is 400mm so only 150mm remains available for use. Many of the island's aquifers have been contaminated by industrial or agricultural wastes, or have been over-exploited, so that the water table has dropped and salt water incursions have contaminated the freshwater.

- Sewage effluent is used for agricultural irrigation.
- A large proportion of public water supply is now provided by desalination of seawater which is very expensive.

Exploitation of new sources of water

The availability of water has a major effect on many aspects of life. It influences where people can live, what they can eat, which industries can be developed, and quality of life.

The quantity, reliability, purity, and location of water all affect the usefulness of a water supply.

To satisfy the growing population and increased per-capita demand, it may be necessary to exploit previously unused resources or increase the exploitation rate of existing supplies.

Precipitation

Rainwater catchment

Header tank

Water used in house

Overflow

Pump used to refill header tank in periods of low rainfall

Overflow

Main storage tank

Aquifer recharge

▲ *A rainwater catchment and storage system that uses surplus water for aquifer recharge*

Rainwater collection

This is increasingly important in areas where public supplies cannot match consumer demand, for example, many cities in India. It also reduces urban flooding after heavy rain.

Collecting rainwater is also important in rural areas where there is no public water supply. The water is often cleaner than other sources such as rivers.

Rivers

River water is often the most convenient source of water. Being long, they are accessible over a large land area. Natural contaminants are rarely a serious problem and human problems were not usually a problem until population density rose to the point where waste from a community upstream did not break down before it reached the next community.

❶ *River water used for domestic use may be contaminated with pathogens*
❷ *Rainwater collection in Kenya.*

The main features that affect the usefulness of a river

- total annual water flow (river discharge);
- flow fluctuations;
- level of natural contaminants;
- pollutants from human activities.

Reservoirs

Reservoirs allow the storage of water from times when there is a surplus of water so that it can be used when there is a shortage. But, even if there is a suitable water supply, many other factors must be considered when choosing a site for a dam and reservoir.

Factors affecting reservoir site selection

Factor	Description
Topography	The main cost of reservoir construction is building the dam while the income created by the reservoir comes from the amount of water it can provide. The ideal topography creates a narrow exit from a large deep basin so that a relatively small dam can hold back a huge volume of water.
Geology	The rock beneath the reservoir must be impermeable so the water cannot percolate into the rock and be lost. The rock should also be strong enough to support the weight of the dam and reservoir, without faults or seismic activity that could cause an earthquake and the collapse of the dam.
Catchment area	This is the area of land over which rain will flow or through the ground and then into a river. So the ability of a reservoir to provide water is controlled by the reservoir site itself and the area that collects water for it. Even if it has not rained recently, there may be a lot of water from previous rain that is on its way to the reservoir. The catchment area does not have to be around the reservoir itself. It may be in a mountain range with the water flowing into a river that carries the water to the reservoir site downstream.
Water supply	Ideally, the rainfall or river inflow should be regular and have a large volume. The climate should not be too hot or dry to cause excessive evaporation losses.
Pollution risk	Land uses in the catchment area should not pose a serious pollution risk to the water. The main risk is caused by toxic pollutants from industry and agricultural pesticides. Pollutants such as sewage and manure are biodegradable and break down relatively quickly. They are unlikely to become as concentrated as they could in a river. If the flooded area of the reservoir was covered with forest, or a lot of dead vegetation is carried into the water, then it may decay anaerobically. This releases methane that adds to global climate change.
Sedimentation	Soil erosion in the catchment area can make the inflow river very turbid, resulting in sedimentation in the reservoir. This gradually reduces the volume of water that the reservoir can hold.
Infrastructure	Building the dam, treating the water and transporting it to the area of demand require workers, building materials, access routes, and machinery. A convenient site near the area of demand may be chosen rather than a site which would supply more water but is isolated and difficult to reach.
Existing land use and land-use conflicts	The use of the land that is to be flooded cannot be so important that it cannot be lost. A loss:benefit analysis must be considered to balance the benefits of having the reservoir against what is lost. In the UK, large urban areas and important wildlife conservation areas would probably be protected, while agricultural land would be less valued. Other countries may assess their priorities differently.

Estuary barrages

An estuary barrage is a freshwater reservoir created by building a dam across an estuary where a river enters the sea. The reservoir has fewer land use conflicts than reservoirs on land that require land to be flooded, but they change important inter-tidal habitats, create an obstacle for shipping and can be polluted by human activities anywhere in the river's catchment area.

Seawater

Desalination of sea water is very energy-intensive and expensive so it is only used in countries where seawater is available and there are inadequate supplies of freshwater.

Sustainable management of water

A range of strategies can be used to ensure future supplies of water are sustainable.

Artificial recharge of aquifers

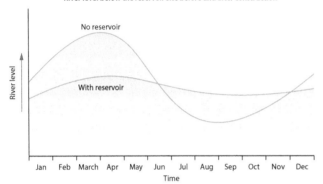

Water from aquifers may be abstracted during dry seasons but the recharge rate may be low during wet seasons when the infiltration capacity of surface rocks is exceeded and surplus runoff flows to the sea via rivers. Aquifer supplies can be maintained by using surplus water during periods of high rainfall to recharge the aquifers by pumping it underground or by diverting it into lagoons where it can infiltrate into the ground gradually.

River-regulation reservoirs

Human activities often increase extremes in river flow such as deforestation or urbanisation within the river's catchment area. Reservoirs can be used to regulate these extremes in river flow.

During periods of low rainfall the reservoir is used to maintain river levels by opening the dam to allow more water into the river.

Following periods of heavy rainfall the reservoir is used to store surplus water to reduce flooding downstream.

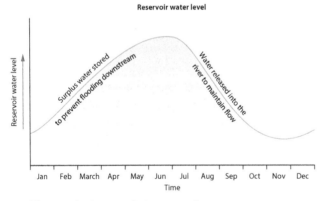

▲ *The use of a river-regulation reservoir*

Inter-basin transfers

Canal and pipe systems may be used to transfer water from areas with a water surplus to areas with a water shortage. This method has been used in many areas including:

⬧ China;
⬧ Russia;
⬧ Australia;
⬧ Wales to England.

Unexploited aquifers

Newly discovered aquifers may increase water supplies, such as in areas of North Africa and North Kenya.

Afforestation

Trees help to reduce soil erosion and reduce the rate of flow of rainwater into rivers. This reduces the fluctuations in river level, helping to reduce flooding after heavy rain as well as maintaining river level during periods of low rainfall.

Water conservation

Water is a renewable resource but the volume that is available for use depends on how it is exploited. Water conservation can use several different strategies.

Low volume uses

These reduce the volume of water needed to carry out particular tasks.

- **Low-water appliances**, for example, washing machines, dishwashers, dual flush toilets, tap timers, low flow shower heads.
- **Xeriscaping:** this involves the management of gardens, parks and urban spaces such as roadside verges and roundabouts by planting them with species that are adapted to dry conditions so that less water is needed to water them.
- **Low-volume irrigation:** drip irrigation delivers water directly to the plants, leading to lower evaporation losses than overhead sprays

Recycling used water

'Grey water' use involves retaining water that has been used but is still quite clean. It is then re-used for other purposes, for example, water used for baths or showers can be used to flush toilets or for garden uses.

❶ *A xeriscaped garden*   ❷ *Drip irrigation*   ❸ *Spray irrigation*

Pollution control

Many activities produce contaminated water which cannot be re-used and may pollute other sources such as rivers. Many effluent treatment processes can be used to treat contaminated water. Examples of water pollution control include:

- oil pollution control;
- sewage treatment;
- acid mine drainage;
- control of heavy metal waste;
- landfill leachate treatment;
- buffer strips next to rivers to reduce fertiliser runoff.

See Chapter 10 for further detail.

Reduced wastage

A lot of the water infrastructure in the UK is old and in poor condition. About 20% of the water intended for public supply is lost from leaking pipes. Leaking appliances can also waste a lot of water, such as dripping taps. Repairs and good maintenance can reduce this.

Paying a fixed fee for water use does not encourage careful use of water. Water meters match the charges that consumers pay to the volume of water used. This encourages the conservation of water as using less water will reduce the bill.

◀ *Water Meter*

Water treatment

The water that is abstracted may not be suitable for use so treatment may be needed. The quality problem may be natural or may be caused by human activities. The treatment processes used depend upon the quality of the abstracted water and the quality requirement of the intended use.

Selected water uses and their quality requirements

Water use	Quality requirement	Problems if quality requirement is not met
Potable (drinkable) water for public water supply	No pathogenic microorganisms Toxins at acceptable levels Water that looks, smells, and tastes good	Public health risks Consumer complaints
Spray irrigation	Low turbidity Low levels of toxins that may be absorbed by crops, for example, heavy metals	Blockage of water pipes Contamination of food
Textile washing with soap	'Soft' water with low calcium ion concentration	Scum forms on textiles
Power station condenser cooling water	No gross solids	Pipe blockage
Industrial boiler water	No dissolved minerals	Mineral deposits would build up, reducing heat exchange and blocking pipes

Water treatment processes

Sedimentation

The water is allowed to remain static to let suspended solids such as silt to settle.

Screens

Many items enter the fluid flow that would create problems for later processes. Metal grills or meshes are used to remove vegetation and litter such as plastic and paper items. See page 270 for more detail.

Aeration

Bubbles of air or water sprays are used to aerate the water and ensure a high dissolved oxygen content. Water sources that are anaerobic may contain hydrogen sulfide from the decay of organic matter, which makes the water smell of bad eggs.

Some dissolved metals that are toxic, or give the water a bad taste, are removed by aeration as they become insoluble.

Flocculation/coagulation and clarification

Clay particles do not settle out in the sedimentation lagoons because electrostatic charges on their surfaces cause them to repel each other. These can be neutralised by adding flocculants such as aluminium sulfate (alum) or polyelectrolytes. They are mixed quickly with the water then passed into the clarifier tank where the particles are allowed to settle.

Filtration

In some treatment plants filters are used to remove any remaining suspended solids and bacteria. These often involve slow flow through layers of sand and gravel.

▼ *Water treatment processes*

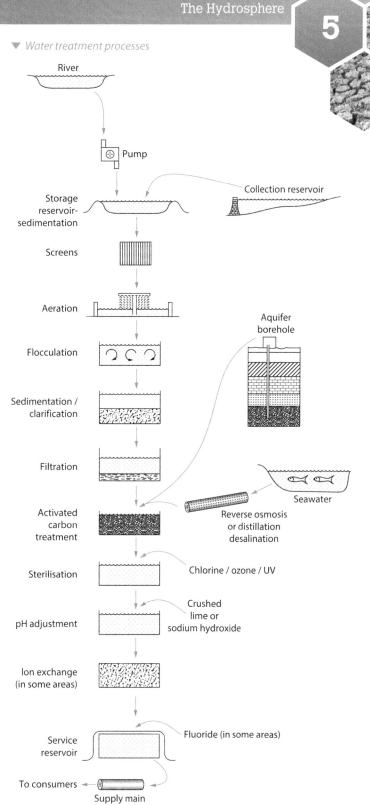

▶ *A sand filter being constructed*

Activated carbon filters

Particles of activated carbon are used to remove organic chemicals such as pesticides , which adsorb onto the carbon particles..

Sterilisation

The addition of chlorine, ozone, or exposure to ultraviolet light, is used to sterilise the water and kill pathogens. Chlorine is the most common method but if the water is from peaty sources then organic matter may be present which could react with the chlorine and produce toxic substances. In this case, ozone is added or UV light is used.

The addition of chlorine should keep the water sterile during distribution but it is gradually lost. Using chloramine keeps the water sterile for longer as it breaks down gradually and releases chlorine.

pH control

Sterilisation with chlorine can make the water too acidic. The pH is adjusted by adding crushed lime.

Fluoridation

Fluorides are added to water in some areas to improve the dental health of people that drink the water.

Ion exchange

Toxic ions such as those of lead, mercury and arsenic can be removed from water using ion exchange resins. The toxic ions adsorb onto polymer beads or particles of zeolite.

Ion exchange is also used to remove calcium and magnesium ions to produce 'soft' water.

▲ *Domestic sterilisation unit*

Reverse osmosis

Seawater is the most abundant source of water but the high salt content makes it unusable except for uses where its composition is unimportant, such as condenser cooling water for power stations.

Removing salt from seawater by desalination is expensive and is only carried out if other sources of water are unavailable.

The saline water is filtered at very high pressure through the partially permeable membranes of very small polyamide tubes. The fresh water that is collected has about half the original volume. The remaining very salty water is returned to the sea. A lot of energy is needed to produce the very high pressures which makes desalinated seawater very expensive.

▲ *Desalination cartridges*

Distillation

Water is boiled by heating and/or reducing the pressure. The steam that is produced is condensed and collected.

Key principles
- Water is a renewable resource.
- The availability of water affects the development of society.
- Poor management can alter the equilibria of the hydrological cycle and deplete supplies.
- Poor management can contaminate supplies.
- Good management can maintain and increase water availability.

The Lithosphere

Chapter topics

▼ Mineral resources extracted from the lithosphere
▼ Geological processes
▼ Mineral exploitation
▼ The environmental impacts of mineral exploitation
▼ Future mineral supplies

The lithosphere is made up of the solid crust and upper mantle. It includes the rocks, mineral resources and soils that provide environmental resources and services that are important to human societies.

Mineral resources extracted from the lithosphere

Many mineral resources extracted from the crust are used to make a wide range of industrial products and construction materials.

Major uses of selected mineral resources

Selected materials	Global annual production/ t	Examples of major uses
Metals		
Iron	1700m	Buildings: girders and steel reinforced concrete Transport: ships, road vehicles, rail track bridges Appliance cases: for example, cookers, fridges, washing machines
Aluminium	53m	Packaging foil, vehicles window frames
Copper	19m	Electric cables, water pipes
Zinc	14m	Steel protection: galvanising Batteries Alloys, for example, brass
Lead	9m	Lead-acid batteries Construction: roof and window flashing Radiation shielding
Titanium	6m	White pigments in paint, paper, plastics Aircraft, spacecraft (as aluminium alloys)
Nickel	2.1m	Metal alloys to increase tensile strength, for example, jet engine turbines
Tin	360 000	Solder Rust prevention in tin plated steel food cans, Glass manufacture
Uranium	66 000	Nuclear fuel for power stations
Cadmium	25 000	Rechargeable batteries

Lanthanum	25 000	Batteries for hybrid vehicles, sponge-alloy hydrogen storage
Neodymium	25 000	Magnets, for example, for electric motors, lasers
Cerium	50 000	Catalytic converters, diesel additives to increase combustion efficiency, LCD screens
Yttrium	10 000	LED lights
Gold	2500	Coins, jewellery, electrical conductors
Mercury	2 000	Fluorescent lamps Thermometers
Indium	710	Electronics, for example, transistors, semiconductors
Gallium	440	Electronics, for example, LED lights, photovoltaic solar panels
Platinum	220	Vehicle catalytic converters Catalyst in the chemical industry
Industrial minerals and construction materials		
Aggregates (sand and gravel)	40b	Concrete, building mortar, glass
Limestone	600m	Cement, crushed for road surfacing and railtrack ballast, building blocks
Salt (sodium chloride)	290m	Source of chlorine for manufacture of paper, plastics, water sterilisation De-icing roads Food additive
Gypsum (china clay)	180m	Building plaster, food additive
Sulfur	75m	Sulfuric acid manufacture to make phosphate fertilisers Pest control
Kaolin (from China clay)	26m	Filler and coating for paper Ceramics, for example, porcelain Filler in paint, cosmetics, toothpaste
Total: all extracted minerals	**55b**	

As industrial and consumer products become more complex, a wider range of elements is used.

Metals used in a mobile phone

Component	Selected elements
Case	Magnesium, titanium, chromium
Electronics	Aluminium, antimony, gallium, mercury, zirconium, silver, platinum
Battery	Manganese, cobalt, nickel, cadmium, terbium, dysprosium, erbium, thulium, ytterbium, lutetium
Speaker and vibration unit	Iron, tungsten, neodymium
Screen	Silicon, cerium, indium

❶ *The structure of an Airbus A380 is 60% aluminium, 10% titanium*

❷ *Tall buildings use steel and concrete for structural strength with glass for the external structure.*

❸ *Concrete is strong, durable and cheap. It is made with lithosphere resources: sand, gravel and cement (mainly limestone, plus sand, clay and shale)*

❹ *The chemical industry uses a lot of stainless steel because it is not very reactive. It is mainly iron and chromium.*

Geological processes that created exploitable mineral deposits

Many geological processes have produced exploitable mineral deposits. Most of them involve the separation of mixtures of minerals to produce localised concentrations of minerals that are sufficiently pure for economic exploitation.

Igneous processes

The processes by which rocks and minerals are created by the cooling and hardening of magma or molten lava are known as **igneous.** Many different igneous processes have produced exploitable mineral deposits.

Hydrothermal deposition

- Igneous intrusions are rocks formed from magma that cools and solidifies within the Earth's crust. The intrusions produce pressurised superheated water at high temperatures that dissolves many minerals from the surrounding rocks. These mineral-rich solutions travel along fissures away from the igneous batholith, cooling as they do so. As they cool, dissolved minerals crystallise and come out of solution. They do this in order of their solubility: the least soluble crystallising first.

- This process of fractional crystallisation starts with a mixture of minerals that could not have been exploited. Once the minerals became separated and deposited, soon after the batholith formed, later exploitation became possible.

- Metal ores that are deposited by hydrothermal processes include tin, copper, lead, silver, gold, and arsenic.

Metamorphic processes

Igneous processes and tectonic movements of crustal plates can alter existing rocks with high temperatures and pressure, without melting them producing metamosphic rocks. High temperatures and extreme pressure can change limestone to marble. Extreme pressure can change mudstone to slate.

Sedimentary processes

Sedimentary processes cause minerals to settle and build up to produce layers of deposited sediment . This deposition and subsequent cementation at the Earth's surface and within bodies of water creates sedimentary rocks and minerals.

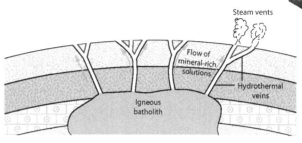

▲ *Hydrothermal veins around an igneous batholith*

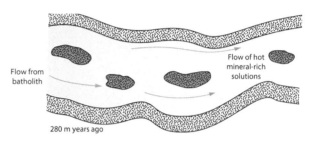

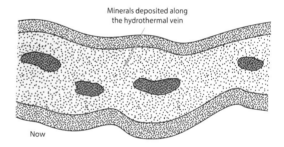

▲ *Mineral transport and deposition in hydrothermal veins*

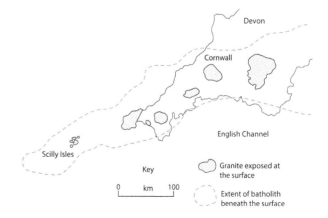

▲ *The igneous batholith under SW England*

133

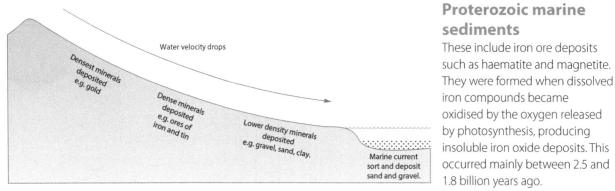

Proterozoic marine sediments

These include iron ore deposits such as haematite and magnetite. They were formed when dissolved iron compounds became oxidised by the oxygen released by photosynthesis, producing insoluble iron oxide deposits. This occurred mainly between 2.5 and 1.8 billion years ago.

▲ *How alluvial processes separate and deposit minerals*

Alluvial deposits

Alluvial processes involve materials that were carried and separated by flowing water. The ability of water to carry solids depends upon the velocity of the water and the density of the solids. Materials that are exploited from alluvial deposits include gold, diamonds, tin ore, gravel, sand, clay.

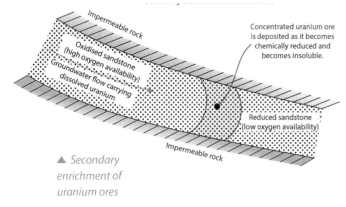

▲ *Secondary enrichment of uranium ores*

Evaporites

If a bay of an ancient sea became isolated, then the water may have evaporated leaving crystallised minerals such as halite (sodium chloride). Evaporites also form in inland seas in desert areas as the water from inflowing rivers evaporates.

Secondary enrichment

Many economically important metals can form minerals that are soluble or insoluble depending upon the conditions, especially the availability of oxygen. They may be transported in solution, by moving water, and then deposited as their oxidation state changes.

Biological sediments

Biological processes are those where living organisms form mineral deposits. These processes often concentra

Biological sedimentary deposits

Original material	Sedimentary deposit produced
Shells of marine organisms	Limestone and chalk
Terrestrial vegetation	Coal
Marine organisms	Crude oil and natural gas

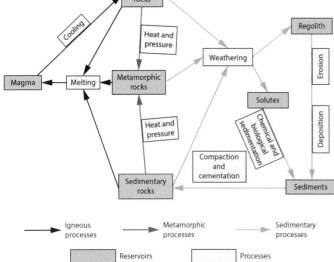

◀ *The rock cycle summarises how igneous, sedimentary, and metamorphic rocks are formed.*

Mineral exploitation

The quantity of exploitable deposits that exists in the crust of every mineral is much greater than we could realistically use. However, most of the deposits are in inaccessible places, or at purities that are too low for current economic exploitation.

Lasky's principle states that: in general, as the purity of a mineral decreases, the amount of the mineral present increases exponentially. So, the major problem with future mineral supplies is not the quantity that exists but the need to develop methods to exploit low-grade deposits.

Lasky's principle

To help with estimates of future availability, it is important to predict which deposits are likely to become exploitable in the future and when. This involves many estimates and uncertainties.

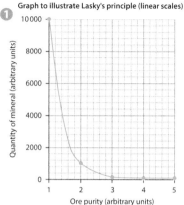

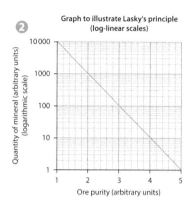

❶ *Graph to illustrate Lasky's principle (linear scales)*

❷ *Graph to illustrate Lasky's principle (log-linear scales)*

Reserves, resource, and stock

The mineral deposits in the crust can be categorised according to whether the technology exists to exploit them and whether this exploitation would be economically viable.

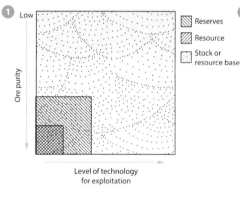

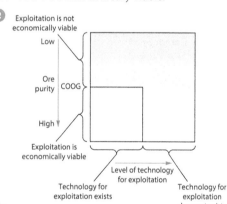

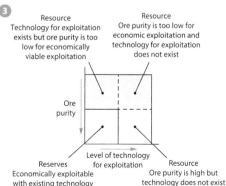

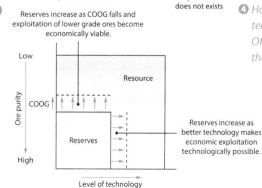

❶ *The relationship between reserves, resource, and stock*

❷ *The effect of ore purity and technology on reserves and resource*

❸ *Factors that prevent exploitation of the resource that is not currently in the reserves*

❹ *How changes in technology and Cut Off Ore Grade affect the reserves*

Mining companies have to plan many years ahead because it takes a long time to prepare a mine before any of the mineral can actually be extracted. This preparation includes gaining detailed information on the mineral that is to be mined. However, the methods that provide this information are expensive, especially trial drilling. So, deposits that will not be exploited in the near future may be investigated with cheaper methods that provide less detailed information. More thorough exploratory investigations would be carried out nearer the time that exploitation may take place.

Stock (also called resource base)

This includes all of the material that exists in the lithosphere. It includes the mineral that can be exploited now, that which will be exploitable when prices rise, or new technologies are developed and that which will never be technologically or economically exploitable.

Resource

The resource is larger than the reserves as it includes all the material that is theoretically available for exploitation. This includes deposits that can be exploited (the reserves) plus those that cannot be exploited now but with realistic increases in prices, or improvements in technology, could be extracted in the future. Resources that are deep, low grade, in a difficult chemical form, or in locations that are currently protected, could all become usable in the future.

Reserves

The reserves are defined as the amount of the resource that can be exploited now, economically, using existing technology. This means that while the size of the resource is finite the quantity counted in the reserves can change. For example, if the market price for the resource increases, or if new extraction technologies become economically viable, then the reserves will increase. If market prices fall then reserves may decrease.

Categories of Mineral Reserves

Category of Reserves	Description
Inferred reserves	The presence of the mineral can be predicted from knowledge of the geological structures present but not enough is known to estimate the amount that can be economically extracted.
Probable reserve	Sufficient information about the deposit is known, so the amount of the mineral that can be economically extracted can be estimated with sufficient accuracy that further exploration is justified.
Proven reserves	Sufficient exploration has been carried out, including trial drilling, to accurately estimate the amount of the mineral that can be economically extracted.

Although the amount of a material that exists may be greater than could ever be needed, there may be other factors that will limit the viability of exploitation:

- ▼ the absence of the technology to exploit the deposits;
- ▼ the financial cost of exploitation may be too great;
- ▼ the environmental impact of exploitation may be unacceptable.

Mineral exploitation

Mineral deposits obviously cannot be extracted unless they have been found. Discovering deposits involves a variety of exploratory techniques.

Remote sensing involves any technique that give information without taking direct samples. The sensing can be done at different distances from the deposits, collecting data on a range of scales: satellite surveys, aircraft surveys, or ground-based surveys.

Larger-scale surveys may be more expensive but they are often very cost effective, providing a lot of information at a relatively low cost per unit area that is surveyed.

Survey techniques

Survey technique	Description
IR spectroscopy	Different minerals emit infrared radiation at different wavelengths and these can be used to identify them
Gravimetry	Gravimeters detect variations in gravity caused by variations in density and mass. Igneous rocks are usually more dense than sedimentary deposits
Magnetometry	Magnetometers detect rocks that are more magnetic such as the iron ore magnetite and ores of tungsten and cobalt
Seismic surveys	These involve sound waves produced by controlled explosions, or a seismic vibrator on the surface. The echoes can give information about the depth, density, and shape of rock strata
Resistivity	Resistivity is the measurement of the difficulty with which electricity passes through a material. In general, sedimentary rocks have lower resistivities than igneous rocks because they have higher water contents.
Trial drilling	The most expensive technique per sampling site but it is the only method that actually produces samples of the rocks underground
Chemical analysis	Laboratory tests confirm the chemical composition and purity of the minerals in the rock samples

Factors affecting mining viability

Proving the presence of a mineral does not mean that economic mining activities can start. A number of factors must be considered to assess the viability of a mine including those set out below.

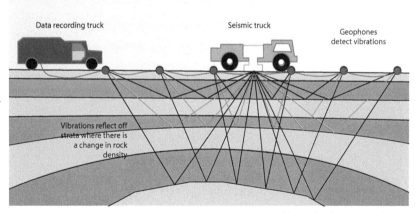

▲ *How seismic surveys detect rock strata underground*

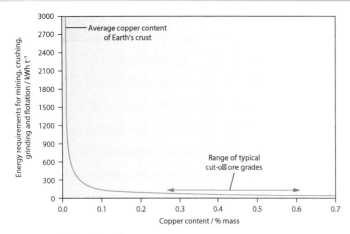

▲ The effect of ore purity on the energy cost of extracting metals

Ore purity

▼ The purity of the ore affects the financial costs of exploitation and the environmental impacts of mining.

▼ If the ore grade is low then:
- more rock will have to be mined;
- more waste materials (spoil) will be produced;
- more energy will be needed for mining and processing;
- more pollution will be generated.

Chemical form

The chemical form of the mineral ore affects the ease of chemical extraction of the metal. For example, aluminium can be extracted from bauxite (aluminium oxide) but not from clay (alumino-silicates) which is much more abundant.

Overburden and hydrology

The overburden is the rock that lies above a mineral deposit. Hard overburden may require blasting which increases costs. Loose overburden may increase the risk of landslides, so the sides of the mine void may have to be landscaped at a more gentle gradient. This may increase the overall area of the mine. Higher precipitation or impermeable rocks below may increase drainage costs.

Depth

Costs rise rapidly as the depth increases. If the depth is doubled then the cost much more than doubles. The sides of the mine cannot be vertical because of the risk of collapse. So the amount of rock that must be removed to reach the mineral rises rapidly as depth increases. As depth increases, the amount of water that flows into the mine from surface runoff or groundwater also rises, increasing pumping costs significantly.

Economic viability

Mining has to be an economically profitable activity, so there must be a balance between production costs and income. The lowest ore purity that can be mined economically, using existing technology, is called the cut-off ore grade (COOG). The COOG changes as technology improves and market prices fluctuate.

Mineral reserves include deposits that are above the COOG.

The impact of changes in market value and technology on the COOG

Change	Impact on COOG
Higher market value	COOG decreases
Lower market value	COOG increases
Improved extraction technology	COOG decreases
Higher energy costs	COOG increases

Transport costs

Transport costs are affected by the distance to market, the ease of bulk transport, the presence of a suitable existing transport infrastructure and whether the bulk of the mineral has been reduced by processing.

Market economics

The market demand and sale value of the minerals control the economic viability of exploiting a specific mineral deposit. The market price is controlled by the demand for the mineral, how much is produced and the costs of extraction and processing. The amount that can be supplied increases relatively slowly as mines are developed but demand can rise and fall quickly. So when demand and supply do not match prices can fluctuate widely. This uncertainty makes the prediction of future markets very important.

Exploiting deposits in regions with existing mining activities produces benefits by having access to the existing infrastructure for transport and energy, equipment supplies, and a trained workforce.

Environmental impacts of mineral exploitation

Only about 1% of the Earth's land surface has ever been mined. The local impacts can be very severe but impacts can spread further through drainage water, atmospheric pollution, the impacts of mineral processing, and infrastructural developments such as transport systems.

Land take

Mineral extraction may cause conflicts with other local land uses.

For most human activities there are choices of location such as where to build a port, road, airport, or housing development. However, minerals can only be exploited where they were deposited. This makes land use conflicts more likely as there is a limited choice of locations that can be exploited.

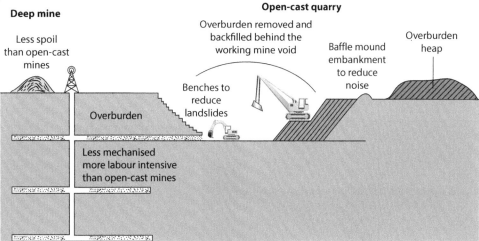

The land area that is required to access the mineral is larger than the area of the mine void (hole) itself. Land is required for associated buildings, access routes, overburden dumping, spoil dumping, and possibly a buffer zone between the mine and neighbouring areas. Open cast mining causes much more habitat loss than deep mining.

▲ The effect of mining on land take and spoil production.

◀ An open-cast china clay quarry, Devon

Habitat loss

The loss of species where the mineral is to be extracted is unavoidable as the surface habitat must be removed.

Removing wildlife by capturing animals and transplanting plants to move them to unthreatened habitats has been attempted but it is rarely completely successful. This is especially true for species that cannot be caught or found easily, as well as those with habitat requirements that are unknown or hard to create.

Habitat restoration, when mining has ended, is often carried out, or new habitats may be created such as a wetland nature reserve in the mine void. In many countries including the UK such restoration can be a requirement of the planning permission given for the mine to be developed. In some cases, the newly created habitat may have greater wildlife value than the habitat that was present before mining started.

About 25% of the sand and gravel used in the UK is dredged from the seabed. To reduce the damage to benthic organisms (those that live on the ocean floor), dredging is usually undertaken where strong currents move the sediments around so few organisms are found here.

❶ *A sand and gravel dredger in the Severn Estuary*
❷ *Unloading sand and gravel in port*

Mining can have serious impacts on the environment, although these are often localised and can be minimised by good mine management.

Loss of amenity

Mining changes the landscape and can create aesthetic problems for local communities. These effects may be reduced by landscaping and tree planting. When the mine closes it can be turned into a community resource so the long term amenity value may be greater than that of the area before mining took place.

Dust

Blasting and vehicle movements creates dust which is lifted into the atmosphere. Water sprays can be used to limit the dust by making dust particles heavier so they settle and by wetting them so they clump together.

◀ *The Eden Project is located in an old china clay quarry*

◀ *Water sprays are used to settle dust on mine roads*

Noise

Mine vehicles and rock blasting are the two main sources of noise. Embankments or 'baffle mounds' built around the mine help absorb and deflect noise.

Blasting in mines does not usually take place day and night but it can be disturbing to local communities, especially if it is unexpected. The disturbance can be mitigated by blasting at set times of the day so the noise is predictable and by restricting blasting times to daytime hours.

Turbid drainage water

Suspended solid particles in mine drainage water can reduce light penetration into rivers and lakes. Sediments can also cover and kill plants and animals.

The turbidity of drainage water can be reduced by using sedimentation lagoons in which the water stands still for long enough for the solids to sink, so the outflow water has low turbidity.

▶ *A sedimentation lagoon used to treat turbid drainage water from a china clay mine*

Spoil disposal

Spoil is the solid waste material left behind by mining. It can include overburden material, unwanted material extracted with the mined mineral, and solid wastes from the chemical processing of the mineral. Spoil needs to be managed and disposed or carefully. Spoil disposal can cause a variety of problems:

▶ **aesthetics:** spoil heaps can damage the scenic beauty of an area. Landscaping can make the spoil heap look more natural and blend in with the surrounding area;

- **stability:** a lack of surface compaction can reduce surface stability and lead to erosion. Instability and erosion can be reduced by landscaping to reduce gradients and by adding soil, nutrients, and by planting with trees or other vegetation. If a spoil heap becomes waterlogged it may become unstable, leading to landslides. This happened in Aberfan, South Wales in 1966 when a coal mine spoil heap slid into a village, killing 144 people, mainly children in the primary school. The risk of landslides can also be reduced by spoil heap drainage;
- **leachate:** rainwater percolating through spoil can dissolve toxic metals and sulfides that produce acidic leachate solutions. Toxic metals that are normally insoluble when inside the rock may be dissolved and become mobile.

Many toxic metals are more soluble under acidic conditions. To manage this mine drainage water can be passed through a filter bed of crushed limestone to immobilize the metal and prevent it being carried into rivers.

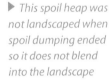

▶ *This spoil heap was not landscaped when spoil dumping ended so it does not blend into the landscape*

Mine site restoration

New uses may be found for sites that have previously been used for mining and mineral processing.

The use of the site after mining will depend on its location, access, topography and any residual problems such as spoil heaps containing toxic wastes.

Many sand, gravel and clay pits have been flooded and developed as wetland wildlife reserves.

Urban development on mine sites may be possible if the ground is stable. If metal wastes are present, the site may be more suitable for industrial use than for housing.

Agricultural use may be possible if the landscape is not too steep or uneven, no toxic materials are present, and the soil is sufficiently fertile.

▶ *The drainage water in this copper mine has a pH of 2*

Future mineral supplies

The mining industry has usually exploited large, easily accessed, shallow, high grade deposits first. Future supplies may be more difficult to exploit, but the development of new technologies may make this easier. Rising prices may reduce the COOG so it would become economically viable to exploit lower grade ores.

Improvements in exploratory techniques

Better remote sensing image resolution

Newer satellites may carry improved sensors which generate greater numbers of image pixels.

Multispectral sensors detect a greater range of wavelengths of visible and infrared light, providing more detailed information on the mineral composition of the Earth's surface.

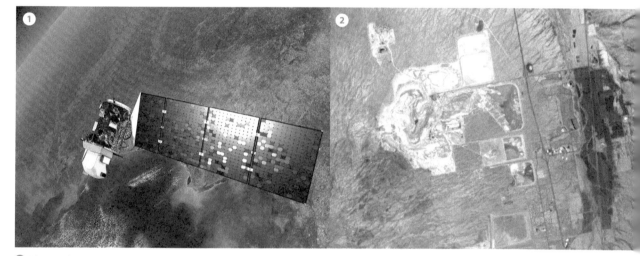

❶ The Landsat 8 satellite carries two sensors that collect visible light and infrared images of the entire Earth's surface every 16 days
❷ An infrared image of a copper mine in Arizona collected by the ASTER sensor on the Terra satellite

Portable field equipment

Laboratory equipment has become smaller and more portable as electronic components have become lighter, more powerful batteries have been developed, and energy consumption has been reduced.

Portable equipment is available for infrared spectroscopy, X-ray fluorescence, and radiation detection. These save time as results are available immediately and it is no longer necessary to wait for laboratory results to be received.

Mechanisation

Deep mining

Using machines allows mining underground where it may be too hot or dangerous for people, for example, deep gold and platinum mines in South Africa, at depths up to 3.8km.

Open-cast mining

Larger machinery in open-cast mines allows overburden and minerals to be extracted more quickly and cost-effectively. Excavators can weigh over 13 000t and trucks can carry up to 300t. Using machinery of this size has allowed deeper open-cast mines to be developed with mines over 600m in depth being possible for more valuable minerals.

Exploitation of low grade deposits

The normal method of extracting a metal from its ore is to smelt it. This involves chemical reduction at high temperatures. The amount of energy needed increases rapidly as the ore purity declines so economically viable exploitation of low grade ores may only be possible if new methods can be developed that do not rely on such high energy inputs and high temperatures.

Bioleaching

The use of living organisms to extract metals from their ores is called bioleaching. The following are examples of this technique.

- Acidophilic bacteria such as *Acidothiobacillus* sp. can be used to extract metals such as copper, zinc, lead, and gold from low grade sources. The bacteria oxidise sulfide ores and produce sulfuric acid which dissolves the metals.
- *Aspergillus* fungi can be grown on scrap electronic components, fly ash from incinerators and catalytic converters. The fungi produce acids that dissolve metals such as nickel, lead, copper, and tin.
- The metals in the solution produced by bioleaching can be separated by electrolysis, or by using carbon filters.

Phytomining

Some plants absorb metal ions from soil or water and concentrate them in their leaves. This can be used as a method of decontaminating polluted sites and as a method of commercial extraction of metals. Once the plants have absorbed the metals, the vegetation is harvested and incinerated. The concentrated metals in the ash can be dissolved using acids, then separated by electrolysis.

Iron displacement

Iron is a more reactive metal than copper and will displace copper ions from solution. The solid iron goes into solution as the copper ions are deposited as solid copper metal which can be collected.

Leachate collection

Rainwater percolating through spoil heaps dissolves soluble metal ions. The draining leachate can be recirculated through the spoil heaps to increase the concentration of metal ions in solution. When the concentration is high enough, the metals can be extracted from the solution by electrolysis.

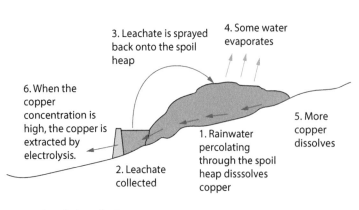

3. Leachate is sprayed back onto the spoil heap

4. Some water evaporates

6. When the copper concentration is high, the copper is extracted by electrolysis.

1. Rainwater percolating through the spoil heap disssolves copper

2. Leachate collected

5. More copper dissolves

▲ *Leachate collection from spoil heaps.*

Rare earth metals

Rare earth metals are used in small amounts in many important applications, especially electrical, and electronic appliances. Exploitable deposits on land are limited and are mainly found in China. Chemical separation is complicated and produces large amounts of toxic wastes. New techniques are being developed such as bacterial adsorption, where dissolved ions of the rare earth metals become more concentrated as they adsorb onto the cell surfaces of bacteria such as *Bacillus subtilis*. The metals can be separated by washing them off the bacteria using acidic solutions, with different metals being washed off at specific pHs.

Deep sea sediments have been found to have relatively high concentrations of rare earth metals including gadolinium, lutetium, terbium, and dysprosium. There is currently no viable method for exploitation of these deposits but they may be developed as the demand for rare earth metals increases..

Some uses of rare earth metals

Appliance	Rare Earth metals
Smartphone	Dysprosium, neodymium, praseodymium, samarium, terbium
Hybrid vehicles	Dysprosium, lanthanum, neodymium, praseodymium, cerium
Fibre optic cables	Erbium, europium, terbium, yttrium
Wind turbines	Dysprosium, lanthanum, neodymium, praseodymium

Polymer adsorption

Metal ions dissolved in seawater will adsorb onto the surface of some polymers and can be collected later. Synthetic polymers can be used, as can natural polymers such as lignin from wood and chitin from shrimp shells discarded by the fishing and aquaculture industries. This method is being developed to extract uranium and may provide a low-energy method of producing fuel for the nuclear power industry.

Exploiting previously inaccessible deposits

Polymetallic nodules

These are also called manganese nodules. They are metal-rich nodules found on the seabed of many of the Earth's oceans. Most are 5 to 10 cm in diameter and are found at depths of 4000 to 5000m. Their origins are not fully understood, but they may have been formed by chemical precipitation of metals around a small solid object such as the shell of a marine organism. They contain about 30% manganese with smaller amounts of iron, nickel, copper, cobalt, and titanium.

Large scale exploitation will be expensive and will require international agreement on the ownership of the seabed and its resources.

▼ *Seabed mining methods*

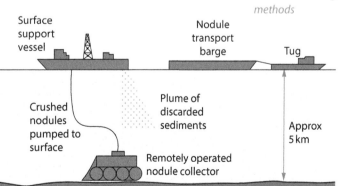

Surface support vessel

Nodule transport barge

Tug

Crushed nodules pumped to surface

Plume of discarded sediments

Approx 5 km

Remotely operated nodule collector

▶ *A polymetallic nodule from the deep ocean floor*

Environmental impacts

Recovering nodules will disturb the seabed and kill benthic organisms that live there.

Separating the nodules from the seabed sediments would increase the turbidity of the water with unknown consequences. Re-deposition of the sediments is likely to kill filter feeders, also covering and killing benthic organisms.

Recycling

Manufacturing industry usually makes new products from freshly extracted raw materials but used materials can also be reused. The wastes may come from two sources:

▼ pre-consumer wastes, for example, the waste trimmings produced by cutting or stamping machines;

▼ post-consumer wastes such as discarded consumer products.

Most of the materials in domestic waste can be recycled if they are separated. This is most effective when undertaken by the public before collection, as this prevents the reduction in quality caused by mixing of wastes, for example, paper and food waste.

Materials separated by the public for recycling

Roadside collection	Taken to local recycling centres
Paper	All categories materials in roadside collections
Cardboard	Batteries
Garden waste	Vehicle engine oil
Metals	Building rubble
Plastic bottles	Soil
Glass	Clothing and other textiles
	Shoes
	Books
	Electrical items
	Light bulbs

Industry can also use recycled elements. However, it can be costly and complex. For example, a comparison of recycling aluminium with using newly extracted aluminium demonstrates a range of advantages and disadvantages.

▼ **Transport:** extraction of aluminium ore involves bulk resources where bulk transport can be used creating major economies of scale and lower unit cost. Recycling may involve the collection and transport of smaller quantities of materials which is more expensive and bulk transport is not possible. However, recycled materials will be lighter than the original raw materials..

▼ **Labour costs:** processing smaller quantities of materials increases labour costs. However, recycling work does not usually require the level of skills or training that

extraction requires so labour costs will be lower.

- **Separation:** alloys of mixed metals cannot easily be separated. So, recycled aluminium alloys cannot be used where pure aluminium is needed.
- **Identification:** it is labour intensive and slow work to identify the composition of recycled materials where the composition is important for reuse.
- **Energy costs:** recycling aluminium saves the energy needed for extraction of aluminium from bauxite. However, this saving may be exceeded by the energy used for transport if small quantities are collected.
- **Public cooperation:** successful post-consumer recycling schemes require public cooperation to separate wastes.
- **Waste losses:** not all used materials can be recycled. Some are unavoidably lost where litter is discarded or placed in general waste for landfill.

Where consumers separate recyclable wastes and large quantities of recyclable waste aluminium are produced, such as large urban areas, the advantages of conserving resources and energy far outweigh the disadvantages.

Cradle to Cradle design

If the lifetime of the minerals in use can be extended then the need to exploit reserves will be reduced. Cradle to Cradle design involves the design of products so that the materials used are able to be reused at the end of their useful lives. This includes easy separation of components and identification of materials. See page 279, Solid wastes, and page 374, The Circular Economy.

Key principles

- An understanding of the lithosphere helps with the management of many environmental systems including metal mineral supplies, agriculture, water supplies, and energy resources.
- Geological processes have produced localised concentrations of exploitable mineral deposits.
- New technologies improve the effectiveness of exploration.
- New technologies increase the efficiency of the extraction of minerals, especially low-grade ores.
- Methods are available to minimise the environmental impacts of mineral exploitation.
- Improved methods of using and re-using mineral resources reduce problems of resource depletion.

Biogeochemical cycles

Chapter topics

▼ The carbon cycle
▼ Human impacts on the carbon cycle
▼ The nitrogen cycle
▼ Human impacts on the nitrogen cycle
▼ The phosphorus cycle
▼ Human impacts on the phosphorus cycle

Many nutrients that living organisms need are processed, converted and recycled by physical processes and living organisms. The interlinked cyclical processes mean that a small quantity of material being continually recycled can support ecosystems over long time periods.

The biogeochemical cycles show the processes that move particular elements between their reservoirs in the biosphere, atmosphere, hydrosphere and lithosphere.

The carbon cycle

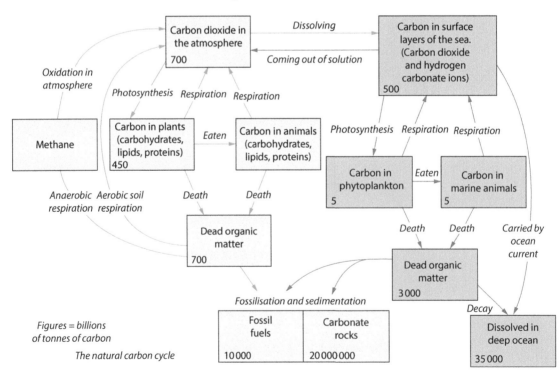

▲ *The natural carbon cycle*

The carbon cycle is naturally in a state of dynamic equilibrium with processes cancelling each other out so there is little or no overall change in the amount of carbon in each of the reservoirs of the cycle.

Main reservoirs in the carbon cycle

Reservoir	Main chemical forms	Quantity /Gt
Atmosphere	Carbon dioxide Methane Carbon monoxide	700 1.2 Trace
Hydrosphere	Hydrogen carbonate ions Dissolved carbon dioxide	Surface waters 500 Deep ocean 35 000
Biosphere	Carbohydrates, for example, cellulose, lignin, starch, sugars Proteins Lipids, for example, vegetable oils and animal fats	Living organisms 470 Dead organic matter 3700
Lithosphere	Carbonaceous rocks, for example, limestone, mainly as calcite (calcium carbonate) Fossil fuels: mainly as carbon and hydrocarbons	Sedimentary carbonates 20 000 000 Fossil fuels 10 000

Human activities alter many of the processes in the carbon cycle. This can alter dynamic equilibria, causing some reservoirs to become depleted while carbon stores increase in other reservoirs.

Main processes of the carbon cycle

Photosynthesis

Photosynthesis captures light energy using pigments such as chlorophyll. It converts low-energy substances such as carbon dioxide and water into high-energy carbohydrates which may be converted into other substances such as proteins and lipids.

Respiration

Respiration releases the energy that was captured during photosynthesis which is then used to drive metabolic processes. Aerobic respiration returns the carbon to the atmosphere as carbon dioxide.

Aerobic respiration breaks down organic compounds more completely and releases much more energy than anaerobic respiration. However, anaerobic respiration allows some organisms to survive and use food sources in oxygen-deficient environments. Anaerobic respiration usually returns the carbon to the atmosphere as methane.

Food webs

Some of the carbohydrates, proteins, and lipids produced by plants are eaten by herbivores, which may then be eaten by carnivores. These feeding relationships combine to make food webs.

Fossilisation

The incomplete decomposition of dead organic matter, often under anaerobic conditions, can produce substances that form long-term carbon stores such as fossil fuels. Some organisms such as molluscs, corals, and many planktonic organisms produce exoskeletons that include calcium carbonate. This may produce rocks such as limestone, which now contain most of the carbon in the lithosphere.

Combustion

The burning of organic materials releases carbon dioxide. Natural fires in forests and grasslands may be started by lightning.

How humans affect the carbon cycle

Many human activities alter the rates of movement of carbon through the cycle. This can unbalance the natural dynamic equilibria of the carbon cycle and change the distribution of carbon in the reservoirs of the cycle.

Changes in Photosynthesis

▼ Deforestation reduces the movement of carbon from the atmosphere into biomass.

▼ Afforestation increases the movement of carbon from the atmosphere into biomass.

▼ Marine pollution with toxic materials can reduce phytoplankton populations. This reduces the absorption of dissolved carbon dioxide. Some phytoplankton naturally sinks to the seabed when it dies, increasing the amount of carbon in marine sediments. Carbon dioxide from the atmosphere would have dissolved in the sea to replace this and maintain the equilibrium between CO_2 in the atmosphere and in solution in the oceans. So, toxic marine pollution that kills phytoplankton can lead to higher atmospheric CO_2 levels.

▼ Algae live on the underside of sea ice around Antarctica. Some of the carbon they absorb during photosynthesis sinks to the seabed in the faeces of krill that eat the algae. If climate change reduces the area of sea ice then less CO_2 may be removed from the sea.

▶ The effects of human activities on the carbon cycle

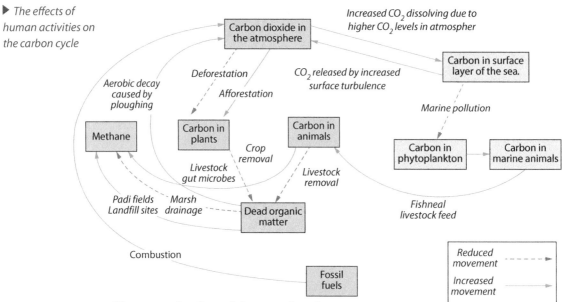

Changes in Aerobic respiration

The carbon in dead organic matter in the soil is gradually released as CO_2 by the aerobic respiration of soil organisms, especially bacteria and fungi.

Ploughing increases the oxygen supply to decomposers living in the soil so aerobic decomposition takes place more rapidly. The amount of carbon in the soil dead organic matter store is reduced and the amount in the atmosphere is increased.

Changes in Anaerobic respiration

In the absence of oxygen, respiration by anaerobic soil organisms releases methane gas. If the methane is released into the atmosphere, it is gradually oxidised to CO_2.

Anaerobic environments produced by human activities:

- rice padi fields;
- landfill sites;
- anaerobic sediments in reservoirs;
- livestock intestines.

Anaerobic environments destroyed by drainage:

- waterlogged fields;
- marshlands;
- peat bogs.

Carbonic acid concentration in the sea

Humans do not directly cause CO_2 to dissolve or exsolve but human activities that affect the concentration of CO_2 in the atmosphere, will alter these processes to create a new equilibrium.

Dissolved CO_2 is in an equilibrium with carbonic acid which dissociates to form hydrogen carbonate and hydrogen ions. The concentration of hydrogen ions affects the pH of the sea so an increase in dissolved CO_2 will reduce the pH of the water.

So as atmospheric CO_2 concentrations rise, dissolved CO_2 concentrations increase, which therefore increases hydrogen ion concentrations and makes the sea more acidic.

Methane releases from fossil fuels

Methane may be released into the atmosphere during fossil fuel extraction.

Combustion

The combustion of fossil fuels and wood releases large amounts of CO_2 into the atmosphere.

Biomass movements

Humans do not directly move large amounts of carbon in biomass between areas, but human activities can produce local changes which have environmental impacts:

- the addition of compost/mulch to improve soil fertility;
- deforestation and crop harvesting leading to reduced soil organic matter and soil erosion;
- the movement of biomass into the sea when sewage is discharged.
- Movement of marine biomass into the terrestrial system by fishing/aquaculture.

Sustainable management of the carbon cycle

The consequences of human impacts on the carbon cycle are serious, especially those that contribute to climate change. A range of strategies have been developed to counteract these impacts.

Conservation of biomass carbon stores

Habitats such as peat bogs and forests contain huge amounts of carbon. Protecting these from exploitation, or damaging land-use change, is important to prevent even higher CO_2 releases.

The use of alternatives to fossil fuels

Renewable energy resources and nuclear power produce lower CO_2 emissions than fossil fuels.

Carbon sequestration

Large-scale tree planting could remove a lot of CO_2 from the atmosphere and slow down or reverse rising CO_2 concentrations. Once a tree reaches full size there will be no further net storage of carbon but the standing tree is a carbon reservoir. If the trees were harvested and kept as wood, for example, in house construction, then replanting would produce additional carbon storage as the new trees grew.

Carbon Capture and Storage (CCS)

This involves capturing carbon, usually as CO_2, so that it is not released into the atmosphere. A range of technologies is being developed.

1. Pre-combustion technology

Changing the fuel used, or the way it is combusted, may be expensive and require the development of new technologies but it may make the removal of CO_2 easier or more efficient. Post-combustion capture may not be practical for many small sources such as road vehicles. It would be better if the fuel could be modified at a large-scale facility where the carbon could be captured before the fuel is used, so that the fuel would not release CO_2 when burnt.

Gasification converts a fuel such as coal into gaseous hydrogen and CO_2. The CO_2 can be removed for storage, then the hydrogen can be distributed for use in vehicles, homes, or industry. When burnt, the exhaust gases contain water vapour but no CO_2.

Oxy-fuel combustion systems use pure oxygen so that only CO_2 and water vapour are produced. The water vapour can be removed by cooling the gases so that it condenses. Capture of the CO_2 is then much easier as it is not mixed with other gases.

2. Post-combustion technology

Carbon dioxide can be removed from the exhaust gases of fossil fuel combustion using several methods:

- dissolving it in a solvent;
- high pressure membrane filtration;
- adsorption/desorption processes;
- cryogenic separation:
- graphene adsorption.

None of these methods is fully developed and the costs for large-scale CO_2 removal are uncertain. The costs are increased because only about 20% of the gases produced by combustion in air is CO_2.

3. Storage

After the CO_2 has been captured it must be stored so that it cannot return to the atmosphere. Most proposals involve storage underground in suitable geological structures such as depleted aquifers, oil fields, or gas fields. It can also be injected into oil reservoirs to provide the pressure needed in secondary oil recovery (see page 187, Secondary oil recovery). Research suggests that CO_2 pumped into fractured basalt may react with the minerals in the rock, producing solid carbonate minerals.

The nitrogen cycle

The nitrogen cycle is an excellent example of how interconnected natural processes can make a natural resource that is not very abundant continually satisfy the needs of living organisms by recycling what has previously been used. Many of these processes are carried out by living organisms, especially bacteria, where the waste products released by one group are the raw materials for another group.

Nitrogen is essential for living organisms as it is a component of many essential biological molecules.

Main reservoirs of nitrogen

Reservoir	Main chemical forms
Atmosphere	Nitrogen gas (N_2) Oxides of nitrogen (NOx)
Biosphere	Living organisms: DNA, proteins (cell membranes, hormones, enzymes) Dead organic matter: proteins, which release ammonium compounds as they decompose
Lithosphere	Soil: ammonium compounds, nitrites, nitrates Rocks: minerals containing nitrogen
Hydrosphere	Dissolved nitrates and ammonium ions.

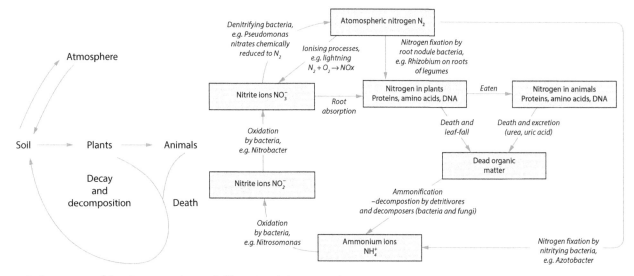

▲ A summary of the nitrogen cycle.   ▲ The natural nitrogen cycle.

The main processes in the nitrogen cycle

A range of physical and biological processes combine to produce the natural nitrogen cycle.

Ionisation

Processes such as lightning and meteor trails provide the energy for atmospheric nitrogen and oxygen to react and produce oxides of nitrogen.

Fixation

Some micro-organisms can chemically reduce nitrogen to ammonia. They may be free-living bacteria in the soil, or they may live symbiotically in the root nodules of legumes.

Food chains

Nitrogen passes between organisms as amino acids and proteins in food.

Nitrification

Nitrification involves the oxidation of ammonium ions to nitrites, then to nitrates, by nitrifying bacteria in the soil.

Denitrification

The chemical reduction of nitrates in soil to nitrogen and nitrogen oxide gases, by denitrifying bacteria in the soil, reduces soil fertility. This normally occurs under anaerobic conditions.

Leaching

The high solubility of nitrates means they are easily leached out of soils into water bodies where they act as nutrients for aquatic plants and algae.

Root absorption

Plants absorb nitrogen as soluble ions, mainly as nitrates but also as ammonium ions.

Ammonification

The amino groups in proteins are released as ammonium ions by the action of bacteria, fungi, and detritivores as they decompose dead organic matter.

Human impacts on the nitrogen cycle

Some human activities alter the rates of natural processes in the nitrogen cycle, while others create new processes. These alter the natural dynamic equilibria of the cycle.

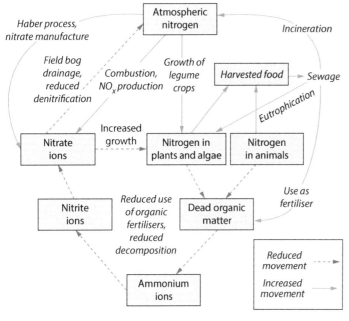

▲ The effects of human activities on the nitrogen cycle

Haber process

This is an an industrial process for producing ammonia from nitrogen and hydrogen, using an iron catalyst at high temperature and pressure. The artificial fixation of atmospheric nitrogen to ammonia uses large amounts of energy. Ammonia may then be converted to nitrates. The main purpose of the Haber process is the manufacture of agricultural fertilisers.

Agriculture

▼ The use of nitrate fertilisers may increase the problems caused by leaching, including eutrophication, if application is followed by heavy rain or if fertilisers are applied close to rivers.

▼ Drainage of fields makes the soil more aerobic. This increases the number of aerobic nitrifying bacteria and reduces the number of anaerobic denitrifying bacteria.

▼ Soil disturbance by ploughing increases the rate of decomposition of dead organic matter which releases more nitrogen oxides into the atmosphere.

▼ Leguminous plants such as peas, beans, and clover may be grown to increase the levels of nitrogen compounds in the soil, which crops can then absorb.

Pollution

Oxides of nitrogen (NOx) are released into the atmosphere by combustion processes and may subsequently increase the quantity of nitrates washed into the soil by rain.

Sustainable management of the nitrogen cycle

Human activities can be changed to ensure that resources containing nitrogen are available while environmental problems involving nitrogen are controlled.

Control of combustion processes

A reduction in the use of fossil fuels would reduce NOx releases. This could be a deliberate choice in an attempt to develop sustainable lifestyles, or it could be caused by the depletion of fossil fuel supplies and the move to other energy resources..

Adopting the principles of the Circular Economy would result in the use of more low-temperature manufacturing processes, for example, the use of polymers produced by living organisms rather than high-temperature processes using fossil fuels. See page 373, Sustainability.

Control of NOx releases

The release of NOx into the atmosphere can be reduced using post-combustion processes such as catalytic converters and urea sprays. See page 253, Control of oxides of nitrogen.

Management of biological wastes

The decomposition of biological wastes releases ammonium ions as the amino acids in proteins are de-aminated. Enzymes produced by bacteria remove amino groups ($-NH_2$) which dissolve as ammonium ions. This process can either cause problems or be useful, depending on where it occurs.

Eutrophication

Biological wastes may be washed into water bodies by runoff or they may deliberately be dumped there. The ammonium compounds are converted to nitrites and nitrates which can cause eutrophication in water bodies. See page 266, Cultural eutrophication.

Organic fertilisers

Wastes such as manure, sewage, and food production wastes may be used as organic fertilisers to increase nutrient and humus levels. They may simply be ploughed into the soil, or applied to the surface, or they may be composted aerobically, or digested anaerobically, before application as a fertiliser. These processes reduce the bulk of the material which makes application easier. It also produces a fertiliser with a better C:N ratio. Composting and digestion reduce the carbon content because CO_2 or CH_4 gases are lost, leaving a more nitrogen-rich fertiliser.

Management of soil processes

Farming practices can be changed to maximise advantageous processes that increase soil nitrate levels, for example, by:

- ▼ cultivation of legume crops;
- ▼ crop rotation;
- ▼ minimal use of pesticides that harm soil biota;
- ▼ control of nitrate leaching;
- ▼ not applying fertilisers during rain or when rain is likely;
- ▼ use of low-solubility fertilisers, for example, urea;
- ▼ use of low-tillage techniques to reduce soil disturbance;
- ▼ uncultivated 'buffer strips' left along rivers;
- ▼ minimal use of nitrate fertiliser where leaching into aquifers is likely.

  See page 335, Strategies to increase agricultural sustainability.

The phosphorus cycle

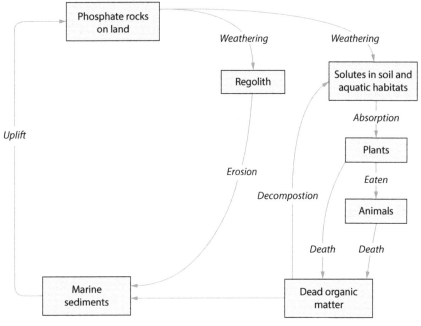

Weathering   *Weathering*

Uplift

Erosion

Absorption

Decompostion

Eaten

Death   *Death*

Phosphate rocks on land

Regolith

Solutes in soil and aquatic habitats

Plants

Animals

Marine sediments

Dead organic matter

▲ *The natural phosphorus cycle*

Phosphorus has several important biological functions. It is a component of bones, ATP, DNA, RNA, cell membranes and proteins.

Phosphorus is more likely to be a limiting factor on biological processes than many other nutrients because most compounds of phosphorus have low solubility and there is no gaseous reservoir of phosphorus.

Main processes involved in the phosphorus cycle

Absorption by roots
Plant roots absorb the phosphates that they will use in metabolic processes. They are not effective at absorbing phosphates so most plants have symbiotic relationships with mycorrhizal fungi. These have extensive networks of fungal hyphae in the soil which increases the surface area for phosphate absorption.

Decomposition
The breakdown of phosphorylated proteins in dead organic matter releases phosphates that are often made more soluble by soil microbes so they can be absorbed by plants.

Sedimentation
The phosphorus in organisms that die and become incorporated into sediments may no longer be available to other organisms, such as planktonic organisms that die and sink to the ocean floor. This reduces the productivity of the surface waters of oceans because phosphorus availability is often a limiting factor..

Mountain building and weathering
Processes that mobilise phosphorus and make it available to living organisms are often slow. The phosphorus in marine sediments may not become available again until continental drift forms new mountain ranges and weathering of rocks releases the phosphates.

Human impacts on the phosphorus cycle

Mining of phosphate rocks

Most phosphorus is mined as calcium phosphate then treated to produce ammonium phosphate which is more soluble.

In the past, large accumulations of bird droppings were mined for the ammonium phosphates they contained. These deposits built up in dry areas such as Peru and some tropical islands, for example, Nauru in the Pacific Ocean. Most large guano deposits have been fully exploited.

Fertiliser use

The use of fertilisers mobilises phosphorus compounds into the environment in more soluble forms. This increases crop production but can also contribute to eutrophication.
See page 266, Cultural eutrophication

Sustainable management of the phosphorus cycle

▼ Shortage of phosphates is the limiting factor on crop productivity for large areas of farmland. The availability of phosphates is reduced by the removal of biomass during harvesting and the loss of phosphates with eroded soil. Maintaining future supplies of phosphates to compensate for these losses by mining rock phosphates is unsustainable.

▼ Biological wastes should be used as fertilisers to maintain phosphate nutrient availability.

▼ Crop breeding programmes are increasing the efficiency of phosphate absorption by crops.

Key principles

▼ Natural processes recycle materials so that they do not become depleted and can sustain life over very long time periods.

▼ The processes of biogeochemical cycles involve many dynamic equilibria and feedback mechanisms.

▼ Human activities alter the rates of the processes of biogeochemical cycles which unbalances the dynamic equilibria and causes reservoirs to build up or become depleted.

Soil

Chapter topics
▼ Soil fertility
▼ Soil erosion

Soil is essential for plant growth in natural ecosystems and agroecosystems. An understanding of the processes that produce soil, reduce erosion, and maintain fertility are important in managing habitats and agricultural productivity.

Soil fertility

Soil fertility is the ability of soil to sustain plant growth.

Features of fertile soil

Water content

Water is essential for all organisms that live in the soil, including the plants. A fertile soil allows good drainage so it does not become waterlogged but still retains enough water for the survival of the soil biota.

Plant nutrients are absorbed in ionic form, dissolved in water.

Soluble materials

Fertile soils contain macronutrients such as nitrogen, phosphorus, and potassium, present in ionic form mainly as nitrates, phosphates, and potassium ions.

Fertile soils also contain micronutrients, including boron, cobalt, copper, iron, manganese, and magnesium.

In a fertile soil toxic ions such as aluminium and heavy metals are adsorbed onto the surface of mineral particles, usually clay, so they cannot dissolve in the water where they could harm soil organisms.

▲ *The behaviour of water between soil particles*

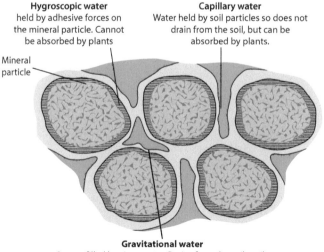

Hygroscopic water
held by adhesive forces on the mineral particle. Cannot be absorbed by plants

Capillary water
Water held by soil particles so does not drain from the soil, but can be absorbed by plants.

Mineral particle

Gravitational water
Spaces filled by air or water. Drains from the soil easily

Air content

Most living organisms in soil and many processes that increase fertility are aerobic, so well aerated soils are likely to be more fertile.

Dead organic matter

Fertile soils usually have a high dead organic matter content, which releases plant nutrients as it decomposes. Dead organic matter also increases water retention and provides food for soil biota.

pH

The pH of fertile soils is usually in the range pH5.5 to pH7.0 which is the range of tolerance for most plants and other soil biota. Acidic soils can increase the leaching of plant nutrients and damage root cell membranes. Under alkaline conditions phosphates become insoluble.

Soil biota

Living organisms are involved in many soil processes that affect soil fertility.

- ▼ Detritivores such as beetle larvae, millipedes, woodlice, and slugs break up dead organic matter and release nutrients into the soil. Worms are detritivores. They also increase soil drainage and aeration by creating tunnels in the soil.

- ▼ Decomposers, including bacteria and fungi, break down dead organic matter. They secrete digestive enzymes and rely on detritivores to physically break up the dead organic matter and increase its surface area.

- ▼ Nitrogen-fixing bacteria convert gaseous nitrogen into ammonium ions.

- ▼ Nitrifying bacteria oxidise ammonium ions to nitrite ions then to nitrate ions.

- ▼ Mycorrhizal fungi form symbiotic relationships with plant roots and aid phosphate uptake by the plants.

Soil texture

Soil texture is the property controlled by the proportions of the different size categories of mineral particles present in the soil.

Soil particle type	Diameter range /mm
Clay	<0.002
Silt	0.002 – 0.02
Sand	0.02 – 2.0

The impact of soil texture on sandy and clay soils

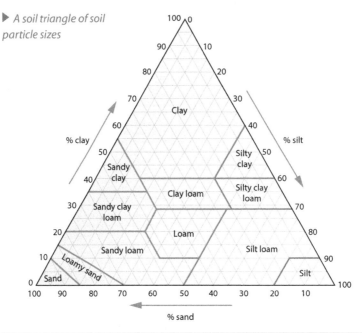

▶ *A soil triangle of soil particle sizes*

Feature	Comparison of sandy and clay soils
Drainage rate	The larger pore spaces of sandy soils allow rapid drainage which reduces the water content but increases aeration. Clay soils are poorly drained.
Capillary action	The tiny pore spaces between clay particles allow water underground to rise towards the surface. There is no capillary rise of water in sandy soils.
Aeration	The pore spaces in well-drained sandy soils are filled with air. Clay soils are more likely to be waterlogged with a low aeration rate.
Nutrient retention	Nutrient ions adsorb easily onto clay particles but not onto sand particles.
Thermal capacity	The high water content of clay soils produces a high thermal capacity so they warm up and cool down slowly. Sandy soils have lower thermal capacities so they warm up more rapidly after cold weather.
Root penetration	Clay particles are held together by the capillary water on the particle surfaces. This makes it harder for plant roots to force their way between the soil particles. Root penetration is easier in sandy soils.
Ease of cultivation	The lack of adhesion between the particles in sandy soils makes it easier to cultivate them than clay soils.

Loam soils have a fairly even mix of sand, silt and clay (often about 40:40:20). They have an ideal mix of properties for cultivating most crops: good drainage, water retention, high nutrient content.

Soil structure

Soil particles form aggregates called peds. The particles are bound together by polysaccharide gums produced by decomposition, by fungal hyphae, by roots, by the action of soil biota and by hygroscopic clay particles. The ped type affects soil properties and fertility.

Crumb peds are small and round. These produce good drainage, aeration and easy root penetration, so they improve soil fertility.

Platy peds are large and flat which reduces drainage, aeration and root penetration, so they produce less fertile soils.

Soil depth

Deeper soils are less likely to become waterlogged or to dry out rapidly. They can also aid good root anchorage.

How human activities affect soil fertility

Aeration by ploughing and drainage

Ploughing and drainage make soils more aerobic. This increases the rates of nitrogen fixation, nitrification, and the decomposition of dead organic matter.

Soil nutrient levels

Farmers increase soil nutrient levels by adding inorganic fertilisers, organic matter or by supporting natural processes that increase nutrient levels such as bacterial nitrogen fixation.

Farming can also deplete soil nutrient levels due to soil erosion, biomass removal, inhibiting natural processes that increase nutrient levels or by increased leaching of dissolved nutrients.

Irrigation

Irrigation increases the fertility of soil where water is a limiting factor on growth. Having sufficient water also allows plants to keep their stomata open and continue gaseous exchange when the soil would otherwise be dry. Water also dissolves nutrients which can then be absorbed by plants in ionic form.

Soil compaction

The excessive use of heavy machinery or high livestock densities, can cause soil to become compacted. This reduces aeration and makes waterlogging more likely, especially when the soil is wet.

pH control

Controlling soil pH helps to ensure nutrients are soluble but not too easily leached.

▲ *Heavy farm machinery can increase soil compaction*

Soil erosion

Soil erosion is a natural process as soil particles are removed by wind or water. In soils that have not been affected by human activities, the rate of erosion is likely to be the same or less than the rate of soil formation. Erosion becomes a problem when it occurs more rapidly than soil formation.

Types of soil erosion

Wind erosion

When some soils are dry, especially those with a low clay content, they are likely to be loose with little cohesion between the particles which would hold the soil together. If it is windy and the soil is unprotected then it may blow away. This is a problem for the area that has lost its soil, but it can also cause problems where the soil is deposited as it may cover crops or land in urban areas.

Water erosion

All forms of water erosion are increased by steeper gradients.

▸ **Rain splash erosion:** when soil particles are dislodged by the splash of a raindrop, soil particles are dispersed in all directions, but those going downhill are likely to travel further. Over time, this can cause the downhill movement of large amounts of soil.

▸ **Surface runoff erosion:** this is caused by surface runoff when the infiltration capacity of the soil has been exceeded. This can occur when the rainfall is heavy or prolonged, or if the soil is relatively impermeable so more of the water flows over the ground surface.

▸ **Slumping and landslides:** when soil on slopes becomes very wet, the increased mass and lubrication of the water makes the downward movement of large amounts of soil more likely. This often occurs when deep soil on steep slopes becomes less stable following deforestation. As the roots that held the soil together decompose, the soil is held together less strongly and landslides following heavy rain become more likely.

▲ *How rain splash erosion transports soil particles downhill*

Areas with seasonal rainfall, such as Sub-Saharan Africa, may suffer from both types of erosion: wind erosion during the dry season and rainfall erosion during the wet season.

▸ *Gulley erosion and slumping in East Africa*

How vegetation reduces the rate of soil erosion

- ▶ Vegetation acts as a natural windbreak, reducing wind velocity and therefore the kinetic energy to carry away soil particles.
- ▶ Vegetation cover and leaf litter reduce the impact of raindrops on the soil surface, so soil particles are less likely to be dislodged.
- ▶ Soil organic matter, including the colloidal material humus, help to bind soil particles together
- ▶ Plant roots hold soil together
- ▶ Plants help to increase the infiltration of water into the soil. This reduces the rate of runoff which reduces water erosion.

Human activities that increase the rate of soil erosion

Vegetation removal

Removing vegetation removes the protection from erosion of the processes detailed above.

Ploughing vulnerable soils

Ploughing breaks up the soil structure, exposing soil particles to erosion by water or wind.

Overgrazing

If the livestock density is too high then the vegetation will be eaten faster than it can grow, increasing the exposure of the soil and the risk of erosion. Disturbance and root damage by hooves increase the risk of erosion.

▲ *Ploughing fields loosens soil and increases erosion risks*

Reduced soil biota

Ploughing, reducing soil organic matter and the use of agrochemicals can all reduce the number of living organisms in the soil.

The living organisms that live in the soil play an important role in reducing soil erosion.

- ▶ Detritivores and decomposers break down dead organic matter, releasing plant nutrients which may increase vegetation cover.
- ▶ Decomposition produces humus which increases adhesion between soil particles.
- ▶ Worms aerate the soil, increasing drainage rates and the infiltration capacity of the soil.

▲ *Degraded soil in Kenya caused by overgrazing*

Soil compaction

The use of heavy farm machinery, high livestock densities and a reduction in soil detritivores make it more likely that soil will become compacted. Compacted soil has smaller interstitial spaces which reduces the infiltration rate so it is more likely that rainfall will produce surface runoff and cause erosion.

Cultivating steep slopes

Surface runoff water flows more rapidly down steeper slopes so it has more kinetic energy to pick up and carry soil particles. Cultivating with techniques that disturb the soil, such as ploughing, add to the erosion risk.

Effects of accelerated soil erosion

Accelerated soil erosion is soil erosion where the natural equilibrium between soil formation and erosion has been broken so that the rate of erosion is faster than the rate of formation.

▲ A river with high turbidity caused by soil erosion

Reduced productivity

When soil is eroded, it is often the most fertile topsoil that is lost. The remaining soil may be less fertile so plant growth may be reduced, leading to smaller harvests.

Erosion may leave shallower soil so root penetration may be more difficult.

Sedimentation in rivers and reservoirs

The soil particles carried into rivers may be deposited if the water slows down and has less kinetic energy. This can occur where the river naturally slows down in reservoirs or on coastlines if the suspended solids reach the sea.

Soil that sediments in a river reduces its flow capacity so the river is more likely to overflow and cause flooding following heavy rain.

Increased atmospheric particulates

Wind erosion increases the level of atmospheric particulates. This can make health problems such as asthma worse.

Desertification

Soil erosion is an important part of the combination of processes that cause the expansion of deserts. It makes it more difficult for vegetation to grow which contributes to further soil erosion and reduced rainfall.

Methods of reducing soil erosion

The removal of the existing community of species to create farmland usually increases soil erosion rates. A range of techniques can be used to reduce erosion rates.

Long-term crops

The growth of crops that do not require frequent replanting and soil disturbance reduces the erosion rate eg permanent grassland or bush and tree crops such as fruit, tea, coffee and cotton.

Zero-tillage cultivation

Cultivation that minimizes soil disturbance reduces the risk of soil erosion. Direct drilling of seeds into the ground causes less disturbance than ploughing and sowing.

Contour ploughing

Ploughing up and down a slope creates gulleys that increase the velocity of runoff and cause more rapid erosion. Ploughing along the contours at 90° to the slope reduces erosion as the water flow is stopped by the ploughed furrows and loses its kinetic energy, so it can no longer carry soil particles. With a slower flow rate, the soil particles are deposited in the furrow. This works well unless the rainfall is so heavy that the furrows overflow.

▲ *Tea is a long term crop that provides a crop without frequent soil disturbance*

Tied ridging

This method is used on land that is almost flat. The field is divided with a criss-cross of intersecting ridges. These retain water when it rains, increasing infiltration and reducing the runoff that may have caused erosion.

Terracing

Where sloping land is cultivated, a series of narrow fields are created with the soil held in place by retaining walls built along the contours. Water flowing over the walls flows quickly, but it slows down as it flows across the fields. Much of this water may infiltrate into the soil.

▲ *Contour ploughing*

Rows of stones

If the gradient is gentle, rows of stones laid along contours can slow runoff and reduce the erosion rate. Any disturbed soil is deposited behind the stone rows.

▲ *Rows of stones placed on contour lines slow water flow and reduce erosion*

Windbreaks

The growing crop reduces the velocity of the wind and reduces wind erosion but the field will be exposed if the plants are removed when the crop is harvested. The protection from the wind is maintained if there are hedgerows or rows of trees around the field. A hedgerow will reduce wind velocity for a distance up to 30 times its height.

Multicropping

Growing more than one crop in a field at the same time can reduce exposure to wind erosion if they are harvested and re-sown at different times because there is always a crop in the field protecting the soil. This works most easily where the farming uses human labour rather than machinery. If the work is done using machinery then wider strips of different crops may be cultivated in a technique called 'strip cropping'. The strips are most effective if they are arranged at 90o to the prevailing wind direction.

Increasing soil organic matter

Any method that retains or adds organic matter will reduce the risk of erosion.

Organic matter on the soil surface such as mulch protect the soil from wind and the impact of rain drops.

As organic matter decomposes it produces the colloidal material humus which helps the soil particles to adhere to each other.

◀ *Spreading manure increases soil organic matter levels*

Livestock management

Stocking density can be controlled to reduce soil damage eg trampling damage.

Livestock movement can be controlled eg reducing access to riverbanks where trampling is more likely to cause erosion into the river.

Livestock may be removed at high-risk times, for example, following heavy rain.

◀ *Livestock trampling can increase soil erosion rates*

The Universal Soil Loss Equation (USLE)

The USLE can be used to estimate soil loss rates and assess the impact of changes in farming techniques.

The USLE formula is $A = R \times K \times L \times S \times C \times P$

USLE formula factors

Symbol	Factor	Description
A	Rate of soil erosion	Annual soil loss
R	Rainfall erosivity factor	Measure of the potential ability of soil to be eroded by rain
K	Soil erodibility factor	Susceptibility of soil particles to detachment by rainfall and runoff
L	Slope length factor	Effect of slope length
S	Slope gradient factor	Steepness of slope
C	Cropping management factor	Impact of vegetation
P	Erosion control factor	Effect of type of ploughing

The USLE can be used to estimate the rate of soil erosion for particular local conditions and cultivation practices.

If the rate of soil formation is known then the sustainability of the situation can be assessed.

Soil erosion rates have been categorised to assess the sustainability of the farming system.

In a particular area, the natural rate of soil formation is 9 t ha-1 yr^{-1}, so erosion rates below this may be considered to be sustainable.

Soil Erosion Class	Rate of soil loss / t ha^{-1} yr^{-1} (tonnes per hectare per year)
Very low (tolerable)	<5.0
Low	5.0 – 10.0
Moderate	10.0 – 20.0
High	20.0 – 30.0
Severe	>30.0

Soil erosion categories

The information in the following tables can be used to estimate the erosion rates for particular farming practices.

R factors for five farms

Farm	R Factor
A	90
B	100
C	110
D	120
E	130

K: factors for selected soil textural classes

Textural Class	K Factor (for soils with average organic matter content)/ t ha-1
Clay	0.49
Loam	0.67
Sand	0.04

C: Cropping management factor (C is calculated using the value for crop type and tillage method)

Crop Type	Factor
Beans	0.50
Wheat	0.35
Horticultural crops	0.50
Fruit trees	0.10
Grazing land	0.02

Tillage Method	Factor
Autumn ploughing	1.0
Spring ploughing	0.90
Mulch tillage	0.60
Zero-tillage	0.25

P: Erosion control factor

Support Practice	P Factor
Ploughing up & down slope	1.0
Contour ploughing	0.50
Strip cropping, contour ploughing	0.25

L: slope length

Slope Length /m	Slope /%	LS Factor
	10	1.38
	8	1.00
	6	0.67
	4	0.40
	2	0.20
30	0	0.07
	10	1.95
	8	1.41
	6	0.95
	4	0.53
	2	0.25
60	0	0.08
	10	2.76
	8	1.99
	6	1.35
	4	0.70
	2	0.30
120	0	0.09
	10	3.90
	8	2.82
	6	1.91
	4	0.92
	2	0.37
240	0	0.11
	10	5.52
	8	3.99
	6	2.70
	4	1.21
	2	0.46
480	0	0.12

The USLE formula can be used to estimate soil erosion rates and how these may be affected by changes in farming practices.

Worked Example

Factor	Factor	Method 1		Method 2	
		Detail	Values	Detail	Values
Erosivity factor for the area	R	Farm A	90	Farm A	90
Soil textural class	K	Loam soil	0.67	Loam soil	0.67
Field length and slope	LS	120m length , 6% slope gradient	1.35	120m length, 6% slope gradient	1.35
Cropping management factor	C	Beans, spring ploughing	0.50 x 0.90	Wheat, mulch tillage	0.35 x 0.60
Erosion control factor	P	Up and down slope	1.0	Contour ploughing	0.50
Erosion rate / t ha^{-1} yr^{-1}			**36.3**		**8.5**

Key principles

▶ Soil is an important but often neglected resource that is vital for sustainable habitat management and agriculture.

▶ The soil in areas unaffected by humans is usually in a state of dynamic equilibrium between soil formation and erosion.

▶ The rate of soil formation is always slow compared with the rate at which erosion can occur.

▶ Human activities often reduce the rate of soil formation and increase the rate of erosion.

▶ An understanding of the processes that affect soil can reduce environmental damage and increase agricultural productivity.

Energy Resources

Importance of energy supplies in the development of society

The amount and forms of energy available have had a big impact on the development of society. Using human labour to do every task is slow, hard work. Using animals, or harnessing the power of water, or the wind released time to develop new activities and make life easier. Changes in energy resources continued with the development of new technologies that harnessed new resources, increased the efficiency of energy use, or allowed energy to be converted into more useful forms.

Smelting of metals using wood and charcoal enabled the development of a range of useful items such as cutting blades, nails, wheel rims, ploughs, and other tools.

The industrial revolution from the 1700s developed the use of coal and coke to produce steel. This was used to manufacture sophisticated machines such as steam engines. These were used in many ways for example, to pump water out of mines, to transport goods, to plough, to drive timber saws and grain-threshing machines, and in textile mills. A major development was the ability to generate power where it was needed by transporting coal in contrast to wind and water power that had to be used where they could be harnessed.

Since the late 1800s crude oil, natural gas, and other fuels have increased the amount of energy that can be used.

Access to large amounts of fossil fuel energy has also enabled the production of a wide range of things including unnecessary products, non-essential travel and has permitted waste of energy.

Secondary fuels such as electricity have become increasingly important. They are often more useful than the primary fuels from which they were produced. Many tools and convenient equipment such as telecommunications systems, motors, lighting and electromagnets in appliances such as audio speakers require electricity and could not be run directly from primary fuels harnessed directly from the environment. Converting energy from primary to secondary fuels is not 100% efficient. This reduces the amount of energy that is available to be used.

Ancient civilizations developed when and where the soil and climate made possible the production of sufficient food to support the population. In contrast, industrial societies developed in places where fossil fuels occurred naturally or where they could be transported easily. Few original industrial centres still use locally available fossil fuels. The increasing use of renewable resources may create new industrial centres locally where energy is harnessed, or more disparately as energy storage and transfer become more effective.

❶ *Traction engine used for ploughing*
❷ *The water wheel that powered a cotton mill*

New uses of energy allowed the development of society: completing tasks more easily or allowing new activities

Per capita energy consumption

As the population has grown, the world's consumption of energy has increased in total as has the per-capita consumption.

Direct uses include energy used by people individually, for example, heating and lighting their homes, cooking, personal transport, use of electrical appliances etc.

Indirect uses include the energy used by commercial organisations, schools, government and industry to provide goods and services and support economic activity, for example, transport of goods, manufacturing processes, water treatment, and energy used in agriculture.

A range of factors create differences in per capita energy consumption in different countries.

Affluence

Higher income enables people to buy more, consume more and use more energy in activities such as travelling more, using less efficient vehicles, heating a larger home and having more energy-using appliances. More energy is used during the manufacture of the additional products bought.

Affluent countries use significantly more energy to construct housing in the production of bricks, glass, tiles and fittings such as carpets, furnishings and appliances.

Not all countries have access to readily available sources of energy. Energy shortages limit transportation, the ability to access water, power equipment and preserve foods.

Supply and demand for energy resources set prices on the world market. Global market prices are usually low enough for more affluent communities to afford to purchase energy for essential uses such as purifying water, running hospitals and transporting food. They may also be able to afford energy for non-essential uses that make life more enjoyable. Poorer communities may be unable to pay for the energy needed for essential uses. This can slow the development of these societies and reduce the quality of life.

Relative cost of energy

In countries where there are large, easily accessible local sources energy is cheap. For example, petrol is much cheaper in the USA than in the UK which means that more petrol can be used for the same cost. This has encouraged the use of larger, less fuel-efficient cars. Fuel efficiency is likely to be a lower priority if energy is relatively cheap.

❶ *Access to energy makes transport of goods and people easier.*

❷ *Farming is easier if abundant supplies of fossil fuels are available*

Some developed countries have a low per capita energy use within their own country. However, they import goods that used a lot of energy in their manufacture in other countries, for example, steel, copper, aluminium. The per capita energy consumption in countries like the UK has gone down in recent years. This is partly due to the decline of industries such as steel and aluminium smelting. These are now produced for us in other countries such as China.

The choice of car has a big impact on energy efficiency

Type of industry

Different types of industries require different amounts of energy

Type of industry	Examples	General level of energy use per unit of economic output
Primary industry	Agriculture, mining, raw material extraction	High
Secondary industry	Heavy manufacturing industry, for example, metal smelting, chemical industry	High
	Light manufacturing industry, for example, car assembly	Medium
Tertiary industry	Services, for example, transport, finance, retail, recreation, education	Low
Quaternary industry	Information and IT	Very low

Social and environmental awareness

Regions and locations which historically had difficulty satisfying demand for energy often have a tradition of managing their energy use carefully. For example, Scandinavia had energy shortages in the past, especially in remote communities and this has driven a strong energy conservation culture.

In the UK, access to large deposits of coal drove the industrial revolution and society's development, but it also meant that energy was used wastefully. As coal mining declined, access to natural gas and oil from the North Sea, extended the extravagant use of energy.

Climate

Climatic conditions affect energy usage as buildings in locations with cold winters require heating and those in very hot areas require air conditioning. High winds increase heat losses while sunny weather increases passive solar heat gains.

How energy is used

Energy is used to create, produce and transport the goods and services that people use.

Types of energy use

Human activities	Examples of energy uses
Agriculture and fisheries	• Fuel for machinery, for example, tractors, and combine harvesters, water pumping, fish farm aeration • Manufacture of chemicals, for example, fertilisers • Food processing, for example, sugar refining, grain drying and milling • Transport of materials and harvested food. • Storage, especially for refrigerated foods • Fuel for fishing boats , water pumping, and aeration in aquaculture
Other industries	• Machinery operation: excavators, rock crushing, pumps, presses, conveyor belts, mixers, cutters, lathes • Heat to melt materials for moulding & casting of metals & plastics • Energy for chemical reactions: smelting of metals, thermal decomposition of limestone in cement manufacture • Heat for baking, for example, pottery, bricks • Heat for distillation, for example, fractional distillation of crude oil • Water treatment for public supply • Sewage treatment
Domestic energy use	• Space heating • Lighting • Running appliances, for example, refrigerators, washing machines, dishwashers, cookers
Transport	• Transport of goods – ships/trains/trucks/conveyor belts/pipelines. • Transport of people – cars, buses, trains, planes

❶ Transport of goods is an increasingly important use of energy.

❷ Energy is important in services such as water and sewage treatment

Changes in energy use

As countries and societies develop energy use changes in terms of the amount and the ways in which it is used.

How per capita and total energy use in a country may change over time

Cause of change	Examples
Energy consumption changes: industrial	As countries such as Brazil, China and India have industrialised, their use of energy has increased rapidly, especially in mining and manufacturing industries. As heavy industry and manufacturing activity have declined in the UK industrial energy use has reduced.
Income levels	Increases in income mean that consumers can afford to pay more for energy, for example, in heating, lighting, and transport. Affluence enables higher consumption of goods increasing the energy required for manufacture and transport. Household appliances such as washing machines, TVs and refrigerators require energy to run. As segments of societies in developing countries such as India and China become affluent domestic consumption rises.
Population growth	Total energy use increases with population growth even if the per-capita use remains the same. If the population of a developing country is growing rapidly it may struggle to increase national energy supplies fast enough to match demand.
Changes in environmental awareness	An increase in environmental awareness may lead to choices that lead to lower energy consumption, such as: • better building energy conservation • choices of vehicle type and usage • choices of consumer goods • food choices • level of recycling

Features of energy resources

The combination of characteristics of an energy resource affects its availability, applicability for specific uses, environmental impacts, and future sustainability.

Renewable/non-renewable

Renewable energy resources naturally re-form relatively quickly so using them does not necessarily reduce future availability, for example, solar, wind, wave, tidal, geothermal, and biofuel energy.

Non-renewable energy resources are either not being formed, or re-form so slowly that current use reduces the amount available for future use, for example, all fossil fuels, uranium.

Depletable/non-depletable

Depletable energy resources are those resources where use can reduce future availability. These include all non-renewable resources but also those renewable resources where unsustainable exploitation may reduce availability, for example, wood, where forests are felled faster than they re-grow.

Abundance

Abundance measures the amount of the resource that exists. This is not the same as the amount available for use as there may be other factors that restrict availability. For example:

- fossil fuels that are deep underground and cannot be extracted;
- winds high above the ground where aerogenerators cannot be located;
- wave power far from the coast where the water is too deep to anchor equipment;
- low intensity sunlight that cannot produce high temperatures.

New technologies and increasing energy prices may make resources that cannot currently be used viable in the future.

Locational constraints

Energy resources are not evenly distributed. Each has its own locational factors.

Energy sources that can only be accessed via extraction, such as fossil fuels and uranium ore, must be located in favourable deposits. (See Chapter 6: Factors affecting mine viability.)

Energy sources that harness natural processes may depend on regional or local features including climate and topography.

Locational factors that control energy resource availability

Energy resource	Main locational factors & required conditions
Fossil fuels	Can only be extracted where economically exploitable deposits exist. Power stations require access to: • fuel supplies; • condenser cooling water (large river/lake/sea); • suitable construction sites.
Nuclear power	High energy density fuel is easily transported Power stations require access to: • condenser cooling water (large river/lake/sea) • suitable construction site.
Solar power	High light intensity Low cloud cover
Wind power	Areas with strong, reliable winds such as: • shallow seas; • open plains; • upland areas. Areas with low land-use conflicts (especially for large wind farms): • not in areas of high ecological sensitivity; • not close to urban areas; • not in areas of high scenic importance.
Wave power	Coastal areas with: • strong, reliable winds over water; • reliable prevailing wind direction; • long fetch: a long stretch of water over which the wind blows.
Hydro Electric Power (HEP)	Areas with: • high, reliable rainfall; • site for a small dam with a large reservoir basin; • large catchment area; • impermeable bedrock; • stable geology.
Biofuels	• Nearby forest areas. • Farmland for biofuel crops. • Farmland for crop/livestock waste. • Nearby urban areas for food waste/sewage.
Geothermal power	Areas with: • hot rocks near the ground surface; • recent volcanic activity.
Tidal power	Areas where: • tidal range is large. • coastal features that focus tidal flow to increase flow velocity or tidal range.

Note: Small scale resources may only be usable locally unless they are close to transport infrastructure: road, rail, ship, pipeline, electricity grid.

Intermittency

If an energy resource is not available at times when it is needed then it is difficult to rely on it, for example, wind, solar, tidal energy.

Predictability

It is important to know how much energy will be available and whether it will meet demand for energy. Some resources are intermittent but the time they will be available can be predicted accurately, for example, tidal power. This means that plans can be made to use alternative resources when they are unavailable. Other resources are both intermittent and unpredictable, for example, solar power and wind power.

Energy density

Energy density is a measure of the amount of energy in a given mass of energy resource, for example, oil, coal, uranium, or wood. For some resources, such as many renewable resources, it is the amount of energy harnessed by a given mass of equipment, for example, the energy harnessed per kilogramme of solar panel.

In general, high energy density energy resources are most useful because:

▼ smaller quantities are needed so storage and transport are easier;

▼ it is easier to reach high temperatures.

The energy density of selected energy resources

Energy density	Energy resources
Highest	Nuclear fusion Nuclear fission
	Hydrogen Fossil fuels
	Wood
Lowest	Wind power Solar power

An energy resource which has a low energy density is often less useful if it is used directly. However, it can still be useful. For example, solar power and wind power have low energy densities but the electricity produced can be used to power technologies with a high energy requirement. The electricity can also be used to produce high energy density secondary fuels such as hydrogen by the electrolysis of water.

Resource availability

The potential contribution of a resource to energy supplies is clearly affected by the amount of energy that is available. It can be difficult to estimate how much of the resource can actually be harnessed. There may be abundant resources which cannot be exploited with any technology that exists, or is likely to be developed, for example, wind at high altitude, very deep coal, or oil under very deep areas of the sea.

Need for energy conversions to increase usefulness

The form in which energy is harnessed is not necessarily the form in which it will be delivered to the end-user. For example, the chemical energy of fossil fuels is converted to heat, potential, kinetic then electrical energy before it can be used to power electrical appliances. Some resources that currently seem to be of little use may become important if appropriate technologies are developed to convert them to more useful energy forms.

Applicability to specific uses

The available energy resources have shaped the way that societies have developed and therefore it can be difficult for society to change to using energy resources with different characteristics.

Renewable energy resources are making a more significant contribution to our energy supplies. They have different characteristics from fossil fuels and nuclear power. While a number can generate electricity none can reach the temperature levels that fossil fuels create or produce liquid fuels in sufficient quantities to power all our vehicles.

Ease of storage

Energy demand and supply levels vary and rarely balance. Being able to store energy is important so that it is available when it is required.

Some energy resources, such as the chemical energy in fossil fuels, can be stored easily especially since they have high energy density where a small mass or volume stores a large amount of energy.

Some energy resources cannot be stored unless they are converted into other energy forms, for example, solar, wind, wave and tidal energy cannot be stored. They can be converted to thermal energy, chemical energy, or gravitational potential energy which can be stored.

Ease of transportation

Energy resources are rarely found in the areas where the demand is highest, so it must be transported. The ease of transport is affected by properties such as the form of energy and energy density.

The transport methods used for different energy resources

Energy resource	Main transport methods	Notes
Coal	Ship, train	Coal is often used in large scale industries such as electricity generation or smelting iron. It is often easier to transport electricity and steel than coal, so power stations and iron and steel works are often located near coal fields, or deep water ports where coal is imported.
Crude oil	Pipeline, ship, rail tanker	Crude oil is transported in large quantities from oil fields to oil refineries where refined products are produced such as aviation fuel, petrol, diesel, lubricating oil, fuel oil and tar. Bulk transport methods are used.
Refined oil products	Pipeline, ship tanker, rail tanker, truck	Products of oil refining are usually distributed to relatively local consumers in smaller quantities than crude oil.
Natural gas	Pipeline, liquefied natural gas (LNG) ship tanker, rail tanker	Natural Gas can be piped easily from gas fields to areas where demand is high, for example, large industries, or urban areas with large numbers of consumers. Natural gas, in its gaseous form, has a low energy density so transport by ship where pipelines do not exist requires liquefaction to increase the energy density. LNG has 160x the energy density by volume of gaseous natural gas but requires refrigeration at -160°C.
Fissile fuel, for example, uranium	Solid fuel rods or pellets by rail or truck	Relatively small quantities of fissile fuels need to be transported because they have a high energy density. They are transported in solid form in containers that are designed to withstand impacts and fires. They may have an outer casing to add further protection.
Biofuels	Road, rail, ship.	Each biofuel has its own transport features. Liquid biofuels, such as alcohol and vegetable oils, have relatively high energy densities so transport over longer distances is practical. Solid biofuels, such as straw and *Miscanthus*, are very bulky with low mass per unit volume so long distance transport may not be practical as the transport energy inputs may be high.
Solar, wind, hydro-electric, tidal, geothermal	Conversion to other energy forms which can be transported	These primary fuels cannot be transported but they can be used to generate electricity that can be transported.
Electricity	High voltage AC or DC electricity grid	Overhead power cables are cheaper to install and maintain than underground cables.

Environmental impacts

The exploitation of all energy resources damage the environment in a variety of ways. Some are obvious such as pollution created during the extraction and use of fossil fuels whereas the link with impacts such as global climate change may be less obvious.

All energy resources cause damage through the manufacture of the equipment required to exploit them.

Some environmental impacts are over-emphasised, for example, people can be upset by the visual impact of constructing solar or windfarms. However, these have no significant impact on the ability of the planet to sustain life.

The environmental impacts of individual energy resources are covered in the following sections on each resource.

Technological development

All technologies have a period of development before they can be used practically. This is followed by a period of further development when the technology is refined to improve it so that it becomes more efficient, more effective, and cheaper. It can be difficult for a new technology to be financially viable during its early development if it has to compete with existing technologies, whose development costs have already been paid for and that have the economic benefits of mass production.

Political/economic influences

Political influences

Governments may decide to provide assistance to particular sections of the energy industry:

- to support the development costs of a new technology, for example, grants for developing new renewable energy technologies;
- to increase national energy security, for example, grants or tax reduction for oil exploration;
- to reduce environmental impacts, for example, EU grants for low carbon technologies.

The support may take several forms:

- financial grants;
- a guaranteed price or market for the energy produced;
- less strict planning regulations/permission to develop favourable sites;
- financial support or compensation for affected communities.

Economic influences

It is not easy to calculate the full cost of using energy. This is because the price paid by the energy user does not always cover the total costs including environmental damage and the costs of mitigating these. Burning fossil fuels causes pollution including acid rain which produces financial impacts elsewhere, for example, through building damage, crop losses, forestry damage and the health effects of atmospheric pollution from vehicles. Such costs are not paid for by energy users. It is also very difficult to assess the costs of some impacts, as these issues are not fully understood, for example, the impacts of global climate change.

The cost of an energy project can be divided into the running costs during its operational life, and the set-up costs to make and install the equipment.

Running costs are paid using the income from the energy produced.

Set-up costs are often paid for with loans on which interest has to be paid, adding to the total cost.

If a renewable energy project is compared with a non-renewable energy project of the same actual cost, the renewable energy project may still be at a financial disadvantage. The cost of renewable energy projects is mostly the initial cost of the equipment, with very low running costs, so most of the expenditure is from a loan. The cost of the non-renewable energy project is mainly the running costs, especially fuel, which will not require a loan with interest payments. So, the renewable project has to cover higher interest payments, making the total cost higher than for the non-renewable energy project.

▶ *Cost comparison of electricity generation from different energy sources.*

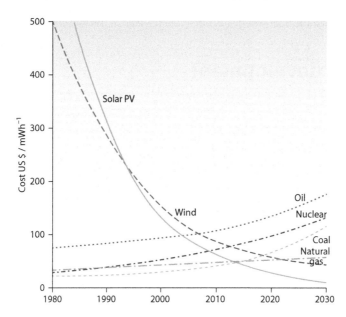

The graphs show mean values for a range of technologies, including estimates for future costs. It is difficult to accurately include all costs such as future decommissioning costs or the costs of environmental impacts.

The sustainability of current energy use

Energy supplies are only sustainable if the amount of energy supplied can be maintained, without unacceptable environmental damage or economic and social impacts. Current global energy use is not sustainable.

Resource depletion

Fossil fuels provide most global energy supplies but they are non-renewable. Their availability must decline in the future as reserves deplete.

New technologies and increased market prices may convert more of the resource into reserves so that they can be exploited, but the principle of resource depletion is still a controlling factor that must eventually restrict supplies.

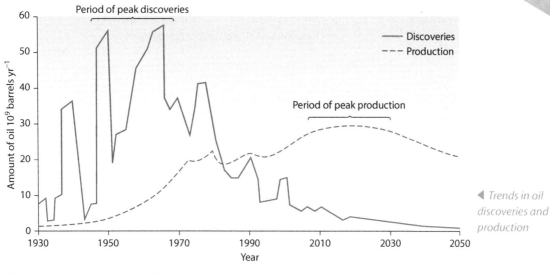

Trends in oil discoveries and production

There are still large reserves of fossil fuels that have not been exploited, but the rate of discovery of new deposits has declined dramatically since the 1980s.

Economic sustainability

The choices made now about energy supplies will affect future economies in many ways.

- Depleted non-renewable resources will become more expensive. Because energy is needed for so many aspects of life, this could reduce future affluence.

- Commitments made now for the long-term use of expensive technologies such as nuclear power could reduce future affluence, although it may help secure energy supplies.

- A failure to invest in the development of future energy supplies may result in shortages for future generations. When a new technology is first introduced it is usually expensive as the development costs are still being paid for and there are no economies of scale in manufacturing that would eventually reduce costs. It is difficult for these new technologies to compete with well-established ones that are cheap such as fossil fuels. Waiting until depleted fossil fuels become expensive and the new technologies become competitive would produce an energy gap because it would take time to develop the technology and necessary infrastructure.

Environmental impacts

All energy resource exploitation has an environmental impact but there are differences in the scale, type, and timing of the impacts.

Many environmental impacts are temporary, local or small, so they do not affect global sustainability. However, the combination of these impacts may be significant.

New technologies may be developed that will reduce environmental impacts, such as the ability to capture CO_2 emissions, but it would be risky to commit to further large-scale fossil fuel use before the technique has been proven.

Features affecting sustainability and energy use can occur before the energy is used, or as a consequence of its use

Impacts before use	Activity/issue	Examples of energy resources/details	For more details see ....
	Fuel extraction	Coal mining, oil extraction	
	Fuel processing	Coal, crude oil	
	Equipment manufacture	Exploitation of energy resources requires equipment that causes environmental damage in material extraction and processing.	
	Site development/operation	Preparing sites for equipment and associated infrastructure causes habitat damage.	
	Transport	The transport of fuels uses fossil fuels.	
	Embodied energy in equipment	Equipment manufacture for every energy resource uses energy, although the amount varies greatly between different resources.	
	Acid mine drainage	Coal mining	
	Subsidence	Coal mining	
	Methane releases	Extraction of all fossil fuels	
Impacts as a consequence of use	**Pollution**		
	Atmospheric pollution	Fossil fuels	
	Oil pollution	Oil, tar sands, oil shales	
	Radioactive waste	Nuclear power	
	Noise pollution	Wind power	
	Thermal pollution	Steam turbine power stations	
	Habitat damage		
	During extraction of the energy resource	Fossil fuels, uranium, biofuel crops	
	Power station and equipment location	All energy resources cause habitat impacts during equipment installation.	
	Ecological impacts of tidal power schemes	Changes in flow velocity, tidal range, sedimentation, turbidity	
	Ecological impacts of HEP schemes	Downstream changes in flow velocity, turbidity, dissolved oxygen. Barrier to movements of wildlife.	
	Pipelines and cables	Oil, gas, electricity	
	Depletion of reserves	Non-renewable energy resources	

Future energy supplies

Energy is such an important part of society that future supplies must be ensured by good planning. The ways in which supplies will be met will be affected by the changing needs of society and the changing energy resources that are available for use.

To plan future strategies, it is necessary to understand how energy resources are used now.

There are many energy resources available to meet future demands. Even resources that do not have the right properties for exploitation could be used if new technologies are developed.

The ways that energy is supplied will change in the future for many reasons, for example:

  ▼ some existing resources such as fossil fuels and wood are becoming depleted;

- concerns about environmental damage are affecting political policies and public opinion;
- current supplies cannot meet the growth in demand caused by increasing affluence and population growth;
- new technologies are becoming available to harness, store, transport, or convert energy into the forms that are required.

Fossil fuels

All fossil fuels were produced by the partial decomposition of dead organic matter under anaerobic conditions beneath layers of sediments that were deposited on the Earth's surface or seabed. These processes took place over long periods of time. Most coal was formed 300 – 400m years ago.

Fossil fuels have provided most of the energy used in the development of industrial society since the 1700s. They have particular features that made them ideal for use:

- They are easy to store.
- They have high energy density so they can power high energy intensity activities, for example, high temperature processes such as smelting steel and powering steam engines. Having high energy density they are also relatively efficient to transport: a given volume or mass contains a lot of energy.
- They are often found in very abundant local deposits.

Many of the richest, most accessible fossil fuel deposits have been depleted, so new technologies are required to exploit remaining deposits.

Features of fossil fuels

When coal was first exploited on a large scale in the 1700s it provided abundant energy for uses that required heat. New technologies allowed this energy to be used to provide mechanical power then electricity. More recently, oil and natural gas have been exploited for similar purposes..

Chemical energy

The chemical energy of fossil fuels is easy to store and easy to convert into the heat energy that is usually required.

Energy density

The high energy density of fossil fuels makes them very useful for many applications.

- The high temperatures produced by burning coal enables the smelting of metal ores.
- Burning fossil fuels reach temperatures that are high enough to produce high pressure steam which can spin turbines and generators in power stations to generate electricity.
- The high energy density of fossil fuels allows a small mass of fuel to do a lot of work, so 5 litres of petrol can carry 1tonne of car for 80 km.
- 75t of aviation fuel can carry a 400t Boeing 747, including 400 passengers, for 5,600km from London to New York. If the fuel had a lower energy density then the weight of the fuel carried may make flight impossible.

Finite resources

Non-renewable energy resources are finite resources so exploitation means they must eventually become depleted. This is important where industrial communities have grown up on local fuel supplies, for example, the heavy industrial towns that were established on the coalfields of NE USA, South Wales, the Midlands in the UK, and the Ruhr region of Germany. Once local supplies are exhausted industry may only survive if supplies from elsewhere can be transported easily and economically.

Available resource

The total quantity of fossil fuels in existence is very large. Many of these deposits are not included in estimates of reserves because the technology to exploit them has not been developed or it would not be economically viable to do so.

- Significant amounts of oil and coal are unexploitable because the deposits are too deep, found in small amounts or located in areas which are difficult to reach.
- A lot of natural gas is trapped in fine-grained impermeable shale deposits.
- Oil shale is a fine-grained sedimentary rock containing solid hydrocarbons, that can yield substantial amounts of oil and combustible gas upon destructive distillation. Most of the organic matter is insoluble in ordinary organic solvents and cannot flow to the surface like crude oil. Therefore, it must be decomposed by heating to release the oil by melting it so that it can flow to the surface. The total contained in shale deposits is greater than our total reserves of crude oil.

Although the quantity of recoverable fossil fuels is very large, their large-scale use may not be possible because:

- it is not economically viable,
- it may cause unacceptable pollution or
- it will involve habitat damage in areas that are ecologically sensitive
- its extraction processes may cause local earth tremors.

Level of technological development

Industrial societies have developed using fossil fuels so the technologies to exploit them are well developed. Many applications that use energy have been developed so that they use fossil fuels such as cars, trucks, ships, aircraft and most power stations. To change to other sources of energy will involve many changes in the infrastructure of society.

Political and international trade problems

High and increasing demand drives energy-hungry countries to satisfy their own energy needs. This can influence political decisions to protect future supplies, at the expense of reducing both local and global environmental impacts.

Crude oil is the basis of most of the world's energy. However, deposits are unevenly distributed across the globe. The majority of oil reserves are in the Middle East. This makes the Middle East region the focus of both trade and political interest.

Economic issues

Economic activity and international trade can drive countries to make decisions based on the cheapest options. This may not be best for the long-term.

When cheap natural gas became available in the UK it contributed to the closure of the deep coal mines even though significant coal deposits remained and could still be extracted. Although North Sea gas reserves will be exhausted in the next thirty or forty years it will not be possible to reopen the coalmines because they have flooded and are unsafe.

Fossil fuel generates economic costs such as pollution damage. These are not paid for by the energy industry but paid by other industries such as agriculture, forestry, or the health service.

Extraction methods and environmental impacts

The extraction, processing and use of fossil fuels as well as the disposal of the wastes produced all have environmental impacts.

Coal

Deep mining and open cast mining are used to extract coal. Deep mining is labour intensive so it is relatively expensive to produce large quantities of coal. Open cast mining is mechanised and is usually more economically viable.. However, as it is necessary to clear all the rock above the coal it is only viable in locations where coal is close to the surface. Deep deposits and very thin seams cannot be accessed by either method.

◀ An excavator used in an open cast coal mine

The environmental damage caused by deep mining is predominantly at the surface through loss of habitat, transport infrastructure and potentially surface subsidence. Open-cast mining causes greater habitat damage.

Oil & gas

Petroleum (crude oil) in liquid form flows through permeable rock and collects in porous rock in pores between the particles. When a pipe is drilled down to these reservoirs oil will be forced to the surface either by the natural pressure of gas above the oil, or by water beneath the oil.

An anticline oil reservoir

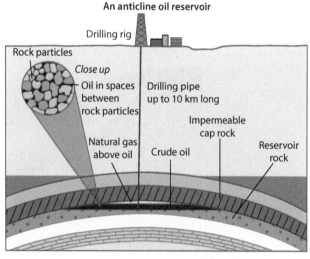

Drilling rig

Rock particles

Close up
Oil in spaces between rock particles

Drilling pipe up to 10 km long

Impermeable cap rock

Natural gas above oil

Crude oil

Reservoir rock

▲ *An anticline oil reservoir*

Deep and open cast coal mines

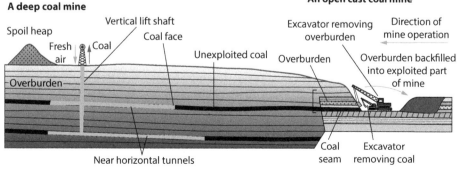

A deep coal mine

Spoil heap

Vertical lift shaft

Coal face

Fresh air

Coal

Unexploited coal

Overburden

Near horizontal tunnels

An open cast coal mine

Excavator removing overburden

Direction of mine operation

Overburden

Overburden backfilled into exploited part of mine

Coal seam

Excavator removing coal

▲ *Deep and open cast coal mines*

Oil spills from oil rigs can cause pollution. Oil-based drilling mud used to lubricate the drill pipes can cause pollution in groundwater, rivers and the sea.

Surplus gas on oil rigs may be burnt or 'flared' to reduce the risk of explosions. This causes atmospheric pollution through pollutants such as sulfur dioxide, carbon dioxide and smoke..

Natural gas is extracted by similar means to oil extraction and is forced to the surface by its own natural pressure.

Environmental impact of fossil fuel extraction

Cause	Environmental impact
Mining of coal	Habitat loss, noise, dust, turbid drainage water, spoil heaps, acid mine drainage, methane releases, derelict sites. More details see Lithosphere See page139, Environmental impacts of mineral exploitation.
Oil extraction and transport	Oil pollution, marine seismic surveys Habitat damage caused by pipeline construction More details see Pollution See page 258, Oil pollution.
Combustion of fossil fuels	Atmospheric pollution: carbon dioxide, sulfur dioxide, oxides of nitrogen, carbon monoxide, smoke Ash disposal More details see Pollution See page 245, Atmospheric pollution.

▶ *A natural gas pipeline during construction*

Fossil fuels cause pollution when they are used. The burning of fossil fuel products such as fuel oil, diesel and petrol releases harmful gases of carbon dioxide, carbon monoxide, oxides of nitrogen, sulfur dioxide and smoke particulates. Coal burning generates large quantities of ash. Natural gas is cleaner, mainly releasing carbon dioxide.

Oil and gas pipelines can cause habitat damage over a significant area especially during construction, although careful route planning, soil replacement and replanting can reduce this.

Main uses of fossil fuels

Fossil fuel	Main uses
Crude oil	Liquid vehicle fuels: petrol, diesel, aircraft fuel, ship fuel oil. Gas fuels for heating: propane, butane Petrochemicals: plastics, fertilisers, pharmaceuticals
Natural gas	Domestic and industrial heating Electricity generation Chemicals: nitrate fertilisers
Coal	Electricity generation Iron and steel industry

New technologies: Coal

The development of new technologies may allow better use of the resources we already use and make it possible for new resources to be exploited.

Coal gasification

Coal that is too deep to be mined can be burnt underground under controlled conditions to produce a mixture of fuel gases including hydrogen, carbon monoxide and methane.

Coal liquefaction

This involves the conversion of coal to liquid hydrocarbons which have applications that solid coal cannot perform such as liquid vehicle fuels.

The coal may be converted to liquids directly using solvents or indirectly using gasification then chemical changes to convert gaseous hydrocarbons to liquid hydrocarbons.

New technologies: Oil

Primary oil recovery

Primary oil recovery is the well-established method that uses the natural pressure of water below the oil or gas that is present above the oil, or dissolved in it. The pressure forces the oil up the production well to the surface. About 20% of the oil is usually extracted.

❶ *A pump-jack fitted at ground level on the production well may be used to increase the flow rate.*
❷ *'Nodding donkeys' are pump-jacks that increase the flow rate from oil reservoirs. This one is in Kimmeridge, Dorset*

A single offshore oil platform can extract oil from many oil reservoirs beneath the seabed

Secondary oil recovery

Secondary crude oil recovery involves pumping water, or natural gas, down an injection well to maintain the pressure and the flow of the oil. Secondary recovery increases the total recovery rate to about 40%.

Some carbon capture and storage (CCS) schemes pump the recovered CO_2 underground to increase oil recovery in addition to storing the CO_2.

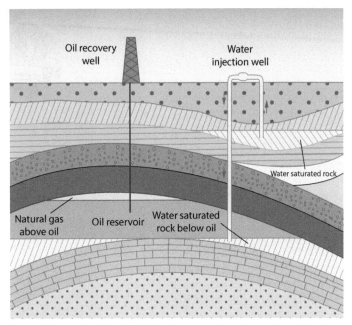

Oil recovery well

Water injection well

Water saturated rock

Natural gas above oil

Oil reservoir

Water saturated rock below oil

▲ *Secondary oil recovery using water injection*

Tertiary oil recovery

Tertiary crude oil recovery includes techniques which reduce the viscosity of the oil. This is also called Enhanced Oil Recovery (EOR).

⬛ Steam may be pumped down to heat the oil. The steam may be generated by burning fuel, or from solar heating schemes, using parabolic concentrators.

⬛ The oil viscosity may also be reduced by controlled underground combustion which heats it up.

⬛ Detergents or solvents reduce the surface tension of the oil and make it flow more easily.

⬛ Bacteria are used to partially digest heavy oil and produce lighter oils that flow more easily. The bacteria also produce carbon dioxide which helps to maintain the pressure and the flow of the oil.

Tertiary recovery typically increases the total recovery rate to about 60%.

▲ *Directional drilling bit. The tungsten carbide teeth grind the rock into fragments. The hole on the left delivers a fine mud suspension that lubricates the drill.*

Directional drilling

Directional drilling allows wells to be drilled that are not vertical. This has many advantages:

⬛ many wells can be drilled from a single platform;

⬛ it is possible to drill underneath locations where drilling rigs could not be placed, for example, urban areas;

⬛ drilling can follow weaker or softer rock strata to make drilling quicker and can target multiple small reservoirs up to 10km from the well head. This can significantly increase total recovery rates.

Subsea production wells

Subsea production wells are located on the seabed and have no platform at the sea surface. They allow operations in water up to 2000m deep, although new developments will allow operations at greater depths.

ROVs and AUVs

Remotely operated vehicles (ROVs) and unmanned autonomous vehicles (AUVs) can be used to carry out seabed surveys and to inspect underwater production equipment and pipelines.

▶ *A remotely operated vehicle (ROV) that can be used to monitor the construction and maintenance of underwater oil operations*

Fracking

Large volumes of crude oil and natural gas are trapped in the pore spaces of shale rocks that have low permeability. These are called tight oil and tight gas. Hydraulic fracturing uses high pressure to open fissures in the surrounding shale rock along which the oil or gas can flow towards a recovery well. Water, sand grains and solvents may be pumped into the fissures to increase the recovery rate.

Concerns over fracking

Experience in the USA shows that fracking can cause environmental problems, however, good management may minimize these. Examples of potential environmental impacts are:

 - ◤ natural gas may enter aquifer water;
 - ◤ chemicals injected underground may enter aquifers, or reach the surface and cause pollution;
 - ◤ toxic metals naturally present in the rocks may become mobile;
 - ◤ large volumes of water are needed;
 - ◤ earthquakes: natural tensions in the crust caused by continental drift and isostatic movements after erosion may cause earthquakes. Fracking may release some of these tensions, but it should not cause earthquakes that could not have occurred naturally.

Potential problems may be reduced using methods such as the collection and treatment of waste water, reuse of waste water, and restrictions on the location of fracking sites in sensitive areas.

Tar sands and oil shales

The liquid hydrocarbons produced from tar sands and oil shales are called 'unconventional oil'. Oil shales include solid hydrocarbons while tar sands include 'heavy' low viscosity oils that do not flow easily.

Tar sands are extracted using two main methods:

 - ◤ the sands are quarried using large excavators. The sand is then treated with hot water. This produces an emulsion of oil droplets that floats and can be separated. One barrel (150 litres) of oil is produced from two tonnes of tar sands. About 75% of the oil is recovered. The waste sand is backfilled into the mine;

▼ *in-situ* production uses steam injection, solvent, or controlled combustion in deep deposits to produce liquid oil that can be pumped to the surface. The high energy inputs make extraction expensive.

- Oil shales are mined then the oil is extracted by heating the shales to drain off the fluid hydrocarbons.
- The recoverable deposits of tar sands and oil shales are much greater than the total reserves of crude oil, however, extraction is expensive so current estimates of economically recoverable reserves are low.

New technologies: natural gas

Natural gas is recovered from underground rock structures of porous, permeable rock using the natural pressure of the gas. The recovery rate is typically 80-90% of the gas present.

Enhanced Gas Recovery

Enhanced Gas Recovery (EGR) increases gas recovery rates using techniques such as the injection of CO_2 or nitrogen around the edge of the gas field to maintain pressure and gas flow.

Methane hydrate

Methane hydrate (or methane clathrate) is a solid ice-like crystalline solid found in locations at low temperatures, such as polar regions, or under high pressure, for example, in oceanic sediments around continents.

Methane hydrate is not exploited commercailly now but could potentially yield more methane than conventional natural gas sources.

Several extraction methods are proposed for exploiting methane hydrate oceanic sediments, for example:

- **water heating** - hot water is pumped into the sediments which melts the hydrate crystals, releasing the methane gas;
- **depressurisation** - drilling into the sediments causes the pressure to drop. The methane gradually dissociates from the hydrate crystal;
- **carbon dioxide injection** - at high pressures, carbon dioxide can also form bonds with ice crystals, but it bonds more strongly than methane. Injecting carbon dioxide could displace methane which could be collected. This could also be used as part of a carbon capture and storage scheme.

So little is known about the ecology of the ocean floor that the environmental impacts are hard to predict. Any methane released that was not collected could enter the atmosphere and contribute to global climate change.

Carbon capture and storage (CCS)

Concerns over global climate change are driving attempts to reduce the use of fossil fuels. Carbon capture and storage (CCS) involves a range of developmental technologies which would store the CO_2 produced by fossil fuel use and reduce CO_2 releases. In theory, this could make extended use of fossil fuels possible. It is unlikely that CCS could be applied to small, dispersed uses such as vehicles. However, it may be possible to use it to capture CO_2 at large power stations then use the electricity to produce non-carbon fuels such as hydrogen. See page 220.

Nuclear power

Nuclear power involves the conversion of small amounts of matter into energy as atomic nuclei split or join - **e = mc²**

where: *e = the energy released*

m = the mass of matter lost

c = the speed of light

In nuclear fission and fusion, a huge amount of energy is released during the destruction of a small amount of matter. Large amounts of energy are released when small amounts of matter from the nuclei of atoms are destroyed.

Nuclear fission involves the splitting of the nuclei of large atoms, such as those of the isotopes uranium-235 and plutonium-239.

Nuclear fusion involves the joining of the nuclei of small atoms, such as those of the isotopes hydrogen-2 and hydrogen-3.

Only nuclear fission is used commercially now, fusion being a research project.

Nuclear fission

The nuclei of the isotopes of some elements with large nuclei may be split if they are hit by neutrons, releasing more neutrons and large amounts of energy.

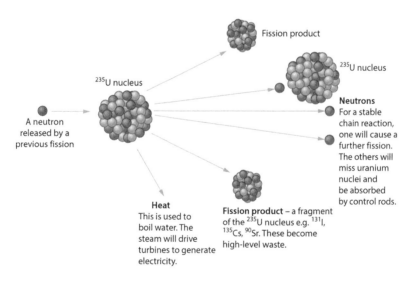

Fission product

^{235}U nucleus

^{235}U nucleus

A neutron released by a previous fission

Neutrons
For a stable chain reaction, one will cause a further fission. The others will miss uranium nuclei and be absorbed by control rods.

Heat
This is used to boil water. The steam will drive turbines to generate electricity.

Fission product – a fragment of the ^{235}U nucleus e.g. ^{131}I, ^{135}Cs, ^{90}Sr. These become high-level waste.

◀ *A nuclear fission chain reaction*

The power output of nuclear reactors normally changes quite slowly so nuclear power is usually used for 'base-load' electricity supplies that are needed all the time.

A number of factors have restricted the growth of nuclear power.

◤ The technology is very complex so it is difficult to use in less technologically advanced societies which cannot support the industrial infrastructure needed.

◤ The complex technology involved is very expensive.

- There is strong public opposition to nuclear power in some countries because of concerns over safety, especially following the reactor accidents at Three Mile Island (1979, USA), Chernobyl (1986, Ukraine), Fukushima (2011, Japan) and the impact such incidents have on the short and long term health of people and the environment.
- There are concerns about possible links between nuclear materials for civil uses and military or terrorist uses.
- Uncertainty over the permanent disposal of radioactive waste.
- Uncertainty over the total costs of nuclear power since no commercial reactor has been fully decommissioned.

Main features of nuclear fission

Energy density

The nuclear fuel used in nuclear power stations has a very high energy density so a small amount of fuel releases a large amount of energy. 1kg of uranium fuel (0.7% U-235) can release as much energy as 13 tonnes of coal. This means that nuclear power stations do not need continual supplies of large quantities of fuel, so they can be located where the transport infrastructure is not as good as that required for a coal-fired power station. Nuclear reactors provide the power for some surface ships and many submarines. They rarely need to be refuelled and do not need an air supply to operate.

▶ *Heysham B nuclear power station in Lancashire is one of 19 commercial nuclear power stations that have operated in the UK. The older ones have been shut down but 8 were still operating in 2017.*

Embodied energy

Although nuclear fuel has a high energy density, the processes required to produce the fuel and the complexity of nuclear power stations require a lot of energy. Coal requires very little processing but uranium must be purified, concentrated, and chemically processed to produce the fuel.

Finite resources

Fissile materials such as uranium and thorium are non-renewable resources, so the quantity that exists declines as they are used. However, depletion will only become a problem if supplies become restricted. This is more dependent on our technological ability to extract them than the actual amount that exists.

A huge amount of uranium exists but most is found in very low purity deposits which cannot be exploited economically at current prices. The energy cost of extracting the uranium, using conventional methods on lower grade deposits, may be greater than would be released when the uranium underwent fission. New technologies in the future may extract the fissile fuel using less energy.

Level of technological development

Nuclear reactors powered by uranium have been used for commercial electricity generation since the 1950s and reactors currently being built are described as 3rd generation reactors. Lessons learned from earlier reactors have allowed improvements in design:

- longer reactor life (60+ years instead of 40+ years);
- more reliable operation;
- lower fuel consumption.

These advances give uranium reactors an advantage over thorium reactors which are less well developed.

Environmental impacts

Impacts of Nuclear energy production

Cause	Environmental impact
• Mining and processing of uranium/ thorium ore to make nuclear fuel	• Habitat loss, noise, dust, turbid drainage water, hazardous wastes
• High embodied energy of materials used	• Contribution to global climate change
• Reactor accidents and radioactive waste	• Health risks of ionising radiation

Political and international difficulties

The possible link between civil nuclear electricity and the preparation of weapons-grade fuel has led some countries to try to restrict the availability of technology to other countries that are considered to be untrustworthy.

Economic issues

New nuclear power stations are such large engineering projects that they are very expensive. The inclusion of new design features and unforeseen problems often causes total costs to far exceed the original estimates.

Very few old reactors have been fully decommissioned. Costs have proved to be much greater than anticipated and funds have often not been put aside from the income during the years of operation to pay for decommissioning. If the cost over-run is paid by the state then nuclear power is receiving a subsidy which makes it appear more economically competitive than it actually is.

Uses of nuclear fission

The main use of nuclear reactors is in the generation of electricity.

Nuclear reactors are also used to propel about 150 ships.

The fission products present in used fuel include isotopes that have other uses such as caesium-137 for food irradiation and americium-241 in smoke alarms.

Future use of nuclear fission

Because nuclear fuel has a high energy density nuclear reactors require very little fuel. This means that power stations can be located where the transport of large amounts of fuels with a lower energy density would be a problem. A reactor only needs to have a few tens of tons of fuel replaced each year, compared with 10 000t of coal that would be burnt every day in a coal fired power station with a similar electricity output.

New technologies

Uranium extraction

Several improved uranium extraction techniques are being developed. These include:

- **polymer adsorption** - uranium dissolved in seawater adsorbs onto certain polymers that are placed in the sea. The uranium can be washed off using acids then collected and concentrated;
- **phosphate mining** - uranium is often present in phosphate deposits and can be separated from the material extracted in phosphate mines;
- **coal ash** - uranium can be extracted from coal ash. This will become economic if the price of uranium rises enough.

New reactor designs

- **Molten salt reactors:** using molten salt as a reactor coolant increases the efficiency of electricity generation because the reactor can operate at a much higher temperature without needing high pressure to prevent the coolant boiling. Liquid cooled reactors are much smaller than gas-cooled reactors, so they are cheaper to construct.
- **Plutonium reactors:** almost all nuclear reactors harness the energy released by the fission of uranium-235, but this only makes up 0.7% of the uranium in the mined ore. The remaining 99.3% is the uranium-238 which is not fissile. However, uranium-238 can be converted into fissile plutonium-239 by neutron bombardment within a reactor. So, the reactor is using up fissile fuel, but it is also producing more fissile fuel from the uranium-238. An isotope that is not itself fissile but can be converted into a fissile fuel by neutron bombardment is called a 'fertile fuel'. These 'breeder' reactors release energy for electricity and can produce more new fissile fuel than they use. They allow much more energy to be harnessed from the original uranium that was mined, however breeder reactors are more complex and expensive to operate. The fission of plutonium does not require the neutrons to be slowed by a moderator so they are often called 'fast reactors' or 'fast breeder reactors'.

▶ *Plutonium fuel breeding cycle: the production of plutonium by neutron bombardment of uranium 238*

$$^{238}_{92}U + ^{1}_{0}n \xrightarrow[\text{Neutron bombardment}]{} {}^{239}_{92}U \xrightarrow[\text{Beta decay}]{\beta} {}^{239}_{93}Np \xrightarrow[\text{Beta decay}]{\beta} {}^{239}_{94}Pu$$

- **Thorium reactors:** thorium-232 is not fissile so it does not release energy when bombarded with neutrons. However, it is a fertile fuel and can be converted to fissile uranium-233. The reactor designs include fuel rods of uranium-233 which release energy and neutrons to maintain the chain reaction. There are also rods of thorium-232 in the reactor core which 'breed' uranium-233 as they are bombarded with neutrons. The uranium-233 can be extracted to make new fuel rods.

Advantages and disadvantages of thorium reactors

Advantages	Disadvantages
• Thorium is three times more abundant than uranium • It is much more difficult to make weapons materials than it is using uranium • Much less radioactive waste is produced • The radioactive waste has shorter half-lives • No fuel enrichment is required	• The breeding rate for uranium-233 is slow, so the fuel is expensive • Uranium-233 releases alpha radiation so it is very hazardous • Being a less-developed technology than uranium reactors, the remaining development costs will be high

Nuclear fusion

Nuclear fusion involves the joining of the nuclei of small atoms such as isotopes of hydrogen, for example, deuterium and tritium. It is the energy source of all stars but producing controllable fusion on a small scale on Earth has proved difficult.

The sources of fuel are:

- ⚐ deuterium (hydrogen-2) extracted from water;
- ⚐ tritium (hydrogen-3) produced by neutron bombardment of lithium.

Development of the methods to produce controlled fusion on Earth has proved complex.

The fusion of deuterium and tritium

$$^{2}_{1}H + ^{3}_{1}H \longrightarrow ^{4}_{2}He + ^{1}_{0}n + \text{energy}$$

Deuterium Tritium   Helium Neutron
hydrogen hydrogen

The production of Tritium

It may be possible to use the neutrons from fusion to produce tritium by the neutron bombardment of lithium.

$$^{6}_{3}Li + ^{1}_{0}n \longrightarrow ^{4}_{2}He + ^{3}_{1}H$$

▲ *The reactions involved in the nuclear fusion of hydrogen and the production of tritium*

Conditions needed for fusion to occur on Earth

Condition	Details
Hydrogen in the form of plasma	The repelling negatively charged electrons around the nuclei must be removed so the nuclei can collide
Heavy nuclei	Nuclei with greater mass have more momentum and are more able to overcome the repelling positive nuclei
Very high temperature	To increase the kinetic energy of the nuclei and increase the chance of nuclei colliding
Vacuum	So the plasma is not cooled by air
Magnetic field	To hold the plasma centrally in the vacuum so it does not touch the sides of the container and cool down

▼ *The inside of the JET torus fusion reactor, Culham, UK*

Toroidal reactors

Most early development has focused on torus reactors such as the Joint European Torus (JET) near Oxford.

Commercial fusion energy on Earth, if it is actually possible, may not be commercially viable for many years. Several new projects are being developed such as ITER. This is a new toroidal reactor that builds on the knowledge gained from JET. It should become operational around 2025. It is planned to:

- ⚐ release more energy than it uses: 500MW output from 50MW input;
- ⚐ maintain fusion for longer periods;
- ⚐ use a blanket of lithium around the reactor to breed new tritium fuel.

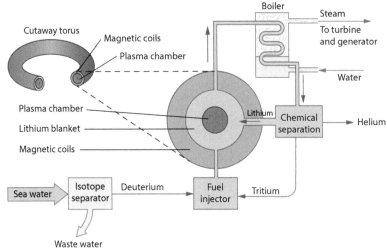

▶ *Design of a torus fusion reactor*

Boiler

Steam

To turbine and generator

Water

Cutaway torus

Magnetic coils

Plasma chamber

Plasma chamber

Lithium blanket

Magnetic coils

Lithium

Chemical separation

Helium

Sea water

Isotope separator

Deuterium

Fuel injector

Tritium

Waste water

▶ *The stages in laser fusion*

1. Laser heating

A small sphere of deuterium / tritium is bombarded with laser beams

2. Expansion

The hot outer layer expands in all directions, including inwards, compressing the middle of the sphere

3. Fusion

Fusion starts in the compressed middle, spreading throughout the sphere, releasing much more energy than was used in the laser heating

Laser fusion

The High Power laser Energy Research (HiPER) project will research the possibilities of using laser fusion. This is a proposed small-scale fusion technology that avoids the problems of plasma containment and refueling that exist with torus reactors. Small spheres of frozen deuterium and tritium would be dropped into an intense laser beam to initiate fusion. Construction is planned to take place from the late 2020s.

Renewable energy resources

Renewable energy resources have properties that are different from the non-renewable energy resources which power modern industrial and technological societies. Before the start of the industrial revolution in the 1700s, renewable energy resources were the only ones available for most uses, so society developed technologies that suited their characteristics. The use of fossil fuels has expanded since the 18th century and their characteristics have moulded the development of new technologies. If we are to use renewable energy resources again as our main source of energy then we will have to either change the way we live or develop new ways of using the renewable energy resources that we harness.

The properties of renewable energy resources

Intermittency

Some resources are not available all the time so they could not be the only source of energy that is used. For example, solar power is not available during the night, it is not always windy

and tidal cycles have periods when water is not moving. Other sources can provide energy continually such as biofuels, HEP, and geothermal power.

Predictability

It is impossible to reliably predict the amount of energy that can be harnessed from some resources, for example, the amount of sunlight reaching the Earth's surface is affected by cloud cover. The amount of wind and wave power available depends on weather systems that cannot be predicted accurately. Some renewable energy resources are usually available when required, for example, HEP using water that was stored in a reservoir or stored biofuels. However, the flow of the tides can be predicted accurately because the future positions of the Sun and Moon are known.

Energy density

The low energy density of most renewable energy resources increases the amount of equipment needed and can make it difficult to power equipment that needs high power or processes that need high temperatures.

For example, solar, wind, and wave powers have low energy densities so relatively large amounts of equipment are needed. Biofuels have a higher energy density and can be used to replace the liquid fossil fuels that are used to power vehicles.

Ease of storage

Many renewable energy resources cannot be stored unless they are converted into other forms of energy, for example, solar power or the kinetic energy of wind power. Biofuels can be stored, as can gravitational potential energy in the water in HEP reservoirs.

Application to current uses of energy

Many modern technologies have been developed that use fossil fuels, for example, the internal combustion engines that power most cars, trucks, ships, and aircraft.

Many renewable resources provide large amounts of energy but it may be low temperature heat or electricity which are not useful for many uses such as powering vehicles.

Environmental impacts

Renewable energy resources usually have low environmental impacts but these can restrict the locations where they are used for example, not locating windfarms in scenic areas. Most impacts are caused by the manufacture and installation of the equipment, for example, solar panels and wind turbines.

Geographical constraints

Most renewable energy resources can only be harnessed where natural processes, or geographical conditions, are suitable, for example, solar, wind and wave power.

Size of available resource

The available resource is usually controlled by the natural processes that produce the resource. The total resource that exists may be very large but geographical constraints and low energy density may limit the amount that can be exploited. For example, all moving air involves kinetic energy but practical exploitation requires higher velocities close enough to the ground that equipment can be located to harness the energy. When wind speed doubles the amount of energy available increases by eight times which is why locating windfarms in the windiest areas is so important.

Level of technological development

Many renewable technologies are not yet fully developed. This may be due to lack of investment or the long time period it takes to perfect the technology.

It is hard for new technologies that need further improvements to compete with well-established technologies such as those that use fossil fuels.

Economic issues

A variety of economic factors has hampered the recent development of renewable energy resources. The advantages of high energy-density fossil fuels have led to the development of equipment, such as vehicles and steam turbine generators, that cannot easily be adapted to run on renewable energy resources. The cost of replacing the existing equipment with new equipment using renewable energy is very high.

The early development costs of fossil-fuel technologies have been paid for and the economies of scale of mass production make manufacture relatively cheap. It is hard for renewable energy technologies to compete economically as costs have to cover current development costs. The equipment is relatively expensive as production runs are often relatively short.

Differences in timing of expenditure and income can also be a problem. For fossil fuel power stations, the fuel costs are spread over the lifetime of the station and can be paid for out of the income, so there are no interest charges for fuel purchase. Most equipment that harnesses renewable energy has no fuel costs. Because almost all the costs are for purchase of the equipment at the start, the costs of the repayment of interest may make an apparently cheap renewable resource financially uncompetitive.

The social and environmental costs of energy use are rarely paid by the energy industry. These could include habitat loss, reduced quality of life, acid rain, photochemical smogs, and global climate change. These costs are higher for fossil fuels than for renewable energy, so society is effectively subsidizing some of the costs of using fossil fuels.

Some renewable energy technologies have reached the point that they can compete with non-renewable energy technologies, especially wind power and solar PV. The rapid growth of electric vehicles will increase the usefulness of renewable energy.

 The Earth's natural energy budget and energy resources

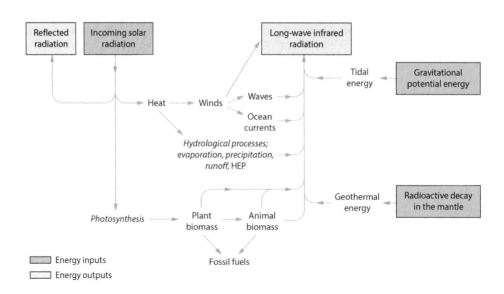

Solar power

The amount of solar energy reaching the Earth is far greater than humanity should ever need to harness. However, there have been problems with developing solar power for reliable, large-scale commercial use.

Problematic properties:

- intermittency: the availability and intensity of sunlight depends upon daily and seasonal cycles;
- reliability: daily and seasonal cycles can be predicted but the changes in energy intensity caused by changes in cloud cover cannot be accurately predicted. Clouds, smoke and dust also scatter the light so that it cannot be focused and intensified using mirrors and parabolic reflectors;
- energy density: the low energy density of solar power requires very large areas of solar collectors to harness significant amounts of energy. The angle of incidence also changes in daily and seasonal cycles so there is no single optimum position for a solar panel to harness solar power. This can reduce the energy density further.

Locational constraints

Solar power can be used anywhere in the world but it is most viable where light levels are highest such as dry sunny deserts. Systems that concentrate sunlight using parabolic reflectors only work where there is no cloud so the rays of light are parallel and reflect onto the absorber. Areas that are a long way from the equator have long summer days which increases the availability of solar power but winter days are short and light levels are low.

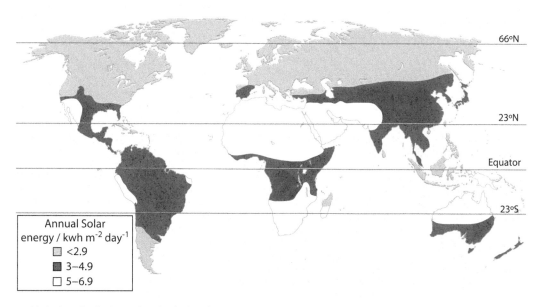

Annual Solar
energy / kwh m^{-2} day^{-1}
- ☐ <2.9
- ■ 3–4.9
- ☐ 5–6.9

▲ *Variations in the intensity of solar insolation*

Harnessing solar power

⊮ **Photothermal solar power:** photothermal systems absorb sunlight to produce heat, usually to heat water for low-temperature uses such as space heating or domestic hot water. The heat harnessed by photothermal panels can be retained in a thermal store for later use. This is usually a well-insulated tank containing a material such as water, sand, or concrete. Molten salt can be used if the energy has been concentrated to produce much higher temperatures.

▲ *Evacuated tube photothermal panels are very efficient because heat loss by conduction and convection is minimised*

⊮ **Passive solar architecture:** buildings can be designed to maximise the absorption of sunlight for heating without the use of active working equipment. Overheating in the summer can be reduced with a fixed solar screen (brise soleil) that deflects the sunlight, adjustable screens or by ventilation.

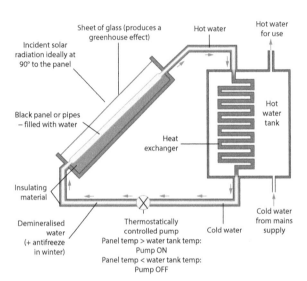

Sheet of glass (produces a greenhouse effect)

Hot water

Hot water for use

Incident solar radiation ideally at 90° to the panel

Black panel or pipes – filled with water

Heat exchanger

Hot water tank

Insulating material

Demineralised water (+ antifreeze in winter)

Thermostatically controlled pump
Panel temp > water tank temp:
Pump ON
Panel temp < water tank temp:
Pump OFF

Cold water

Cold water from mains supply

▲ *A thermostatically controlled photothermal solar panel*

❶ *A solar atrium that increases passive solar heating*
❷ *Light tubes can be used to transmit light from the outside of a building to rooms inside a building that has no external windows. The light is reflected along a reflective tube.*

⊮ **Heat pumps:** a heat pump uses the change in state of a fluid from liquid to gas to absorb heat from the environment and releases it within a building when the gas condenses to a liquid. The change in state is caused by changes in pressure using a compressor pump to cause the gas to condense and a pressure relief valve to cause the liquid to boil. The heat source may be the atmosphere or the ground. Heat pumps absorb heat energy from low energy-density sources and produce higher temperatures in the building to be heated. The heat energy released into the building can be four times as much as the energy to run the heat pump, although less is released if the temperature of the heat source is lower NB heat pumps can also harness other sources of heat such as geothermal energy..

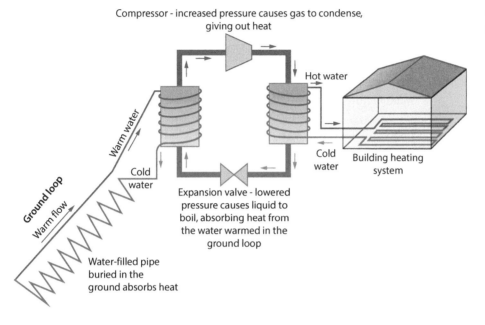

◀ A ground source heat pump

▷ **Photovoltaic (PV) solar power:** when a PV cell absorbs photons of light, electrons are dislodged from atoms in the upper layer of the PV cell. These will flow along an electrical conductor from this electrically negative layer to the relatively positive lower layer. The moving electrons provide the electric current to power electrical appliances. A wide variety of improved PV cells have been developed. Some have lower efficiencies but are cheaper to manufacture, while more expensive ones may have higher efficiencies at converting light to electricity. Many early uses of solar PV were for isolated uses of electricity, often with a rechargeable battery for night-time operation. Solar farms are now used to deliver electricity for grid-connected uses.

Efficiencies of different PV cell designs

Type of PV cell	Maximum efficiency
Multi junction	46.0%
Single junction gallium arsenide	29.1%
Crystalline silicon	27.6%
Organic cells	20.1%
Amorphous silicon	13.6%

Environmental impacts

▼ **Manufacture of solar panels:** making solar panels requires the extraction and processing of materials such as metals, plastic, paints, and silicon. Making PV solar panels produces toxic wastes such as silicon tetrachloride and small amounts of cadmium. These can be controlled but this adds to the manufacturing costs.

▼ **Impacts during use:** solar panels do not require much maintenance, although cleaning requires water which may be scarce in the areas best suited to solar power. Large solar farms can occupy land that could have been used for other purposes, although there are very large areas of urban roof space that could have panels installed without any land use conflicts. In desert areas, they can make land productive although there may be environmental impacts on local flora and fauna.

New solar power technologies

Solar Technology	Features
Multi-junction photovoltaic cells	Multiple layers made of different materials, each of which absorbs different wavelengths of light. This means that a greater amount of the available light is absorbed and converted to electricity.
Anti-reflective surfaces	PV cells with smooth surfaces reflect about 30% of the light that hits them. Having a grooved or textured surface reflects light into the cells rather than away from them. Some designs mimic the structure of the corneas of moth eyes which are very efficient at absorbing light.
Concentrating Solar Power (CSP) with thermal storage	Parabolic reflectors are used to increase the energy density. The light is absorbed by tubes of oil which is used to heat molten salt in large insulated tanks. The salt is heated to temperatures up to 550°C that can be used to boil water and drive steam turbines whenever electricity is required. This overcomes the problem of solar power being intermittent.
Photovoltaic/ thermal hybrid systems (PVT systems)	The efficiency of PV cells drops at higher temperatures as the electrical resistance increases. Hybrid systems absorb heat for uses such as space or water heating. This cools the PV cell and increases its efficiency.
Transparent PV cells	PV cells that allow most of the light through can be incorporated into windows. Some are so transparent that they look like ordinary windows, while others can be used to provide shade and reduce overheating.
Heliostats	A heliostat alters the angle of a solar panel so that it is always at the optimum angle for absorbing sunlight.
Self-cleaning panels	Nanohydrophopic surfaces.

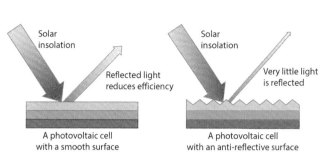

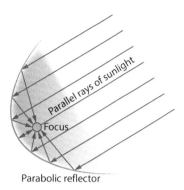

❶ *Photovoltaic cells with anti-reflective surfaces are much more efficient*

❷ *A parabolic reflector can be used to focus sunlight and produce much higher temperatures*

Hydro-electric power (HEP)

The gravitational potential energy of rainwater that lands on upland areas can be harnessed as kinetic energy as it flows downhill. Practical exploitation depends upon a large enough volume of water being available and suitable topography that creates high water pressure or high flow velocities. The kinetic energy of flowing water has been used for thousands of years to provide mechanical power and, more recently, to generate electricity. Water wheels have been replaced by turbines which are more efficient.

Locational constraints to harnessing HEP

The ideal sites include the following features:

- large water catchment area;
- high total rainfall, evenly distributed throughout the year;
- low water turbidity;
- impermeable bedrock beneath the reservoir;
- low seismic activity;
- suitable topography – narrow exit to a large basin;
- no serious land-use conflicts;
- close to consumers, or electricity grid, to reduce transport costs.

▲ *A heliostatically controlled solar PV panel*

◀ *This water wheel provided power to grind grain until the 1940s*

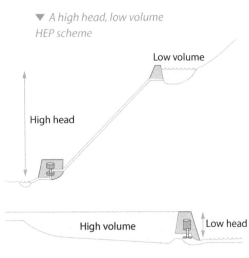

▼ A high head, low volume HEP scheme

▲ A low head, high volume HEP scheme

Environmental impacts

Building the infrastructure for HEP impacts the environment through the creation of the reservoir and in changes to flowing in and out of the reservoir.

▸ **Reservoir creation:** dam construction requires large amounts of material such as rock, sand, gravel, and cement. Extraction, processing, and transport of the materials requires energy. Access roads may also be required. The reservoir created by the dam will flood land which can cause the loss of wildlife habitats, farmland, and homes. The reservoir provides an area of static water in which suspended solids and dead organic matter carried by the river sink. Decomposition of the dead organic matter can produce anaerobic conditions and the release of methane gas. The reservoir can also have a positive impact on wildlife by providing a new habitat for aquatic wildlife.

▸ **Impacts on the river:** sedimentation in the reservoir can reduce turbidity downstream and the replenishment of nutrients onto the flood plain around the river. The natural flow fluctuations of the river are replaced by the water flow that is controlled by the power station operators. This may involve a constant flow rate to produce the maximum power output. The reservoir stores surplus water when the flow rate of the river upstream is high. The reservoir is used to maintain water flow through the power station when river flow is lower. Some HEP stations are used to meet peaks in demand for electricity, so the water flow rate through the dam can vary greatly. The environmental impact of changes in flow rate depend upon the difference between the natural and new flow regimes.

▲ A high head, low volume HEP scheme in Scotland

HEP impacts on flow regime

Natural flow regime	New flow regime	Environmental impacts
Seasonal flow extremes between wet and dry seasons	Constant flow	Dry season sandbanks used by nesting birds or turtles are lost The loss of periods of high flow allows sediments to build up so gravel fish spawning sites are lost The loss of high river levels downstream stops the seasonal flooding of the surrounding land which may be essential for plants, breeding fish, and other aquatic species
Constant flow	Sudden flow increases	Increased turbidity caused by high flow rates makes it difficult for fish-eating birds to see their food. Reduced light penetration makes photosynthesis by aquatic plants more difficult. Species that cannot resist high flow rates may be washed away.

The dam and reservoir divide the river into two sections which prevents the movement of aquatic species. Fish such as salmon and sturgeon cannot move upstream to spawn. Aquatic animals that live in flowing water, such as platypus, may not be able to pass the dam so populations become isolated.

❶ *The dam of a low-head high volume HEP scheme*
❷ *A fish ladder that allows fish to get around the dam*

Low-head turbines

Some new developments allow increased use of low-head locations where the water drops a short distance.

- **Waterwheels:** waterwheels are less efficient than turbines but they do not suffer from screen blockages with leaves and litter which can affect turbine systems.
- **Kaplan turbines:** these are axial flow turbines with blades that can be rotated to allow for variations in water flow. They can harness up to 90% of the kinetic energy of the flowing water.
- **Helical turbines:** these turbines are similar to the Archimedes' screws that were used in several ancient civilizations to raise water. They are turned by water flowing down the screw to generate electricity. The turbines have a high efficiency and can use water with a high turbidity without being damaged. Almost all of the electricity for Windsor Castle in Berkshire is generated by two helical turbines. Fish can be carried down the turbine without being harmed.

▼ *A run of river helical turbine*

- **Micro-hydro schemes:** these are small scale projects, usually used by small rural communities. The environmental impact of damming rivers has restricted the use of HEP on many rivers. Micro-hydro schemes divert part of the flow of a river to drive a turbine but do not create a barrier across the whole river.

Large HEP schemes

These are being constructed in many countries with expanding industrial economies, for example, China, Brazil.

Wind power

Differences in atmospheric pressure are produced by regional differences in heating by solar energy. Winds blow to equalize these pressure differences.

Harnessing wind power

Early uses of wind power harnessed the kinetic energy of the winds to drive machinery such as grain mills and water pumps. Modern wind turbines generate electricity. Most aerogenerators have blades or vanes that rotate around an axis in either the vertical or horizontal plane known as Vertical Axis Wind Turbine (VAWT) and Horizontal Axis Wind Turbine (HAWT).

Advantages and disadvantages of different wind turbines

Turbine type	Advantages	Disadvantages
HAWTs	Technology is more advanced and well established than VAWTs	Stress cracking can occur at the base of the blades, caused by cyclical gravitational forces.
	Higher efficiency than VAWTs	Taller towers are needed to keep the blades above the ground.
		The weight of the generator requires a stronger tower than for VAWTs where the generator can be at ground level.
VAWTs	Turbines are driven by wind from any direction so they can be used where winds are turbulent such as cities	No very large VAWTs have been built.
	Turbines do not need to be turned to face into the wind so there is no need for a motor	Lower efficiency as the blades are not absorbing wind energy throughout their rotation.
	VAWTs are quieter than HAWTs	
	Operate at lower wind velocities	

Aerogenerators absorb the kinetic energy of moving air, so the air behind a turbine moves more slowly. Individual turbines must be spaced so that they are not in the 'wind shadow' of the nearest turbines.

▶ *A windfarm of HAWTs*

Locational constraints

▶ **Wind velocity:** the reliability and strength of winds are affected by the latitude, with the windiest areas being in temperate and polar regions. The topography of an area will also affect wind velocity as the friction and turbulence of surface features can slow the wind down. Areas which often have higher wind velocities are:

- coastal areas;
- upland areas;
- flat areas;
- the sea.

Harnessing wind power in the windiest areas is important as higher wind velocities produce much more power. A doubling in velocity results in an eight-fold increase in kinetic energy.

▶ **Isolation:** small-scale use of wind power can provide electricity for isolated uses such as small rural communities. Large-scale wind farms may be located near the existing electricity grid to avoid the cost of laying new cables to join the electricity grid.

▶ **Land use conflicts:** conflicts can arise from a range of conflicting needs and preferences but these can often be mitigated. For example:

- **Ecological impacts:** turbines may be located away from bird migration routes, high bat populations, or sensitive habitats such as bogs where turbine foundations or access tracks may affect the hydrology of the area.
- **Land requirement:** the turbines in a windfarm require a large area of land over which the aerogenerators can be dispersed. To minimise the 'wind shadow' effect aerogenerators are normally spaced with an interval of three to five times the diameter of the blades. The land between the aerogenerators can still be used for other purposes such as agriculture, so the actual amount of land that is 'lost' is much smaller than the overall area of the windfarm.
- **Telecommunication interference:** aerogenerators can interfere with radio and radar systems.
- **Public opposition:** some people object to windfarms so they are often located away from scenic and urban areas.

❶ *An onshore windfarm constructed in a remote area but close to the existing electricity grid*

❷ *Offshore windfarms receive stronger, more reliable winds and cause fewer land use conflicts*

❸ *Aerogenerators do not disturb livestock*

❹ *A small windfarm on an isolated island. The blades are downwind of the tower so the nacelle is turned by changing wind directions without needing a motor*

Environmental impacts

▶ **Manufacture and installation:** as with all energy resources, material manufacture and installation have environmental impacts during the production of the materials and their transport and installation.

▶ **Noise:** rotating aerogenerators are much less noisy than many other everyday anthropogenic sources of noise such as domestic appliances and roads. However, for people who live very close to aerogenerators, the rhythmic sound may be irritating. More aerodynamic blade designs and direct drive aerogenerators with no gearbox are quieter.

▶ **Habitat damage:** the habitat area that is destroyed by the foundations of an aerogenerator is relatively small but more habitat is required for access paths and transformers.

▶ **Bird strikes:** the rotating blades of aerogenerators may kill birds. This is most likely if the aerogenerators are located along ridges where migrating birds soar, along migration routes, or where birds congregate such as wetlands. Careful location of aerogenerators can reduce the risks of bird deaths. VAWTs are less likely to cause bird deaths than HAWTs as the blades are seen more easily.

▶ **Bat deaths:** the changes in air pressure caused by the passing blades can kill bats. Bats usually fly when wind speeds are low which is when wind turbines are generating little electricity. In areas where there is a high risk of bat deaths, turbines may be stopped during periods of low wind velocity.

New wind power technologies

Blade-tip fins

The fins reduce turbulence and wind resistance which increases blade efficiency.

Nacelle brushes

Blade-nacelle brushes reduce the amount of air escaping between the base of the blades and the central nacelle (hub). This increases the amount of kinetic energy absorbed by the blades.

Direct drive turbines

Most wind turbines have a gearbox to ensure the generator turns at 3000rpm. This produces the 50 cycle per second alternating current (AC) electricity that has to be fed into the national grid. The Gearbox is expensive and a common cause of mechanical breakdown. Friction within the gearbox reduces efficiency and increases the wind velocity at which the blades start to rotate.
The extra weight in the nacelle requires the tower to be stronger which requires more materials and is more expensive.
Direct drive turbines do not have a gearbox. They are more reliable, quieter, cheaper, and start to generate electricity at lower wind velocities. The generator produces DC electricity which is converted to AC electricity that can be fed into the electricity grid using an inverter.

Helical VAWT blades

VAWTs with straight blades do not rotate smoothly as some positions absorb more energy than others. This reduces the efficiency of the electricity fed into the grid and can lead to strain and stress fractures. Helical blades rotate more smoothly and avoid these problems.

Wind-assisted ships

The intermittency of winds and the difficulty of sailing against the wind direction mean that commercial shipping is unlikely to solely use wind power. However, wind assisted ships that use wind power to reduce the energy provided by the ship's engine have been designed and built using vertical aerofoil wings, mechanically controlled sails, or a kite-sail.
The Maltese Falcon demonstrates a sail rig that was designed for use on wind-assisted cargo ships. It can be operated by a single crew member.

Many other designs of wind power equipment have been proposed or demonstrated but have not yet become established technologies.

Wave power

The friction of winds blowing over water creates waves. The kinetic energy of the vertical movement of the water can be harnessed.

Locational constraints

The kinetic energy of the waves is greatest where:

▼ mean wind velocities are high and winds are consistent in strength and direction to allow the wave height to increase;

▼ there is a long 'fetch' – distance of open water over which waves can build up.

Harnessing wave power

A wide variety of technologies have been proposed or demonstrated to use the vertical movement of water caused by waves. Competition with well-established energy technologies has delayed their development.

▶ *Point absorber wave power*

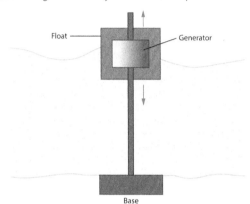

▼ **Point absorber:** point absorbers have a floating structure which rises and falls as waves pass. This is attached to a non-moving base located on the seabed or in static deep water. The movement of the floating part turns a generator, for example, Power Buoy.

▼ **Overtopping/Terminator device:** breaking waves force water into a storage reservoir which is above sea level. The water flows back to the sea passing through a turbine which generates electricity. Sea walls may be used to increase the height of the waves and therefore the volume of water that enters the reservoir, for example, Wave Dragon.

▶ *Overtopping device wave power*

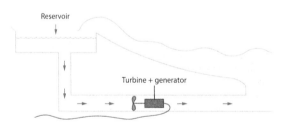

▼ **Oscillating Wave Surge Converter:** as waves pass, water moves both horizontally and vertically, producing a cycle. The oscillating horizontal or vertical movement pushes a flat plate which moves pistons to pump fluid over a turbine to generate electricity. For example, Oyster.

Oscillating wave surge converter

As waves pass, water moves both horizontally and vertically, producing a cycle. The oscillating horizontal or vertical movement pushes a flat plate which moves pistons to pump fluid over a turbine to generate electricity. e.g. Wave Clapper

▶ *Oscillating wave surge converter*

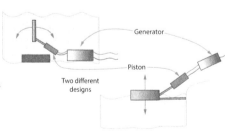

- **Surface attenuator wave power:** this is a hinged floating device. As waves pass, the moving sections push and pull pistons which force a fluid over a turbine, generating electricity, for example, Pelamis.
- **Oscillating water column wave power:** the rise and fall of water, as waves pass, forces water up and down in a submerged chamber. The air that is forced in and out flows over turbines, generating electricity, for example, Islay Limpet.

▲ *An oscillating wave surge converter built by Eco Wave Power*

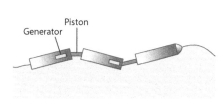

▲ *Surface attenuator wave power*

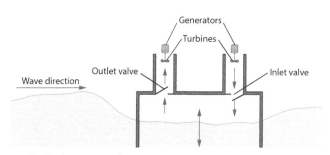

▲ *Oscillating water column wave power*

▼ *Pistons between the sections of Pelamis*

Design problems

- Equipment must be able to withstand storms and corrosion.
- It can be difficult to anchor equipment off stormy coasts or in deep water.
- It may be expensive to transport electricity from isolated areas, where wave energy can be harnessed, to the consumers.

Environmental impacts

Wave power systems have very limited environmental impacts. As with all energy systems, equipment manufacture and installation has environmental impacts. The anchoring of floating systems affects the seabed but can also create new habitats.

Biofuels

Biofuels include the energy resources where photosynthesis has recently captured sunlight and stored it in materials such as vegetable oils or carbohydrates. Biofuels include any energy resources that have been produced by biological processes sufficiently recently that they can be renewable.

Some biofuels are deliberately produced, while others are waste products of other processes and activities. Globally, more people use wood as their main energy source than any other energy resource, mainly in LEDCs. Newer methods are being used to produce biofuels in MEDCs.

Harnessing biofuels

A range of crops can be used as biofuels, including

- wood;
- combustible crops, for example, *Miscanthus* (elephant grass), coppiced willow;
- alcohol from carbohydrate crops, for example, sugar cane, sugar beet, cereal crops, wood;
- biodiesel from vegetable oils such as sunflower, palm nuts, and oilseed rape.

❶ *Miscanthus (elephant grass) is a high yielding biomass crop.*
❷ *Coppiced willow is usually cut on a three-year cycle*

Waste products can also be used as biofuel:

- methane from anaerobic digestion of wastes such as sewage, crop, and forestry waste and food waste;
- combustible crop waste, for example, straw;
- incineration of combustible domestic refuse;
- landfill biogas.

❶ *Straw is a cheap biofuel as it is a waste product. It's low energy density means it must be used close to the area where it was grown*
❷ *Anaerobic sewage sludge digesters*

Advantages of biofuels

- The supply rate of energy crops can be controlled, unlike most other renewable energy resources.
- Biofuels can be stored until they are needed so it is easy to match supplies to demand
- Biofuels such as vegetable oils and sugar can be used to make vehicle fuels to replace petrol or diesel.
- The fuels themselves are 'carbon neutral' and release the same quantity of carbon dioxide as they absorbed in photosynthesis during growth
- The energy density of alcohol and biodiesel is nearly as high as that of fossil fuels.

Disadvantages of biofuels

- The supply of biofuels from wastes is limited to the amount produced by the source activity
- The large areas of farmland required for biofuel crop production may compete with food production or encourage the clearance of wildlife habitats to create more farmland.
- The energy density of straw, wood, and *Miscanthus* is lower than that of fossil fuels.
- The intensive farming techniques used to grow some biofuel crops may release nearly as much carbon dioxide as using fossil fuels directly instead of using them to grow biofuels.

Locational factors

Biofuel crops have the same locational constraints as most arable crops, such as the need for fertile soil, suitable climate, and topography that makes cultivation easy.

Biofuels that come from wastes are produced wherever the source activity is located, for example, landfill sites and sewage works near urban areas, or arable crop wastes and forestry waste in rural areas.

Environmental impacts

The wide range of biofuels creates a range of environmental impacts.

Biofuels that are produced as a part of an agricultural production system can cause environmental impacts through habitat loss, fertilizer use, pesticide use and the impacts of using fossil fuels to drive machinery.

▲ *A large scale biogas plant in Kenya that digests plant waste from flower farms*

New biofuel technologies

- **Hydrogen from algae:** some types of algae produce hydrogen during photosynthesis if they are deprived of sulfur. This hydrogen can be harnessed to be used as fuel.
- **Anaerobic digestion:** anaerobic digestion is being applied to a wider range of biological materials, for example, crop wastes and marine algae. Small scale projects using manure or sewage are becoming common in LEDCs.

▲ *This small scale biogas plant in Kenya uses the manure from one cow and produces enough methane for a family's cooking needs*

Geothermal power

The radioactive decay of isotopes of thorium, uranium, and potassium in the Earth's mantle releases heat. This heat may be moved towards the surface of the crust by molten magma or hot water. The heat may be exploited for space heating, hot water, or for electricity generation.

Harnessing geothermal power

Geothermal heat can be harnessed in several ways.

▼ **Low temperature schemes**
- **Geothermal springs:** groundwater that has been heated by hot rocks underground may come to the surface in hot springs. This can be used for district heating.
- **Geothermal aquifers:** hot groundwater may be pumped to the surface from underground aquifers to be used in district heating schemes.

▼ **High temperature schemes**
- **Geothermal steam systems:** groundwater at very high temperatures may be brought to the surface using an extraction borehole, producing high temperature steam at the surface that can be used to generate electricity.
- **Hot dry rock systems:** where there are hot rocks near the surface but no groundwater, two boreholes may be used. Water is pumped down an injection borehole and steam is recovered using a second borehole. Fracturing the rocks underground may increase the permeability of the rock and the surface area exposed for heat absorption.

Locational constraints

Geothermal power stations that use steam turbines need a heat source with a temperature above 150°C. This requires relatively recent volcanic activity so that hot rocks are near the surface of the crust. In other areas, the hot rocks are so deep that drilling down to reach them is uneconomic.

Environmental impacts

Geothermal power has relatively few environmental impacts as long as it is carefully developed.

▼ **Infrastructure:** steam and hot water pipes can provide obstacles to the movement of large mammals.

▼ **Gaseous emissions:** the hot water extracted from the ground can release gases such as small amounts of carbon dioxide and hydrogen sulfide.

▼ **Waste water:** water wastes can contain salts and heavy metals.

◄ *A geothermal borehole drilling rig in Kenya*

New geothermal technologies

Low temperature fluids: new turbine technologies are being developed that use liquids which boil and turn turbines at lower temperatures. Water as cool as 60°C can be used to boil butane or pentane. This may allow areas with lower temperature rocks to be used for electricity generation, including some areas in the UK.

Tidal power

The gravitational attraction between the Earth and the moon creates tidal flows of water that produce two periods of high water and two periods of low water in each 25 hour cycle. The gravitational effect of the moon depends upon its position in relation to the Sun which also has a gravitational effect on the tides, although it is smaller. When their effects combine, there are 'spring tides' where the tidal range is greater. When their effects work in opposition, there are 'neap tides' where the tidal range is smaller.

In most areas of the sea, the speed of water flow is too slow for it to be harnessed, but coastal features and seabed topography may focus the flow, increasing the velocity of the water and increasing the tidal range.

Harnessing tidal power

▼ **Tidal barrages:** a tidal barrage is a dam across an estuary or bay in which turbines are located so that all the water flowing in or out of the lake created behind the barrage flows over the turbines. A barrage makes the maximum use of the tidal flow of water in and out of an estuary or bay, but the financial costs are high and environmental impacts are great.

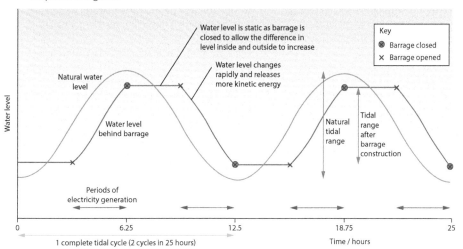

◀ *The changes in water level and periods of electricity generation associated with a tidal barrage*

▼ **Tidal lagoons:** a tidal lagoon surrounds a selected part of an estuary or bay. Only a part of the area is affected and the most environmentally sensitive areas can be avoided. Some schemes propose multiple lagoons next to each other. If electricity is being generated but demand is low, water can be pumped into a lagoon producing a water level higher than sea level. Electricity can be generated later when demand is high but there is no tidal water flow.

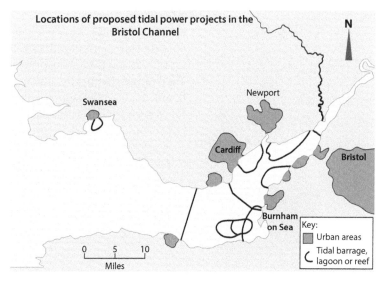

▲ *Locations of proposed tidal power projects in the Bristol Channel*

- **In-stream turbines:** these are fixed to the seabed and absorb the kinetic energy of the natural tidal flow. These harness much less energy than a barrage or lagoon, but the environmental impacts are very low as in-stream turbines do not have any significant impact on the tidal flow.

◀ In-stream tidal turbines

Advantages and disadvantages of Tidal power

Advantages	Disadvantages
• The positions of the Sun and Moon can be predicted so the times and ranges of the tides are also predictable • A tidal barrage on a large estuary would have a large electricity output compared with most other renewable energy schemes	• The intermittent periods when electricity generation is possible make it difficult to meet a continual demand • There are few suitable sites for the construction of a barrage where the flow of water would produce enough electricity to be economically viable • The environmental impacts of barrages are large compared with the impacts of most other renewable energy schemes

Locational constraints

Gravitational forces affect all water bodies but sites that are suitable for the economic exploitation of tidal water flows are rare. The seawater normally moves quite slowly but coastal features such as estuaries and headlands may concentrate the flow and increase the water velocity. If the tidal range is large and the mass of moving water is large then harnessing tidal power may be viable.

Environmental impacts

- **Tidal barrages:**
  - **Materials:** the large size of a barrage requires very large quantities of material for construction - sand, gravel, rock, cement, tarmac etc. These have environmental impacts during extraction, processing, transport, and installation.
  - **Tidal range change:** the barrage reduces the ease with which the water can flow in or out of the lagoon, so the low tide level is never quite as low and the high tide level is never quite as high.

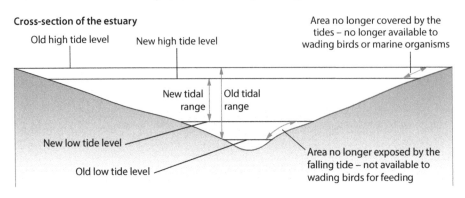

◀ The changes in tidal range caused by a tidal barrage

- **Sedimentation:** water flow in and out of the lagoon behind the barrage is only possible through the turbine channels in the barrage, so there are areas of very fast flow where sediments are eroded and carried away. In other areas with slower flow, sediments may be deposited and build up. The extended periods of static water at high and low tide will allow sediments to settle, so general turbidity will be lower. This will allow light to penetrate to deeper water, increasing temperatures and allowing more photosynthetic organisms to survive.
  - **Pollutant concentration:** pollutants from human activities around the lagoon or in the catchment areas may build up in the lagoon.
- **Tidal lagoons:** these have similar impacts to barrages but on a smaller scale. As they do not involve the whole estuary, there are more opportunities to avoid impacts on the most sensitive features, such as not creating a barrier across the main channel so that migratory species can still pass through.
- **In-stream turbines:** these do not block the natural tidal flow so they do not have the impacts of tidal barrages or lagoons. All tidal turbines produce noise that may affect marine animals such as whales and dolphins. The effect is localised but the installation of a large number of in-stream tidal turbines, dispersed over a large area, could have a larger impact than the turbines in a barrage or lagoon.

New tidal power technologies

As tidal power has not been widely used, there are still a large number of proposed designs that have not yet been tested. One proposed design is a tidal reef. This is similar to a barrage in crossing an estuary but it is not as tall, so water can flow over the top of the reef, allowing the movement of fish and other marine organisms and the flow of water across the full width of the estuary.

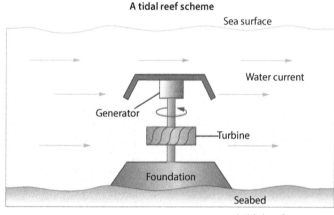

A tidal reef scheme

▲ *A tidal reef scheme*

Summary

The transition of society from being powered by fossil fuels to being powered by renewable energy will require many changes including the following:

- new technologies to harness a greater amount of energy and at a higher efficiency;
- large-scale energy storage systems;
- changes to the energy transport infrastructure and vehicle designs;
- changes in the technologies that use energy.

Secondary fuels

Primary fuel comes directly from the environment but may not be in a form that is easy to use. However, it may be possible to convert it into another energy form and be used as a Secondary Fuel.

Electricity

The generation of electricity involves the conversion of energy from a range of original primary fuels. The forms of energy that can be converted directly to electricity are kinetic energy, chemical energy, and light. Several energy conversions may be needed to convert the energy of the primary fuel into an energy form that can be converted to electricity.

▶ *The energy conversions involved in converting primary fuels into electricity*

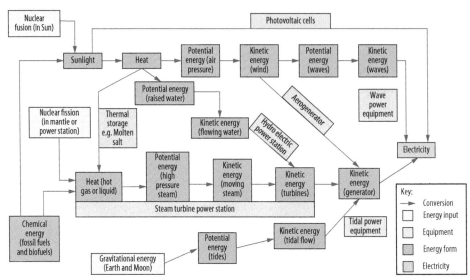

Electricity from kinetic energy

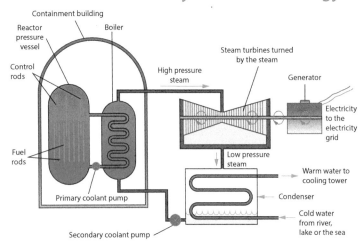

▲ *Main features of a nuclear power station*

Kinetic energy can be used to make electricity by spinning an electrical conductor within a magnetic field in a generator. This is called a generator. The kinetic energy may be harnessed directly, as with wind or water power, or it may be produced by converting other types of available energy such as heat energy. In conventional power stations, heat is used to boil water then the movement of the high pressure expanding steam is used to spin turbines which spin the generators.

Feature	Function
Nuclear reactor	The heat generated by nuclear fission is used to heat the primary coolant (pressurised water)
Control rods	Control rods absorb neutrons. They are lowered into the reactor or raised out of it to control the power output
Boiler	The hot primary coolant heats water which boils to produce high pressure steam
Steam turbines	The kinetic energy of the high pressure steam is absorbed and spins the turbines
Generator	The rotating turbines turn the generator which produces electricity
Condenser	The steam which has cooled and lost its pressure is condensed using cold water from a river, lake or the sea. The condensed steam is reused in the boiler

Electricity from light energy: photovoltaic cells

Photons of light that strike the surface of the photovoltaic cell displace electrons which make the surface layer negatively charged. These free electrons can flow along a conductor to the lower layer which is relatively negatively charged. The moving electrons can be used to power electrical appliances.

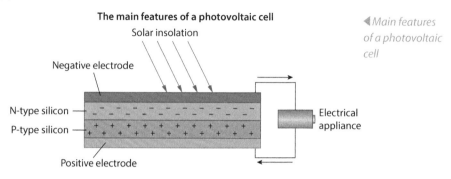

The main features of a photovoltaic cell

◀ *Main features of a photovoltaic cell*

Electricity from chemical energy

Chemical energy can be converted to electricity in reactions where one chemical accepts electrons at an electrode and another chemical releases electrons at another electrode. The electrons flowing between the electrodes can be used to power electrical equipment.

Electrochemical cells are used in batteries to store chemical energy that can be converted to electricity. When the chemical reactions take place, the battery loses its ability to produce more electricity.

Rechargeable batteries use electricity to reform the chemicals that produce electricity.

Fuel cells also use electrochemical cells to store energy in chemicals such as hydrogen and alcohols. However, they will not lose their ability to produce electricity as long as a fresh supply of fuel is available for the chemical reactions.

Fuel cells use hydrocarbons, alcohols, hydrogen and oxygen. The simplest type of cell uses hydrogen and oxygen as fuel. Hydrogen releases electrons while oxygen accepts them. The resulting hydrogen and oxygen ions combine to create water.

Advantages and disadvantages of using electricity

Advantages	Disadvantages
• No pollution is caused when it is used. • Converting electricity to other energy forms (for example, sound, light, heat, movement) is straightforward. • Transportation is easy via conducting cables.	• Converting primary fuel to electricity is not very efficient. • Storing electricity is difficult as there are no large scale options currently available. • The initial production of electricity may be highly polluting.

Transport of electricity

The locations where electricity can be generated are often geographically limited, so it may be necessary to transport the electricity using a grid of electrical cables. Laying cables underground is expensive and the cables need to be cooled, which requires energy for pumping the coolant fluid. Overhead cables can cause aesthetic problems in scenic areas and birds may be killed if they collide with the cables.

Hydrogen

Hydrogen is a reactive gas which can be produced by the electrolysis of water using electricity from surplus primary energy sources. This enables unreliable or intermittent energy supplies to be efficiently used by converting them into a form of energy that can be stored.

Uses of hydrogen

Two main methods are used to release the chemical energy from stored hydrogen, namely:

- **combustion to produce heat** which is then used to heat buildings, water and industrial processes, or to boil water and create steam to drive turbines and generate electricity;
- **fuel cells**. This is an electrochemical process which combines oxygen and hydrogen to produce water and thereby releasing energy.

◀ *Pylons and cables of the UK national grid*

The hydrogen economy

Storing excess energy helps address the disadvantages of energy resources which are only available intermittently.

There are a number of methods that can be used to store hydrogen, although each approach has disadvantages.

Hydrogen storage

Form of storage	Process	Disadvantage
Compressed gas	A compressor pumps upto 700 times the normal volume into storage tanks	Energy is required to run the compressor
Liquid	Liquefied under high pressure at a very low temperature	Energy is required for refrigeration and to run the compressor
Metal hydride systems	Hydrogen is adsorbed on to the surface of a metal matrix enabling low pressure hydrogen storage.	The storage tanks are larger and heavier than a petrol tank that stores the same amount of energy
Ammonia	Surplus primary energy is used to produce ammonia (NH_3)	Some energy required but much less than the alternatives as the process does not require such high pressures or low temperatures.

Those advocating hydrogen storage argue that it enables communities to be fueled renewably from an abundant, convenient energy. This proposal is known as the 'hydrogen economy'. Current energy supplies would continue to be used to satisfy current demand and hydrogen would be used to store any surplus energy. This energy would continue to be stored until it was needed to meet an increase in demand, or a supply shortage created by unreliable or intermittent supplies.

The stored hydrogen would be used directly to power heating and vehicles or in steam-turbine power stations or fuel cells to generate electricity.

The development of a hydrogen economy does not require hydrogen to be the main energy source actually used by consumers. Primary energy, such as biofuels, can be stored and would only be used when available and when there was demand. This means that energy losses created during energy conversions, if all the primary energy had been used to make hydrogen, would be reduced.

Unlike many renewable energy resources, hydrogen has a high energy density and therefore could replace fossil fuels for many uses, such as powering vehicles.

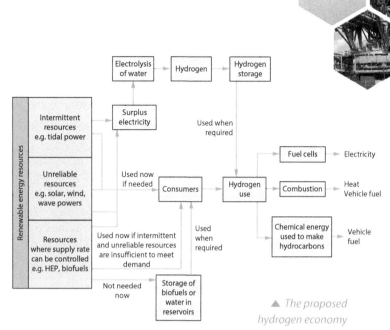

▲ The proposed hydrogen economy

Energy storage

Energy storage solves a number of problems. It means that:

- a larger quantity of fuel can be accumulated for more economic transportation;
- energy production rates can be kept constant for the most economic use of equipment and workers, for example, coalmines, oil and gas wells.
- any surplus energy from intermittent supplies can be stored until it is required, for example, wind and solar power. This process of storing a surplus to meet a future shortage is called peak shaving.

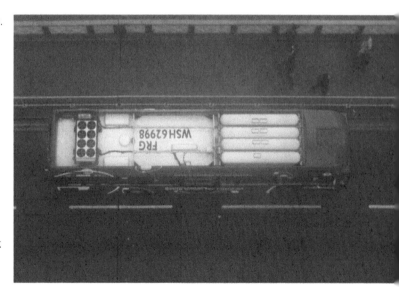

▲ A hydrogen fuel cell bus with storage tanks on the roof

Causes of fluctuations in energy supply

- Use of intermittent energy resources, for example, solar power, wind power, tidal power
- Bulk delivery of transported energy resources, for example, oil, coal, biofuels.

Causes of fluctuations in energy demand

▶ Short-term weather-related fluctuations

▶ Seasonal fluctuations

▶ Weekday/weekend fluctuations in industrial use

▶ 24 hr day/night fluctuations

▶ Short-term behaviour-related fluctuations: mealtimes, TV 'pickup'

Large scale storage of electricity is not yet possible yet there can be a surplus of electricity generated. The reasons for this include:

▶ base-load power stations generating electricity 24 hours a day even though much less electricity is needed during the night because it is uneconomic to turn the power stations on and off;

▶ fluctuations in demand, for example, after meals or TV breaks, lower industrial demand outside core working hours. The demand for electricity may drop more rapidly than power station output can be reduced.

▶ If generated electricity is unused then it is lost through heat from the cables.

Developments in energy storage technologies

Peak shaving using pumped–storage HEP

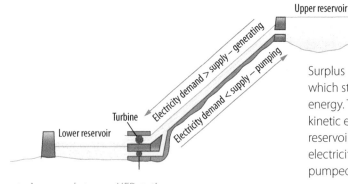

▲ A pumped-storage HEP station

Surplus electricity is used to pump water uphill, which stores the energy as gravitational potential energy. The potential energy can be converted to kinetic energy through water flowing to the lower reservoir turning the turbines and generating electricity to meet any peaks in demand. So pumped-storage HEP stations can be much more responsive to changes in demand than stations powered by coal, gas or nuclear fuels. They can go from standby to full power in less than 15 seconds, so they can meet sudden increases in demand.

Compressed gas

Surplus energy can be used to drive a pump that compresses air. The compressed air can be released later to power machinery. This method has been used on a small scale since 1870. Current research focuses on large-scale systems which could produce over 200MW of power from compressed air stored in underground caverns, for example, in salt mines. Compressing the air produces a lot of heat. This may also be stored, such as in hot oil or molten salt thermal storage. A compressed air system with heat storage can recover over 90% of the original energy.

Chemical energy

Stored fossil fuels, biofuels, and hydrogen store chemical energy. Batteries and fuel cells can be used to store chemical energy. Rechargeable batteries enable the original chemicals to be reformed using electricity so that the batteries can be reused. However, for fuel cells to continue to operate new fuel and oxidant chemicals must be supplied.

The braking system in this cliff railway drives a compressor to compress a gas and store potential energy. This recovered energy can be used to help push the carriage up the hill again.

Rechargeable batteries

Factors affecting rechargeable battery viability

- The efficiency of the storage cycle: the percentage of the electricity used during recharging that is available later.
- The number of charge-discharge cycles that can be carried out.
- Energy density.
- Cost per unit of energy stored.
- Recharging speed.
- Self-discharge during periods of non-use.
- Safety issues: toxicity, fire risk.

Examples of rechargeable battery types

Widely used	Being developed
Lead acid	Lithium-air
NiCad (nickel – cadmium)	Gold nanowire
LiIon (lithium ion)	Graphene
LiPoly (lithium polymer)	Sodium-ion
	Bio batteries

A lead-acid battery storage system

Types of storage systems

▶ **Vehicle to Grid (V2G) systems:** these are systems where energy can be transferred between the national electricity grid and vehicle batteries. The batteries of road vehicles represent a big source of energy for the electricity grid if other sources cannot provide enough energy to meet demands. The proposal is that all vehicles are plugged into the grid when they are parked for long periods. If there is a peak in demand for electricity then a small proportion of the energy from the vehicle batteries may be used. This avoids the cost and environmental impacts of using rapid-response, low-efficiency, high-cost power stations such as open-cycle gas turbines. Surplus energy from the grid can also be used to recharge vehicle batteries.

▶ **Power to gas (P2G) systems:** these use surplus electricity to produce gaseous fuel which can be stored. Water is electrolysed to produce hydrogen. This can be used to produce methane that can be fed into the natural gas pipe network.

▶ **Heat energy:** heat energy is unavoidably lost from hot materials by conduction, convection, and radiation so long-term storage of heat energy is difficult. However, short-term storage of thermal energy can be efficient, especially if few energy conversions are involved. Thermal storage systems include the use of molten salt, high volume hot water stores, and the use of high thermal mass materials. The material used for the heat store should have a high specific heat capacity so that the greatest possible amount of heat energy can be stored in a given volume. Such materials are said to have a high thermal mass.

▶ **High volume storage:** as the volume of a heat store increases, the surface area:volume ratio goes down, so the rate of heat loss declines as there is a smaller surface area for each unit of storage volume. Very large heat stores can be used for inter-season energy storage, such as absorbing surplus solar energy from the summer for heating buildings in the winter.

▶ **Molten salt:** molten salt has advantages over water for thermal storage if high temperatures are required. Potassium nitrate has a much higher boiling point than water, so it is used at temperatures up to 550°C to store heat from CSP photothermal systems. The heat can be used later to boil water in a steam-turbine power station and generate electricity when needed. A hot water storage system could only reach such high temperatures if it was kept under pressure which would increase the costs.

▶ **High thermal mass building materials:** buildings constructed of materials with a high specific heat capacity, such as concrete, warm up and cool down comparatively slowly. This reduces overheating during hot weather and therefore reduces the need for air conditioning. It also reduces the need for heating at the beginning of cold weather as the building materials will keep the building warm for some time.

▶ **Kinetic energy:** flywheels can be used as a temporary store of kinetic energy. The rotating flywheel can be used to drive machinery or generate electricity when needed.

▶ **Electricity supercapacitors:** early capacitor designs store electricity as electrical charge on flat plates of conducting materials, separated by an insulator. New 'super capacitors' use an electrochemical process and have an energy density 10 to 100 times higher. In the future, it may be possible to use supercapacitors for the large-scale storage of electricity.

▼ *This flywheel stores energy from surplus renewable energy supplies to meet later peaks in demand in a small island community.*

Energy conservation

Energy is conserved by increasing the efficiency of energy use and by avoiding the wastage of unnecessary use. This means that the amount of energy needed for a task is reduced. The efficiency is measured by the proportion of energy that actually achieves the desired activity. Energy used for tasks that are thought to be unnecessary can be seen as wastage. However, what defines such tasks is often a matter of opinion.

It is important to distinguish between low efficiency and wastage. For example, a smaller vehicle may be much more efficient in its use of energy than a large vehicle yet driving it just for fun is still wasteful.

Transport energy conservation

The activity that uses more energy than any other is transport. As societies have developed and individuals have become more affluent they have been able to travel more, afford goods from around the globe and eat foods that have been transported long distances. Transport systems have become faster, more convenient and able to carry larger numbers of people or quantities of goods. Transport infrastructure and larger forms of transport have enabled industries to develop in a wider range of places away from the sources of raw materials such as metal ores, limestone and coal.

Bulk transport

Carrying larger loads on fewer vehicles is more energy efficient than using a large number of small ones. Although more energy is used to move the larger vehicle the larger load it can carry is likely to give it a greater overall efficiency.

Other factors also determine the type of transport used:

- flexibility of routes and destinations, for example, the inconvenience of public transport compared with 'door to door' transport;
- the need for rapid transport of goods such as perishable foods;
- the level of fuel tax.

Vehicle design

The energy from the fuel is converted to kinetic energy to propel the vehicle. The fuel conversion should be as efficient as possible, minimising the conversion of energy into unwanted forms of energy and maximising the amount of energy that can be used to push the vehicle forward.

There are many different ways to reduce the quantity of fuel used and to increase the efficiency of energy conversion.

Aerodynamics/hydrodynamics

Reducing friction as a vehicle moves through the air or water reduces the amount of energy needed to propel it.

▼ *A truck with an aerodynamic fairing to smooth the air flow over the cab and trailer*

Regenerative braking/Kinetic Energy Recovery System (KERS)

To slow a vehicle down, its kinetic energy must be converted into another energy form. Conventional braking systems use friction brakes to convert the kinetic energy to heat, which is lost to the atmosphere. More fuel must then be used to accelerate the vehicle again. Regenerative braking systems convert the kinetic energy to an energy form that can be used or stored rather than being wasted.

1 A hybrid car that has a petrol engine and an electric motor which uses energy recovered during braking

2 This train recovers energy during braking. It is used to generate electricity which is returned to the overhead cables

Road vehicles use a generator to convert kinetic energy to electricity which is stored as chemical energy in a battery. This can be used to produce electricity that propels the vehicle using an electric motor. Some railway locomotives also use a generator to slow the train but the electricity produced is fed back into the national grid.

Reduced mass

Reducing the weight of a vehicle will reduce fuel consumption. This can be done in a number of ways, for example:

- plastics are used in cars instead of metals where strength is less important. Composite materials, such as carbon fibres, can also be used and have a higher strength: weight ratio than metals;
- steel alloys containing carbon, titanium and vanadium create high strength steel so that thinner, lighter body panels can be used;
- lighter neodymium speaker magnets can replace ferrite ones;
- replacing cast iron engine blocks with lighter aluminium ones;
- redesigning wiring routes so that shorter cables are used and the wiring is lighter;
- using higher energy density batteries which have a lower mass per unit of stored energy;
- designing vehicles with rounded 3D surfaces rather than angular corners creates a smaller surface area so less material is needed and weight is reduced;
- no-bleed aircraft engines that have an electric generator which powers electric motors to control equipment such as wing flaps and the rudder. These are lighter than the pneumatic equipment used on most aircraft which run on pressurised 'bleed' air from the jet engine.

Wheel design

As air-filled or 'pneumatic' tyres rotate, the weight of the vehicle squashes the tyre changing its shape. When the vehicle moves frictional heat is created by this continual change in the tyre shape and the movement of air inside the tyre. Underinflated tyres lose even more energy. Less energy is lost by using solid wheels but these give a bumpy ride, unless vehicles using them run on rails, such as trams and trains.

◀ *Steel wheels that run on rails give little resistance to rolling as they do not deform and change shape as they rotate.*

Fuel combustion efficiency

Internal combustion engines are not able to burn 100% of the fuel they use. If the combustion can become more efficient then less fuel is wasted. Combustion efficiency can be improved through:

- ⬛ efficient exhaust gas removal - having more valves per cylinder ensures the waste combustion gases are removed more completely so do not mix with the new fuel;
- ⬛ better engine temperature control for example, by using a thermostatically operated fan that only operates when the engine temperature is above the optimum temperature;
- ⬛ ignition control and servicing - the timing of the ignition spark in petrol engines is important to burn fuel efficiently so it is critical to ensure that engine ignition timing is always correct, for example, through electronic ignition control or regular engine servicing.

Vehicle design for end of life

Traditional vehicle design focuses on the ease of manufacture of components and their assembly to create the vehicle. A newer concept is to design vehicles to minimise the environmental impacts of the disposal of vehicles when they are scrapped. This includes several principles:

- ⬛ use of recyclable materials where possible;
- ⬛ easy identification of components and their composition, for example, by being stamped with code numbers to identify their composition;
- ⬛ easy dismantling and separation of components;
- ⬛ use of reusable components for use in new vehicles;
- ⬛ use of compostable materials for components that cannot be recycled.

▲ *A bus with a self-inflating system to ensure the tyre pressure is always correct*

Embodied energy

Most of the energy used by a vehicle during its life is the energy to propel it but a significant amount is in its embodied energy. For a typical car, this is equivalent to its fuel consumption for 1 ½ years. If the car is made with recycled materials then its embodied energy will be much lower.

Mode of vehicle use

How a vehicle is driven affects fuel efficiency. When a vehicle travels slowly a lot of energy is used just to run the engine rather than to move the vehicle. When it travels fast energy is wasted through overcoming air resistance. Therefore there is an optimum speed for efficient energy use which for many cars is about 56mph.

If a vehicle is unable to travel at its optimum speed, for example, because of traffic congestion, then fuel will be wasted. So, automatic stop/start systems which cut out the engine when the vehicle is stationary and traffic management systems that encourage free traffic flow will increase energy efficiency.

Driving smoothly, in higher gear and avoiding sudden breaking and acceleration will also improve fuel efficiency.

Transport infrastructure and management systems

▲ *Variable speed limit signs*

Integrated transport systems road/rail/cycle

The most energy-efficient method of transport is not necessarily the same for the whole length of a journey but it is often inconvenient to change vehicle during a journey. Park and ride schemes or facilities to carry bicycles on trains help.

Active Traffic Management (ATM)/'Smart motorways'

Variable speed limits can be used to prevent the serious congestion that causes delays and wastes energy.

Driverless cars

The development of driverless cars may result in smoother traffic flow and reduced fuel consumption.

Building energy conservation

Building design

Orientation

Energy losses are generally greater through windows than through walls but the solar gains through a window depend upon its orientation in relation to sunlight.

The use of a room may affect the area of windows needed and the room temperature.

In the northern hemisphere, passive solar gains through windows are greatest through south-facing windows, while losses are greatest on the north side of the building.

The choice of position of different room types can reduce overall energy use. Rooms that need to be warmer may be placed on the side of the building that has greatest passive solar gains.

Building surface area

The shape of a building and whether neighbouring buildings are joined affects the surface area through which heat can be lost. Buildings with a low surface area:volume ratio will lose heat less easily.

High thermal mass materials

Temperature management in buildings can involve resisting periods of over-heating and periods of low temperatures. Using materials with a high thermal mass can help to reduce temperature extremes. They can absorb heat to reduce over-heating or emit heat to reduce heating requirements.

Concrete and water both have a high thermal mass.

Choice of materials

Low embodied energy materials

Many buildings require large amounts of cement for mortar and concrete. The manufacture of cement requires a lot of energy so buildings that use cement have a high embodied energy.

Alternative materials that have lower embodied energy values are available.

- Limecrete is an alternative to concrete. The embodied energy of concrete is roughly double that of limecrete.
- Rammed earth is an alternative to concrete block walls.
- Lime mortar is an alternative to cement mortar.

Earth sheltered buildings

During cold weather the ground is usually warmer than the air and the flow of the air over a building increases heat losses. Sinking some of the building into the ground can reduce heat losses

Use of insulating materials

Space heating is the biggest domestic use of energy.

A building with a constant internal temperature has a dynamic equilibrium where heat inputs equal heat losses. If the heat losses can be reduced then the inputs can also be reduced.

A range of energy conservation methods have been used for many years to conserve heat energy as shown in the table.

▼ The south-facing side of an earth-sheltered building

Heat conservation method	Details
Low thermal conductivity materials	Insulating materials in roof, walls, and floor, for example, mineral wool, polystyrene, wool, shredded paper The static air between the glass panes in double glazing is a poor thermal conductor Curtains and internal window shutters reduce contact between warm internal air with cold window glass
Reduction of convection of warm air against cold external surfaces	Double glazing creates a layer of static air that is too narrow for convection to occur
Reduced radiation losses	Reflective foil layer on panels of insulating materials
Reduced loss of warm air	Draught proofing seals around doors and opening windows

A number of factors affect the rate of heat loss from a building including:

- ▼ the temperature gradient: the difference in temperature between the inside and outside of the building;
- ▼ the thermal conductivity or resistance of the materials that form the external walls, windows, and roof;
- ▼ the loss of warm air from inside;
- ▼ the chilling effect caused by wind and rain.

Energy conservation programmes usually focus on reducing the temperature gradient, increasing material thermal conductivity and preventing the loss of warm air.

Improved insulating materials

Most insulating materials reduce conduction by trapping airspaces in a porous structure. The most effective systems often have prefabricated boards with a reflective foil layer to reflect infrared radiation. Some insulating materials have low environmental impacts because they are manufactured from waste such as recycled paper, straw, vegetable oil or wool.

Window energy conservation

Multiple layers of glass with spaces between them reduces the energy loss through windows. The gap should be as large as possible, but not so large that convection currents can start. This optimum gap depends on the gas used to fill the gap and the area of the window.

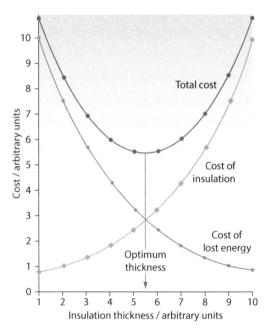

▲ *The effect of insulation thickness on heat loss*

Heat loss through different glazing systems with optimum gap sizes

Glazing system	U value W/m² °C
Single glazing	4.7
Double glazing, air fill	2.8
Double glazing, low-e glass	2.1
Double glazing, low-e glass, argon fill	1.9
Triple glazing, low-e glass, argon fill	1.4
Quadruple glazing, low-e glass, krypton fill	0.74
Quintuple glazing, low-e glass, xenon fill	0.51
Double glazing, vacuum fill (0.2mm gap)	1.4

Low emissivity (low-e) glass has a surface coating that reflects long wavelength infrared energy back into the building.

Glazing which has the gap between the panes filled with inert gases is more expensive but it has lower thermal conductivities.

It is not practical to have a wide vacuum gap because the panes need to be held apart with spacers which cannot be long, so vacuum double glazing is used where there is not space for gas-filled multiple glazing.

Thermal conductivity of different gases

Gas	Thermal conductivity (relative units)
Air	1
Argon	0.67
Krypton	0.37
Xenon	0.21

Ventilation

Heat recovery during ventilation

Heat exchangers can be used for ventilation with minimal heat losses. The heat of the air leaving the building is passed to the air coming in. The counter-current flow of stale and fresh air in the heat exchanger ensures efficient heat transfer.

Automatic ventilation

Large glazed areas increase passive solar gains. This may be excessive during very sunny weather.

Over-heating can be reduced using thermostatically operated automatic screens, self-opening windows, and solar screens.

▼ *How a heat exchanger reduces the waste of heat energy*

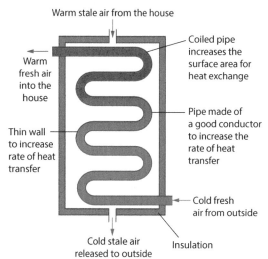

Warm stale air from the house

Coiled pipe increases the surface area for heat exchange

Warm fresh air into the house

Pipe made of a good conductor to increase the rate of heat transfer

Thin wall to increase rate of heat transfer

Cold fresh air from outside

Cold stale air released to outside

Insulation

Energy management technologies

Occupancy sensors

These work in a similar way to most burglar alarms: they detect sources of infrared energy and movement. However, they are different in that they turn appliances off if they cannot detect occupants in the room.

Programmable thermostats

The temperature required in a room can vary at different times of the day and on different days of the week. These changes may vary between different rooms in the building. Having programmable thermostats makes it easier to adjust the heating of a large number of rooms and avoid energy wastage by unnecessary heating.

Water heating

Heat loss from hot water is reduced if it is heated as it is supplied or as soon beforehand as possible. If hot water must be stored then a well-insulated tank should be used.

Reducing the volume of hot water used will also save energy. This can be done by:

- showering instead of having a bath;
- using a water-saving washing machine or dishwasher;
- using the eco-cycle programmes which are designed to use less heated water;

◀ *A brise soleil solar screen that allows sunlight into the building when the sun is low in the sky but shades the building when the sun is high in the sky*

Low energy appliances

Selecting low energy domestic appliances can reduce energy use.

'Low-energy' appliances

Appliance	How energy use is reduced
Lightbulbs	CFL lamps replaced with LED lights
Washing machine	Low energy washing machines have: • faster spin cycles so the clothes need less drying • cold and low temperature wash cycles which use less energy to heat water
Dish washer	Newer dishwashers use less water so less heating is needed
Cooker	Modern cookers have double or triple glazed door windows so heat losses are reduced.
Refrigerator	Low-energy fridges have a more efficient compressor, for example, a linear compressor. This doesn't need oil lubrication as the pumped fluid acts as the lubrication. This reduces maintenance and increases reliability. It is also much smaller so it has a lower embodied energy.
Television/computer monitor	Plasma screens use 25% of the electricity used by the cathode ray tubes they replaced. LED screens use about 50% of the electricity used by plasma screens.
Electronic appliances	New materials in transistors reduce energy use, for example, replacing silicon with germanium.

Human behaviour

In developed and affluent societies the relatively low cost of energy enables the use of energy on unnecessary items and activities which are fun, entertaining, impressive, or we are just too lazy to stop. Energy wastage can be reduced by changes in behaviour. Simple changes include:

- turning lights off when they are not required;
- turning thermostats down to prevent unnecessary over-heating;
- turning appliances off rather than leaving them on standby;
- only heating water that is needed, for example, small quantities in a kettle or when boiling vegetables;
- installing individual radiator thermostats and turning them down in unused areas.

Industrial energy conservation

Heat recovery

Industrial waste, in liquid and gaseous forms, is often hot. The heat energy can be recovered through heat exchangers and transferred to the incoming cold gas or liquid.

Heat exchangers pass hot and cold liquids through a container. They do not mix as one liquid is carried in pipes.

Increased efficiency of the heat exchange can be achieved through better design, for example:

- the surface area for heat exchange can be increased by using long, narrow pipes;
- pipes are made of a good thermal conductor, for example, copper;
- the hot and cold fluids flow in opposite directions: counter-current flow;
- the flow rate is reduced so that there is more time for effective heat exchange.

See Heat recovery during ventilation page 231

Insulation

The amount of heat energy required to keep materials warm is equal to the amount of heat being lost. By reducing the rate of heat loss there will be an identical reduction in the heat inputs required.

As with domestic insulation, heat loss can be reduced by using an outer layer made of a material that has a low thermal conductivity/high thermal resistance. Insulating pipes, storage tanks, and furnaces can save a lot of energy.

High volume storage

Surface area is an important factor affecting heat loss. Reducing the surface area by using a large tank rather than multiple small tanks to store hot fluid will reduce heat loss. Surface area and the resulting heat loss can also be reduced by changing the shape of a tank or container, for example, a sphere has the smallest surface area for any volume.

Combined Heat and Power (CHP)

CHP power stations recover much of the heat lost in electricity generation and uses it for space heating in buildings, for example homes, fish farms and greenhouses. The maximum efficiency of a modern thermal power station, at converting the energy of a combustible or nuclear fuel into

▼ *A comparison of the energy efficiency of conventional and Combined Heat and Power stations*

Conventional power station

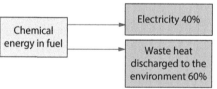

Combined heat and power station

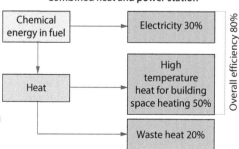

Overall efficiency 80%

electricity using steam turbines, is about 40%. The remaining 60% is lost as waste heat energy, mainly through the cooling water used to condense steam, through the cooling towers, or into a river, lake or the sea. In many CHP stations the efficiency of electricity generation is deliberately kept below 40%. This increases the temperature of the hot water and increases its usefulness.

▼ A hot water store that uses hot condenser water to heat a housing estate

Integrated manufacture

Energy can be saved when material manufacturing processes are located on the same site. The saving can be achieved by:

▼ waste heat from one industry being used by another (see page 388, Kalundborg);

▼ integrating processes, for example, iron and steel; the process of converting iron into steel requires impure iron to be molten so in an integrated works the molten iron from a blast furnace is directly converted to steel without letting it cool down first. This saves the energy that would have been used to heat it up and re-melt it;

▼ reducing the energy that would be used to transport materials between sites by locating inter-dependent industries near each other.

Recycling

As well as reducing waste and the use of new resources, recycling can also reduce energy use as producing new products from used materials often uses less energy than making them from fresh raw materials. For example, manufacturing an aluminium drinks can from recycled aluminium only takes 1/20 of the energy required to make it from raw aluminium ore. This is because most of the energy involved in making a new can is used in converting aluminium ore into aluminium metal.

While more energy is used in producing a bottle from glass than producing it from plastic, a glass bottle can be refilled or recycled. If glass bottles are reused enough then the total energy use is lower.

Recycling is not always energy efficient as there can be economies of scale through mass production and large scale mining when manufacturing items from new raw materials. Recycling can involve higher energy use from the transport and processing of smaller quantities of material.

▲ Molten iron from a blast furnace being taken to the steel furnace. It is used before it has had time to cool down.

Mass reduction

If a product can be redesigned to make it lighter then less energy will be used in its manufacture and transport. Modern glass milk bottles weigh half as much as early designs.

Plastic bottles and cardboard cartons are lighter than glass bottles but they cannot be washed and reused. Recycling them takes more energy than washing but their lighter weight may save more energy in transport than is used in recycling if their use involves being transported long distances.

Electricity infrastructure management

Peak shaving/pumped storage HEP

Peak shaving involves the storage of surplus energy so that it can be used later, to meet demand if other supplies drop or to meet a peak in demand. See pxxx

High voltage grid

The resistance to the flow of electricity in a cable causes a loss of electrical energy as it is converted into heat which is lost from the cable. The loss of energy is related to the amount of electricity flowing (Current) rather than its 'pressure' (Potential Difference or voltage). The electrical power is the product of current and voltage.

Power (Watts) = Current (Amps) x Potential Difference (Volts)

Electricity grids use transformers to control the current and voltage of the electricity distributed in the grid to minimise energy losses. The national grid transports electricity at very high voltage (400 000v) so that the current can be reduced to minimise energy loss, while maintaining the power delivered.

IT management of electricity supplies

IT systems make it possible to accurately predict demand for electricity and monitor and adjust electricity supplies quickly. This reduces the waste of energy caused by generating electricity for which there was no demand.

Location of new generation capacity and distribution infrastructure

The electricity generating equipment that is used in the future may be in new locations, for example, offshore windfarms rather than power stations on coalfields. This will require the construction of new grid infrastructure.

Key principles

- ▶ Energy supplies have played a vital role in the development of society.
- ▶ The properties of energy resources affect their usefulness in meeting demands.
- ▶ The large-scale use of some energy technologies relies on the development of other technologies such as energy storage.
- ▶ The energy resources used in industrial societies in the 20th century will not be the main ones that are used at the end of the 21st century.
- ▶ The use of every energy resource has an impact on the environment. Each resource has its own unique impacts.
- ▶ Changes in energy use must achieve sustainability in terms of resource availability and environmental impacts.
- ▶ The development of new technologies is making new energy resources more usable.
- ▶ New technologies are increasing the efficiency of energy use.

Pollution

Chapter topics
- ▼ Properties of pollutants
- ▼ General strategies to control pollution
- ▼ Sources, effects and control of pollution
    - Atmospheric pollution
    - Pollution of water
    - Heavy metals
    - Solid wastes
    - Noise pollution
    - Ironsing radiation

Pollution involves the release of substances or forms of energy into the environment that cause harm, especially to living organisms. Pollution is usually caused by human activities, but natural processes can have the same effects, for example, oil leaks from natural oilfields, smoke from forest fires, or volcanic eruptions releasing acidic gases and dust.

The chemical industry produces a large number of new chemicals each year. An understanding of the behaviour of existing chemicals helps in predicting the behaviour of new chemicals so that decisions can be made about setting acceptable emissions, developing control methods, and establishing monitoring programmes.

Properties of pollutants

The properties of a pollutant determine the length of time it may cause a problem, the level of harm it can cause, and where and how far it might travel. Understanding how the properties of pollutants cause problems can help us anticipate and prevent pollution.

State of matter

Whether a polluting material is a solid, liquid, or gas affects its ability to be dispersed by moving water or air. In general, solids are deposited close to the source while gases are transported easily in the atmosphere.

Energy form

The different pollutants that are energy forms, such as noise, heat, ionising radiation or light, have widely varying impacts because of the way the energy behaves.

Density

The density of a material will affect its dispersal. Denser materials require more kinetic energy to keep them suspended, so they are more likely to be deposited closer to the source, for example, lead dust has a high density. Some gases are denser than air and settle close to ground if there is insufficient wind to disperse them, for example, hydrogen cyanide released at Bhopal, India, in 1984, remained very close to the source.

Persistence

Persistence is a measure of the length of time that a pollutant remains in the environment before it breaks down chemically (degrades).

Persistence can be measured as the time it takes for half of a pollutant to break down. This is called the environmental half-life ($T_{\frac{1}{2} \text{ ENV}}$). It is not a precise measure because the rate of breakdown can be affected by environmental conditions such as light, temperature, oxygen levels, pH, or the presence of bacteria.

Pollutants with different degrees of persistence

High persistence	Low persistence
CFCs Organochlorine insecticides, for example, DDT	Sewage Pyrethroid insecticides

The process of breakdown is called degradation and can be categorised according to the feature causing breakdown:

- ▼ biodegradation: caused by living organisms, usually bacteria;
- ▼ photodegradation: caused by light.
- ▼ Thermal degradation: caused by heat.

Toxicity

This is a measure of how poisonous a substance is to living organisms. The harm is usually caused by damage to proteins, especially the inhibition of enzyme action.

Examples of toxic pollutants

Pollutant	Toxic action
Carbon monoxide	Prevents blood from carrying oxygen by binding to haemoglobin in red blood cells
Lead	Inhibits enzyme action in nerve cells
Acids	Inhibit protein action by changing the molecular shape, for example, the active site of an enzyme
Cyanide	Inhibits enzymes involved in aerobic respiration

Specificity

Specificity is a property of toxic pollutants and is used to describe variations in toxicity to different groups of organisms. Specific toxins are more toxic to some groups than others. Non-specific pollutants have similar toxicities to all groups.

Pyrethroid insecticides have high toxicity to insects and low toxicity to mammals so it is relatively safe for humans to use them in insect pest control in areas with livestock. However, they have high toxicity to fish so they should not be used near rivers or fish farms.

Reactivity

The reactivity of a pollutant can affect the severity of the pollution caused, either increasing or reducing the problems caused.

How reactivity affects the severity of pollutants

Pollutant	Reactivity	Effect on pollution
CFCs	Low, except in the presence of UV light	CFCs are relatively stable in the troposphere, but are broken down in the stratosphere where they release chlorine
NOx, ozone, hydrocarbons	High	React with each other to produce PANs which are more toxic

A reactive pollutant may degrade rapidly such as sewage, or it may react with other substances to produce secondary pollutants, for example, the action of ozone in acid rain and photochemical smog.

Primary and secondary pollutants

A primary pollutant is one that is released by human activities.

A secondary pollutant is one that is produced by chemical reactions between one or more primary pollutants, often with non-pollutants.

Adsorption

Some pollutants can become attached to the surface of materials such as soil particles, or aquatic sediments. This can immobilize them so they cannot cause pollution problems, but it is also possible they may be released later to cause problems after a period of time when their presence was not obvious, for example, the disturbance of lake sediments by storms releasing phosphates or PCBs.

Solubility in lipids/water

Substances that have high solubility in water are easily dispersed in water bodies, for example, nitrates. This can reduce the pollutant concentration but may allow the pollutant to affect a larger area.

Lipids are organic compounds that are fatty acids or their derivatives and are insoluble in water. Substances that dissolve in lipids may be able to pass through phospholipid cell membranes and be stored in oil or fat deposits within cells, for example, mercury, or DDT.

Bioaccumulation

This is the process by which the amount of a substance within an organism increases. It often involves the long-term ingestion of small doses of a liposoluble pollutant. The original doses may have been too small to be toxic, but they may eventually build up to reach toxic levels. Liposoluble pollutants are more likely to bio-accumulate because they may be stored in lipids. Water-soluble pollutants tend to be excreted from the body more easily.

Biomagnification

Substances that bioaccumulate may become more concentrated as they pass along a food chain, becoming concentrated into a progressively smaller biomass with each successive trophic level. Organisms in later trophic levels often have longer lifespans and build up even higher concentrations, especially if they are endotherms (warm-blooded) that have a higher food intake because of their higher metabolic rates so they are likely to ingest more of the pollutant.

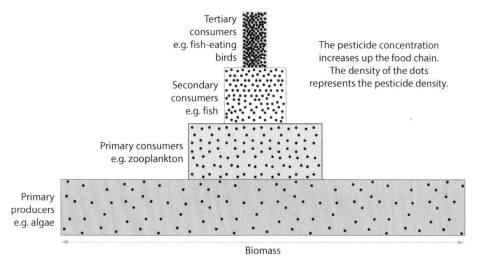

The pesticide concentration increases up the food chain. The density of the dots represents the pesticide density.

◀ *This pyramid of biomass shows how persistent liposoluble pesticides can bioaccumulate within organisms and biomagnify in food chains*

Synergism

Synergism in pollution involves two or more pollutants where their effects interact to create a different effect, usually a more serious one. The pollutants themselves do not interact to produce a new pollutant (that would be a secondary pollutant), it is the effects that interact, for example, ozone damages leaf cuticles which enables sulfur dioxide to cause more damage to the newly exposed living cells.

Mutagenic action

Mutagens are agents which cause changes in the chemical structure of DNA by damaging chromosomes by rearrangement of the DNA structure. These changes are known as mutations.

Gonadic effects (cells in ovaries or testes)

A mutation in an egg, or sperm cell, or in an embryo, may cause a birth abnormality in the offspring produced.

Somatic effects (general body cells)

A mutation in a body cell may make it behave abnormally as the damaged DNA cannot control normal cell function. The death of individual cells is rarely a problem as they can be replaced by the division of other healthy cells.

A serious consequence of DNA mutations in body cells that are not killed is cancer, where uncontrolled cell division produces a tumour.

Examples of mutagenic pollutants

- Ionizing radiation
- UV light
- Chlorinated organic substances, for example, PCBs, dioxins
- Cadmium
- Asbestos

Carcinogenic action

Carcinogens are mutagens that cause cancer. The cell multiplication caused by a carcinogen produces a mass of tissue called a tumour. The tumour may eventually cause health problems by preventing normal tissue function.

Teratogenic action

Teratogens cause birth abnormalities by preventing normal gene expression. They do not change the DNA structure but inhibit the function of proteins and enzymes that the DNA would normally have controlled. The birth abnormality cannot be inherited by future generations because the DNA structure is not affected.

Examples of teratogenic pollutants

- Mercury
- The herbicide 2,4,5-T (no longer used)

Mobility

The ability of a pollutant to move in the environment depends upon other properties, especially its state of matter, density, and solubility in water. Pollutants that are more mobile are likely to travel greater distances and affect larger areas, although dilution may reduce the severity of the effect.

Examples of pollutants with different degrees of mobility

Pollutants	Mobility
Lead dust	The high density of atmospheric lead dust causes most particles to be deposited close to the source.
Smoke particles	Smoke particles are easily washed out of the atmosphere by rain, or settle if the air is relatively static. Smaller particles settle more slowly.
Sulfur dioxide gas	Sulfur dioxide is soluble in water and is easily removed from the atmosphere by rain, usually within 250km of the source.
CFCs	CFCs are chemically stable and have low solubility in water, so they remain in the atmosphere for a long time and disperse throughout the whole atmosphere.

Effects of environmental features

The environment into which a pollutant is released can have a big impact on the extent and severity of the pollution caused. Identical amounts of the same pollutant released in different locations may have very different impacts.

Features affecting degradation

Chemical reactions involving a pollutant may cause it to degrade and produce less harmful materials but they may also allow the production of secondary pollutants.

Temperature

Most chemical reactions occur more rapidly if the temperature is higher. Degradable pollutants such as sewage will break down more rapidly at higher temperatures, but more rapid degradation can increase problems such as deoxygenation.

Light levels

Light can provide the activation energy that drives chemical reactions involving pollutants, for example, photochemical smogs and the photodegradation of some pesticides.

Oxygen

Oxygen is involved in many chemical and biological reactions involving pollution including:

- aerobic bacterial decomposition of sewage;
- oxidation of sufide ores producing sulfur dioxide.

The oxidation state affects the solubility of many metals.

pH

pH can affect the solubility of substances. Many heavy metals, such as lead, are more soluble and therefore mobile under more acidic conditions.

Pollutant interactions

The behaviour of a pollutant may be affected by the presence of other pollutants such as:

▼ the interaction of NOx and hydrocarbons in photochemical smogs;
▼ the combined effects of phosphates and nitrates in eutrophication.

▲ *Fast flowing turbulent rivers have high dissolved oxygen levels.*

Factors affecting dispersal

Wind and water currents

The velocity and direction of air and water currents will affect how far a pollutant is dispersed, but also how much it is diluted.

Temperature inversions

Atmospheric temperatures in the troposphere normally decline with increasing altitude. The temperature of warm pollutant gases, released at ground level, makes them less dense and more buoyant than the cooler surrounding air. This allows them to rise, disperse, and become diluted. They cool down as they rise but, because the surrounding air is also cooler, they remain buoyant and continue to rise and disperse.

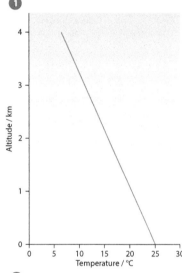

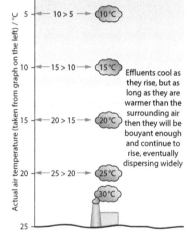

❶ *How effluent gases rise under normal conditions. inversion.*

❷ *How a temperature inversion prevents the dispersal of pollutant gases. Under certain circumstances the layer of air closest to the ground may be colder than normal. This colder air is more dense and less buoyant so any pollutants released there may also become cold and dense. This means they cannot disperse easily and become more concentrated. This situation is called a temperature inversion.*

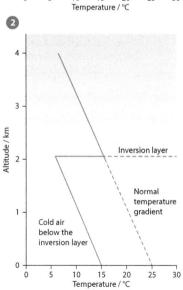

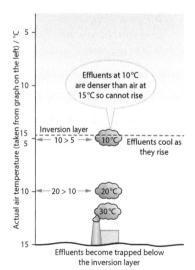

Factors that allow temperature inversions to form

▶ Valleys: where colder denser air can collect.

▶ Low wind velocity: so that the air layers with different temperatures do not mix.

▶ Cloudless skies: so that infrared energy can be radiated from the ground, allowing the ground to cool down.

▶ Mist or fog during the day: water vapour that condenses in the cooler ground layer has a high albedo and will reflect sunlight and slow the heating of the ground that would cause the temperature inversion to be broken down.

▶ *A temperature inversion in a valley Under certain circumstances the layer of air closest to the ground may be colder than normal. This colder air is more dense and less buoyant so any pollutants released there may also become cold and dense. This means they cannot disperse easily and become more concentrated. This situation is called a temperature inversion.*

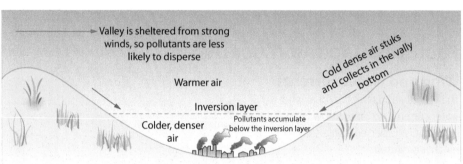

▶ *How a temperature inversion changes over a 24 hour period.*

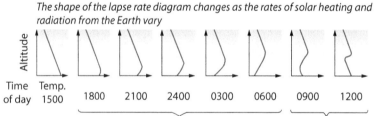

The shape of the lapse rate diagram changes as the rates of solar heating and radiation from the Earth vary

Air near the ground becomes colder as infrared radiation radiates from the Earth which becomes colder. The cold ground cools the air above

The air that cooled overnight becomes warmer as sunlight warms the ground

Many cities are in valleys where high pollutant emissions may cause serious problems as they become concentrated during temperature inversions such as smoke smogs and photochemical smogs.

The presence of adsorbent materials

Pollutants may adsorb onto materials such as clay particles or organic materials in aquatic sediments. Adsorption may immobilise the pollutant and stop it causing problems. Radioactive caesium-137 released into the atmosphere by the nuclear accident, at Chernobyl in 1986, was washed out of the atmosphere by rain. Much of the caesium that was washed into soil has adsorbed onto clay particles, so it is immobile and any radiation released is absorbed in the ground. Many naturally occurring toxic metal ions are immobilised by being adsorbed onto soil clay particles, for example, aluminium and lead.

General strategies to control pollution

Critical Pathway Analysis (CPA)

The purpose of CPA is to predict the movement of potential pollutants in the environment to assess the severity and location of the pollution that may occur. If a potential pollutant would be diluted and dispersed, or carried to locations where the impacts would be acceptable, then no further action may be needed. If the potential pollutant would become concentrated, or would be carried to important or sensitive locations, then it may be necessary to control these releases.

Factors that may be included in Critical Pathway Analysis

Properties of the pollutant	State of matter Density Solubility in water/lipids Chemical stability
Features of the environment	Wind and water currents Geology pH Oxygen availability Temperature

CPA could be used to monitor the movements of any mobile, persistent pollutant but it is mainly used to monitor the dispersal of radioactive waste discharges. Predicting the pollutant pathways means that environmental monitoring can focus on the sites most at risk of pollution with no need for sampling of sites that were never likely to be polluted.

Environmental sampling can be used to check the accuracy of the CPA predictions.

Critical Group Monitoring (CGM)

CGM is a specific method of assessing the risk of public exposure to pollutants. It assesses the risk to members of the public who, because of their lifestyle, are most likely to be at risk. This group of people is the Critical Group. If their risk is acceptably low, then it is assumed that all other members of the public have an even lower risk.

CGM is not normally used to detect damage to health caused by the pollutant. It is used to monitor exposure and assess potential risks before health impacts occur. If an unacceptable risk is identified then emissions can be controlled to reduce future exposure.

Emission control strategies

Environmental factors such as air quality, meteorological conditions, hydrology and emission source affect the dispersal of pollutants. Some factors can be managed, for example, emission location and timing.

Control of emission location

The severity of pollution is affected by the location where the discharges are released. Although the emission location is normally determined by the location of the source, there may be some choices that affect the severity of the pollution caused, such as:

- marine discharges where water currents will dilute and disperse emissions;
- emissions downwind of urban areas.
- not discharging waste onto permeable rock above an aquifer

Control of emission timing

Changes in the timing of emissions can affect the severity of pollution.

How emission timing can affect pollution

Timing	Impact on pollution
Tidal cycle	Emissions into tidal rivers when the tide is coming in will be carried upstream. Emissions when the tide is going out will be carried out to sea where they will disperse.
Temperature inversions	Atmospheric emissions during a temperature inversion are less likely to disperse. Polluting activities may be restricted in some cities during temperature inversions for example, the use of diesel vehicles or industrial combustion.

Principles of pollution control

There are a number of principles that affect the decision of how to control pollution.

The polluter pays principle

If the organisation or person that causes pollution is responsible for any problems caused then there is an obligation to prevent it.

If the costs of preventing the damage caused by the pollution are less than the costs of the damage, then there is a clear financial incentive to prevent it.

This approach works best if there is little chance of the polluter escaping their responsibilities.

The incentive to comply is greater if financial penalties are high.

The precautionary principle

This approach assumes that a waste will cause pollution if released, until research confirms it is unlikely to do so when release may be permitted. This is safer than releasing a waste that has not been analysed in the hope it is safe, then waiting to see if problems occur.

This principle means that being unaware of a problem that is not yet understood is not an excuse and does not reduce responsibility.

Selection of the control method

A range of different approaches can be used in selecting the method used to control pollution.

Pollution control methods

Control method	Examples
Production prevention	Desulfurisation of fossil fuels before combustion.
Prevention of release	Electrostatic precipitators for smoke control. Catalytic converters for control of NOx, CO and hydrocarbons in vehicle exhaust emissions.
Post-release remediation	Oil spill clean-up methods. Phytoremediation of land contaminated with heavy metals.
Alternative processes	Use of electric vehicles instead of diesel or petrol vehicles. Use of pyrethroid pesticides instead of the more polluting organochlorines, for example, DDT. The use of renewable energy resources instead of fossil fuels.

The efficiency of pollution control

Pollution control can be expensive. The relationship between cost and the efficiency of control is not linear.

It is rarely practical to reduce pollutant emissions to zero. The impact of low level emissions may be acceptable, so paying for controls to a higher standard may be judged to be unnecessary. A decision must be made about the acceptable level of emissions.

In general, emissions should follow the 'ALARA' approach. This means that emissions should be As Low As Reasonably Achievable. This can be achieved by selecting new equipment that is 'BATNEEC'. This means it is the Best Available Technology, Not Entailing Excessive Cost.

To achieve acceptable environmental conditions often requires changes in emission controls. As industries expand or cities grow the number of pollutant sources may increase. So, the methods used originally may no longer be sufficient.

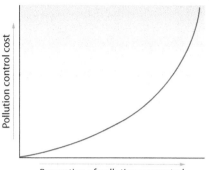

▲ the relationship between pollution control costs and the effectiveness of control

Atmospheric pollution

Pollutants in the atmosphere often behave very differently from those in water, or on the ground. For example:

▼ rapid movement due to winds leads to dispersal over a large area;

▼ interaction with electromagnetic radiation such as UV (ultra violet) or visible light from the Sun can cause chemical reactions to occur, leading to the production of secondary pollutants.

Smoke and smoke smogs

Smoke is made up of the atmospheric particulates produced by the incomplete combustion of carbon-based materials. Smoke is often categorised by the size range of the particles:

▼ PM10: particulate matter less than 10 microns in diameter;

▼ PM5: particulate matter less than 5 microns in diameter;

▼ PM1: particulate matter less than 1 micron in diameter.

Particle size is important because smaller particles remain in the atmosphere for longer so they are more likely to be inhaled.

Toxic chemicals found in smoke can include fluorides, aluminium, lead, acids and organic compounds such as phenol.

Smoke can act synergistically with other atmospheric pollutants such as sulfur dioxide. The exact composition of smoke depends upon its source. The main sources of smoke are:

▼ combustion of coal, diesel, general combustible wastes especially in urban areas;

▼ combustion of crop waste, wood fuel, grasslands, forests in rural areas

❶ Smoke emissions from an oil fired power station
❷ Diesel trucks release smoke, especially if they are poorly maintained

Effects of smoke pollution

► On humans: respiratory disease, for example, bronchitis, asthma, lung cancer. Chemicals on or in smoke particles can kill the cilia in the bronchioles which makes it more difficult to clear inhaled particles and bacteria from the lungs. This can increase the risk of infections. Some of the chemicals may be carcinogenic.

► On other living organisms: reduced photosynthesis as smoke blocks light. Substances in the smoke particles may be toxic, for example, heavy metals and acids.

► On non-living objects: smoke particles can damage buildings due to the acids and organic solvents they may contain. Cleaning dirty buildings is also expensive.

► On the climate: Large releases of smoke can reduce temperatures because the high albedo of the smoke reflects light so it does not reach the ground where it may have been absorbed and converted to heat. It was thought that an impact of large-scale nuclear war would result in so much smoke reaching the stratosphere that the Earth would cool significantly for several years. This scenario is called a 'Nuclear Winter'. It could make survival on Earth much more difficult as crops would fail, livestock would die, and many natural ecosystems would be disrupted.

► smoke particles are small and can remain suspended in the atmosphere for long periods, especially in the stratosphere where there is no rain to wash it out;

► smoke in the stratosphere can also deplete the ozone layer;

▼ *A temperature inversion to the west of London*

Smoke smogs

When smoke and fog are present together a smog may occur.

Smoke + Fog = Smog

Fog tends to form when moist air is cooled until it reaches its dew point. The water vapour condenses as airborne droplets of water. Temperature inversions make the formation of fog more likely.

Smoke that is part of a smog is more easily inhaled.

Smog has a very high albedo so the temperature inversion can last for long periods of time, allowing pollutant levels to rise to a high level.

The London smog of 1952

The position of London in a valley has caused atmospheric pollution problems since the 1200s. These became worse as the city grew.

In December 1952, there was a five day period when anticyclonic weather conditions produced clear skies and low wind velocities so a temperature inversion formed and atmospheric pollutant levels rose.

About 12,000 deaths were caused by this smog, mainly people who were old, very young, or had existing respiratory health problems.

▼ *An experiment in London using CMA (calcium magnesium acetate) as a road surface coating. Suspended particles stick to the coating and are not resuspended*

Smoke pollution control measures

Legislation: Clean Air Act (1956). This restricted the use of fuels that produce smoke in large urban areas of the UK.

Domestic sources: increased use of fuels that do not produce smoke, for example, natural gas, electricity.

Transport sources: Diesel Particulate Filters (DPV) fitted in the exhaust pipes of diesel engines trap up to 80% of smoke particles.

Industrial sources

- Electrostatic precipitators: effluent gases are passed through a chamber with many electrically charged wires or plates. The smoke particles within the gases are attracted to the charged wires and plates and collect together. As the particles accumulate they fall to the floor as 'fly ash'. This pollution control method is often used in coal-fired power stations.
- Cyclone separators: this process is based on the same principles as many vacuum cleaners. Like the air and waste drawn into a vacuum cleaner the effluent gases are forced to rotate in a cylindrical chamber, which throws the suspended particles to the outside surfaces of the chamber where they fall and collect. This cleans the gases which are then discharged via a pipe from the centre of the cylinder.

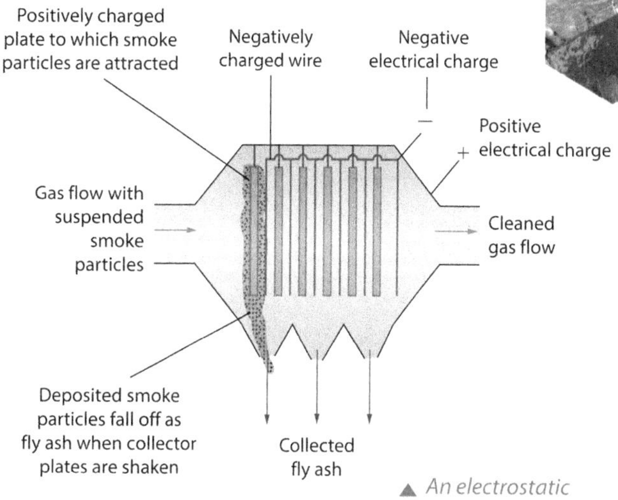

▲ *An electrostatic precipitator*

- Scrubber: a scrubber uses a fine water spray to wash out suspended solid particulate matter and dissolve soluble gaseous pollutants.
- Coal treatment - heating coal allows the tar that causes smoke production to be drained off. This produces smokeless coal.
- Bag filters remove smoke particles from effluent gases by trapping them on a fabric filter.

More efficient combustion technology

- A lot of smoke particles are made of organic matter which has not completely burnt. If more oxygen is supplied and efficiently mixed the smoke particles can be completely burnt to gases.
- Diesel engines produce most smoke when the driver accelerates too quickly so too much fuel enters the engine for the amount of oxygen available to burn it. Turbo chargers enable more air and therefore more oxygen to be delivered to the combustion chamber which increases the efficiency of the combustion.

❶

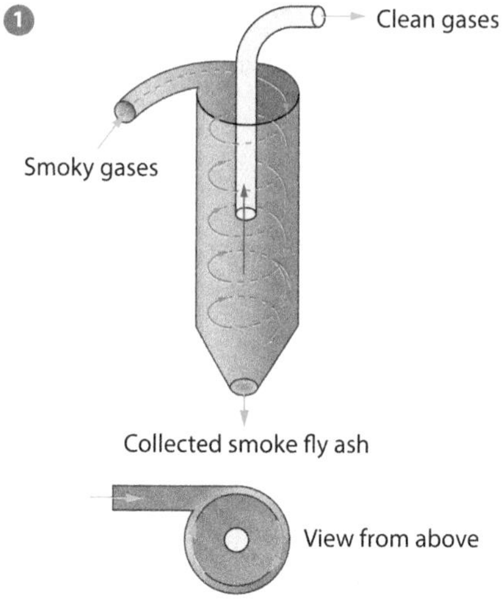

The speed of rotation forces the smoke particles to the outside. The clean exhaust air is removed from the middle.

❷

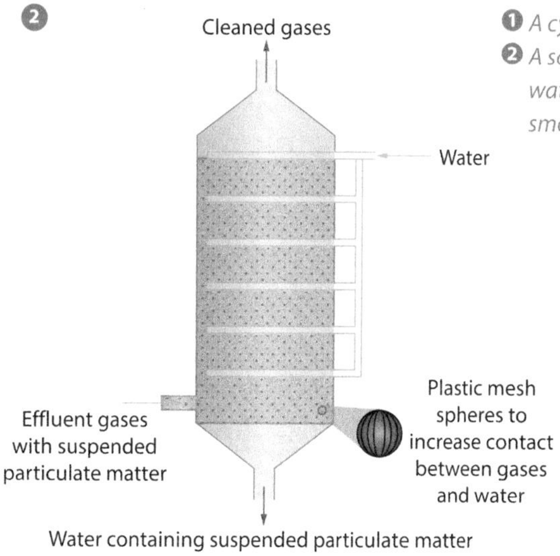

❶ *A cyclone separator*
❷ *A scrubber in which water sprays remove smoke particles*

Photochemical smogs

The use of the word 'smog' here is misleading as they do not involve smoke or fog but they do involve urban pollution during temperature inversions, often in valleys, so there are some similarities with 'true' smoke smogs.

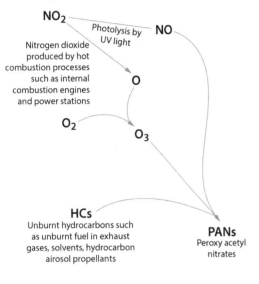

NO$_2$
Nitrogen dioxide produced by hot combustion processes such as internal combustion engines and power stations

Photolysis by UV light → **NO**

O

O$_2$

O$_3$

HCs
Unburnt hydrocarbons such as unburnt fuel in exhaust gases, solvents, hydrocarbon airosol propellants

PANs
Peroxy acetyl nitrates

Pollutants involved

Photochemical smogs involve a wide variety of reactions between primary and secondary pollutants, in the presence of sunlight, including UV light.

Sources of primary pollutants

In urban areas most oxides of nitrogen (NOx) are released in the exhaust gases from petrol and diesel engines. NOx are not produced by the fuel combustion itself. They are formed by the nitrogen and oxygen from the air that are drawn into the engine, then react with each other under the high temperature and pressure conditions in the engine. Nitrogen dioxide is toxic at high concentrations but these are normally only reached in more polluted cities. However, in the presence of sunlight and other pollutants such as hydrocarbon vapours, much more toxic secondary pollutants can be produced such as Peroxy Acetyl Nitrates (PANs).

❶ Large industrial plants such as oil refineries are major sources of NOx, especially in countries where there are no strict emission regulations

❷ An atmospheric pollution monitoring station

Unburnt hydrocarbons come from a variety of sources, especially unburnt fuel in engine exhaust gases, fuel evaporating from fuel tanks, and spillages.

Photochemical pollutant effects

NOx increase the risks of respiratory infections such as colds, flu, and bronchitis. They can also make existing health problems worse such as asthma and heart disease.

PANs are toxic at concentrations much lower than those at which NOx become toxic. They cause eye irritation, breathing difficulty, asthma, emphysema, and an increased risk of heart attacks.

Tropospheric ozone contributes to the production of PANs but is also toxic itself, causing asthma, bronchitis, and heart disease.

Some cities are particularly prone to photochemical smogs because of their topography, heavy vehicle use, and climate. These include Los Angeles, Mexico City, Paris, Beijing, and Athens where traffic congestion is severe, the climate is sunny and temperature inversions are common.

◀ *Pollution trapped by an early morning photochemical smog over Mexico City.*

Control of photochemical smogs

NOx and hydrocarbons can both be controlled using catalysts such as platinum and palladium in exhaust pipe catalytic converters.

NOx are chemically reduced in catalytic converters to re-form the oxygen and nitrogen gases that originally reacted together. Catalytic converters are used in the exhaust systems of vehicles with petrol engines and many with diesel engines.

Unburnt hydrocarbons can be controlled using several methods:

▼ catalytic converters oxidise hydrocarbons to carbon dioxide and water;

▼ vapours at filling stations can be collected, condensed, and returned to the main fuel tank;

▼ vapours can be collected and passed through an activated carbon filter where the hydrocarbons adsorb onto the carbon particles.

If the primary pollutants are controlled, the secondary pollutants will not be formed because the reactants will not be present.

Chemical reduction of NOx

$$NOx \longrightarrow N_2 + O_2$$

Oxidation of hydrocarbons

$$HC + O_2 \longrightarrow H_2O + CO_2$$

NB the chemical reactions are not balanced because a range of NOx and HCs may be involved.

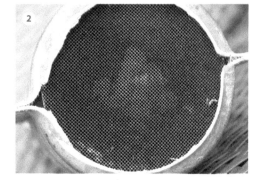

❶ *The control of NOx and hydrocarbons using a catalytic converter*
❷ *Cut-away catalytic converter showing the high surface area 'honeycomb' structure for chemical reactions*
❸ *The collection of hydrocarbon vapours at a filling station*

Acid rain

All rain is naturally slightly acidic (pH 5.6) because naturally occurring carbon dioxide in the atmosphere dissolves to produce a dilute solution of carbonic acid which is a weak acid. 'Acid Rain' is the general name given to any precipitation that is more acidic than pH 5.6.

Acid rain is the combination of the pollution problems caused by a range of acidic gases and other pollutants that contribute to the problem.

Pollutants involved in acid rain

Main gases

- Sulfur dioxide dissolves in water to produce sulfurous acid.
- Sulfur dioxide may be oxidised in the atmosphere by gases such as ozone to produce sulfur trioxide. Sulfur trioxide is dissolved to produce sulfuric acid which is a much more powerful acid than sulfurous acid.
- Oxides of nitrogen dissolve to produce nitrous and nitric acids.

Other gases

Hydrogen chloride dissolves to form hydrochloric acids. Ozone is involved in the oxidation of sulfur dioxide to sulfur trioxide. It also harms plants directly.

Sources of the gases involved in acid rain

Gas	Main sources
Sulfur dioxide	Combustion or oxidation of materials containing sulfur, especially burning coal and smelting sulfide ores.
Oxides of nitrogen	High temperature combustion, especially in power stations and petrol and diesel internal combustion engines.
Ozone	A secondary pollutant produced by photochemical reactions involving oxides of nitrogen.
Hydrogen chloride	The combustion of coal and the incineration of wastes containing chlorine, for example, PVC plastic waste.
Sulfur trioxide	Oxidation of sulfur dioxide by ozone

Effects of acid rain

▼ *Pollution damage to York Minster*

Impact on non-living things

Acid deposition corrodes metals, causing damage to railway lines, metal railings, water pipes, pylons, and overhead powerlines.

Limestone structures such as buildings and statues are damaged as the acids dissolve the surface layers and weaken the stone structure of porous limestone.

Impact on living organisms

Acid rain can harm living organisms directly by the acids in the rain, or indirectly where they cause other environmental changes that are harmful.

Direct effects on living organisms

Acids are harmful to all living organisms although the range of tolerance differs between species. Low pHs denature proteins in cell membranes and can inhibit enzyme action.

Tissues which have living cells exposed to the environment are most likely to be damaged by acid rain, for example, the cells inside leaf stomata, plant root hairs, germinating seeds, fish eggs, and fish gills. Invertebrates with exoskeletons may die as the acids dissolve the calcium compounds that form the skeleton.

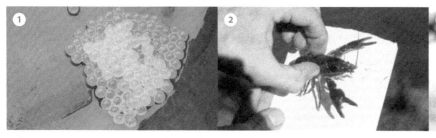

Lichens are very sensitive to acidic conditions and their size, state of health, abundance and diversity may be used in a biotic index to monitor acid rain pollution (see Pxxx).

Sulfur dioxide can create breathing difficulties and increase the frequency of respiratory problems such as asthma attacks.

Indirect effects on living organisms

The solubility of many metal ions is affected by pH, often becoming more soluble at low pH.

The acidic solutions, produced by acid rain that percolate through soil, can leach metal ions from the soil. Important plant nutrients such as calcium (Ca^{2+}) and magnesium (Mg^{2+}) are usually lost first. Once these have gone, other ions are mobilised which would normally be adsorbed onto the surface of clay particles and would therefore be immobile and would not take part in normal soil chemistry. They include toxic ions such as aluminium (Al^{3+}) and lead (Pb^+).

These toxic ions inhibit enzyme action in plant root hair cells and other soil organisms such as detritivores and decomposers. The mobilised toxic ions may be leached into rivers and lakes where they can harm aquatic organisms.

Metal ions leached out of the soil may also affect human health. Lead is a neurotoxin and there is some evidence that aluminium ions may be a factor associated with some neurological disorders.

❶ *Fish eggs have exposed living cell membranes which are easily damaged by pollutants*

❷ *Crayfish have calcium-based exoskeletons that are damaged by acidic conditions*

❸ *Lichens are sensitive to acids*

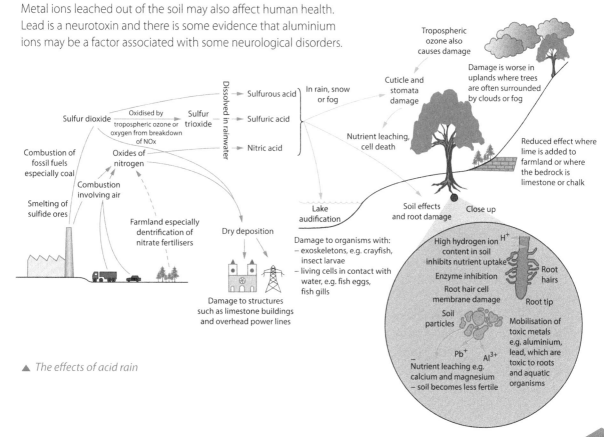

▲ *The effects of acid rain*

Environmental factors that affect the severity of acid rain

Environmental factor	Impact on acid rain
Soil lime content	Soils with a high lime content include $CaCO_3$ which neutralises acids and reduces the impact of acids on soil pH.
Fog	Acid precipitation that falls as rain may have a relatively brief contact with the leaves of vegetation. In areas that have long periods of fog, the acidic water droplets may be in contact with the leaves of trees for long periods of time so the damage caused by the acids may be increased.
Snow	In areas where all precipitation is rain, the impact of the acids may be spread over long periods of time. Areas that have a lot of snow may accumulate acidic snow. If this melts quickly then the pH of the meltwater may be very low, harming life in the soil and rivers.

Control of acid rain

Control of oxides of sulfur

Natural gas desulfurisation: involves the removal of sulfur from the fuel before it is burned. In some areas of the sea, for example, the North Sea and within 25 miles of the California Coast, only low sulfur fuels may be used by ships

▼ **Natural gas:** hydrogen sulfide is removed from natural gas after it has been extracted to prevent corrosion damage to refinery and pipeline equipment and to the appliances in which the gas is used. This also prevents the production of sulfur dioxide when it is burned. It is removed by dissolving it in an amine solution or reacting it with iron particles.

▼ **Crude oil desulfurisation:** sulfur compounds are removed from crude oil during distillation using molybdenum catalysts in the process of hydrodesulfurisation.

▼ **Coal desulfurisation:** most of the sulfur in coal is present as solid iron pyrites (FeS_2). This can be removed by washing and streaming. The coal is crushed then put in a stream of flowing water. The flow rate is fast enough to carry the coal away but leave the denser pyrites behind

Flue-gas Desulfurisation (FGD): several processes can be used to remove sulfur dioxide from the power station emissions released after fuel combustion.

▼ **Dry flue-gas desulfurisation (Dry FGD):** flue gases are passed through a bed of crushed calcium carbonate. The sulfur dioxide reacts with the calcium carbonate producing solid calcium sulfur.

Reaction summary:

$$2CaCO_3 + 2SO_2 + O_2 \rightarrow 2CaSO_4 + 2CO_2$$

Calcium carbonate · Sulfur dioxide · Oxygen → Calcium sulfate

If the effluent gases have been cleaned to remove smoke particles, then the calcium sulfate produced may be pure enough to make gypsum building plaster.

▼ **Wet flue-gas desulfurisation:** this involves sodium sulfite scrubbing where the flue gases are bubbled through a sodium sulfite solution.

Reactions:

$$Na_2SO_3 + H_2O + SO_2 \rightarrow 2NaHSO_3$$

Sodium sulfite · Water · Sulfur dioxide → Sodium hydrogen sulfite

The sodium hydrogen sulfite produced by the absorption of sulfur dioxide can be heated. It breaks down to produce sodium sulfite and water, which are reused, and concentrated pure sulfur dioxide, which is a valuable industrial raw material that can be converted to solid sulfur or sulfuric acid.

Control of oxides of nitrogen

Low temperature combustion: less NOx is produced using lower temperature combustion techniques, such as fluidised bed combustion, where an increased surface area for combustion maintains rapid combustion without the need for high temperatures.

Catalytic converters: a chamber in the exhaust pipes contains a catalyst such as platinum which chemically reduces NOx back to nitrogen and oxygen gases. For the reaction equation see page 248.

Urea sprays: NOx can be removed by reacting it with urea.

$$2CO(NH_2)_2 + 4NO + O_2 \qquad 4N_2 + 2CO_2 + 4H_2O$$

| Urea | Nitrogen monoxide | Oxygen | | Nitrogen | Carbon dioxide | Water |

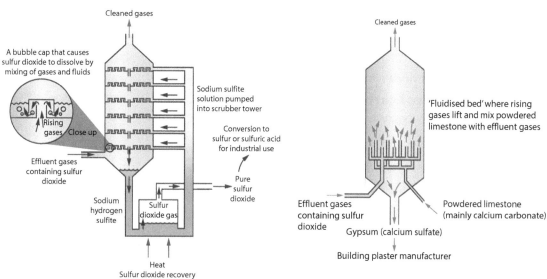

▲ *Wet flue gas desulfurisation*   ▲ *Dry flue gas desulfurisation*

Tropospheric ozone

Stratospheric ozone occurs naturally and is important for life on Earth as it reduces exposure to harmful UV light. However, tropospheric ozone is a pollutant, produced as a result of human activities, and is toxic to living organisms.

Effects of tropospheric ozone

Ozone is toxic to plants and reduces growth rates of trees and agricultural crops.

In humans, ozone causes breathing difficulties and increases asthma rates.

Tropospheric ozone is also involved in the production of secondary pollutants in photochemical smogs and acid rain.

Sources of tropospheric ozone

Tropospheric ozone is a secondary pollutant produced by photochemical reactions involving oxides of nitrogen

Summary reactions

1 Nitrogen dioxide is broken down by UV-A sunlight. This is a 'photochemical reaction'.

$$NO_2 \longrightarrow NO \quad + \quad O$$

Nitrogen   Nitrogen   (Monatomic)
dioxide   monoxide   oxygen

2 The monatomic oxygen reacts with 'normal' (diatomic) oxygen to produce ozone.

$$O \quad + \quad O_2 \xrightarrow{\text{UV-A}} O_3$$

Monatomic   Diatomic   Ozone
oxygen   oxygen   (Triatomic oxygen)

Control of tropospheric ozone

Tropospheric ozone is a secondary pollutant so levels can be controlled by reducing levels of the primary pollutants that produce it. Nitrogen dioxide is produced by internal combustion engines, power stations, and other high temperature combustion involving air. Methods to reduce these releases will reduce ozone levels by preventing its formation.

Carbon monoxide/CO

Carbon monoxide (CO) is produced when carbon-based materials are burned with a shortage of oxygen, such as the incomplete combustion of hydrocarbons, especially petrol and diesel in vehicle engines.

Effects of carbon monoxide

Carbon monoxide binds to haemoglobin and prevents it from carrying oxygen from the lungs to tissues around the body. If too much of the haemoglobin in the red blood cells is inactivated by carbon monoxide then brain damage may occur and possibly death.

Low concentrations of carbon monoxide can increase the health problems caused by chronic heart disease.

Control of carbon monoxide

Exhaust catalytic converters oxidise carbon monoxide to carbon dioxide. Although carbon dioxide is also a pollutant, the increase in CO_2 emissions caused by oxidising the CO is very small compared with other emissions of CO_2.

Pollution of water

Rivers, lakes and the sea have been used as a place to dump wastes for a long time.

Factors that affect the concentration of pollutants

The water cycle is a natural purification process. When water evaporates as water vapour it is pure. It then falls as rain and flows to the sea carrying dissolved and suspended materials (including pollutants) with it. When the water evaporates, the pollutants are left behind and may become more concentrated.

Features of the water body

When wastes are released into the water they cause pollution. However, whether this becomes a problem is determined by the features of the water body and properties of the waste material released.

- ▼ **Effluent quantity**: the amount of pollutant released will clearly affect the concentration. If the concentration of pollutant in the water is low many pollutants are not harmful.
- ▼ **Volume of water**: the larger the body of water the more the waste will be diluted.
- ▼ **Residence time of the water**: The shorter the residence time of the water the more likely that the pollutant will be carried away by flowing water and not accumulate.

Factors which affect degradation

Degradation is the process by which substances are broken down. It involves both biotic and abiotic processes. Biodegradation involves microorganisms, while physical processes include chemical and photochemical reactions. A number of factors determine the rate at which degradation takes place.

High levels of sunlight or UV may cause photochemical degradation.

Dissolved oxygen: this increases the rate at which aerobic bacteria break down sewage.

Higher temperatures; these increase the rate of most reactions.

environmental conditions will also control the new substances produced. In aerated surface waters pollutants are more likely to be oxidised. Oxidation of organic pollutants often causes them to break down into less harmful substances. In deeper water where pollutants are part of the sediments they are likely to be chemically reduced, for example, inorganic mercury wastes being changed to methyl mercury, which is much more hazardous.

Removal rate

Pollutants become less of a problem if they become part of the sediment in a body of water. This effectively removes them from the water. Pollutants such as phosphates and pesticides can become adsorbed onto sediment particles.

Dispersal

Currents in the water will move pollutants away, dispersing them through the water so that the pollutants become diluted. Understanding where and how this happens can help determine where to locate suitable sites for effluent discharge.

The dilution of pollutants through dispersal in lakes and the sea can reduce the harmful effects and may give the impression that the pollutants have disappeared. In fact, pollutants that persist over time and do not biodegrade may gradually become more concentrated. If this becomes a problem, it may be difficult to solve due to the large volume of water affected.

There may also be processes which cause the pollutants to re-concentrate, for example, the bioaccumulation along a food chain of heavy metals and some pesticides.

Some water bodies are at particular risk of being polluted. See the table below.

Water bodies likely to be polluted

Cause of pollution	Examples of water bodies
Industrial areas	River Tees, River Tyne, River Danube, River Rhine
Areas with large human populations	River Ganges
Lakes and enclosed seas in which pollutants may collect	Mediterranean Sea, Great Lakes of North America
Heavy shipping	English Channel, Persian Gulf, St Lawrence Seaway
Oil terminals and ports	Rotterdam, Persian Gulf

Thermal pollution

The main source of hot water is steam turbine power stations that use cold water from a lake, river, or the sea to condense steam. The coolant water is returned to its source at a higher temperature.

Effects of thermal pollution

The warm effluent water can have ecological effects, especially on dissolved oxygen concentrations, as the maximum amount of oxygen that can dissolve in water is controlled by the temperature.

Most aquatic organisms will be killed by high temperatures because proteins (especially enzymes) are denatured. The few organisms that can survive above 40°C are said to be thermophilic (heat-loving). These high temperatures are rarely reached in aquatic ecosystems, even where hot effluents are being discharged. However, water at lower temperatures can still harm aerobic organisms indirectly because the solubility of oxygen declines as the temperature increases.

Low oxygen levels are rarely a problem in the atmosphere because each litre of air contains about 210cm³ of oxygen. Anaerobic conditions are normally only found where a volume of air has become enclosed and deoxygenating processes have occurred, for example, in the decomposition of organic matter. Deoxygenation is much more likely to be a problem in water because at 20°C a litre of water holds a maximum of 6cm³ of dissolved oxygen which is less than 3% of the amount found in air.

Some aquatic organisms are often near the lower end of their range of tolerance for dissolved oxygen. An increase in temperature may cause oxygen to come out of solution, leading to the death of sensitive organisms.

◀ *The relationship between temperature and the maximum possible amount of dissolved oxygen. Note: The line shows maximum levels. Processes which remove oxygen may result in values below the line, but values above the line are impossible as the water is already saturated with dissolved oxygen.*

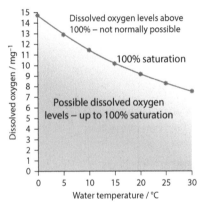

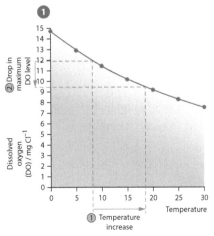

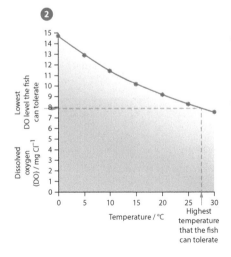

❶ *How an increase in temperature reduces the maximum dissolved oxygen level*

❷ *How the minimum dissolved oxygen level that a fish species can tolerate affects the maximum temperature they can survive*

▲ Hot condenser water being discharged from a power station

Higher water temperatures can also cause physiological changes:

- increased metabolic rates of many organisms, so more energy is used, leaving less surplus energy for growth;
- increased rate of development of eggs so they hatch earlier;
- non-indigenous species, introduced from habitats with warmer climates may thrive and out-compete indigenous species;
- pollutant toxicity is often greater as toxins are metabolised more rapidly;
- resistance to disease may be reduced.

Control of thermal pollution

Cooling towers are used to cool power station effluent water so that it does not cause deoxygenation.

Water used to condense steam in a power station is taken from a nearby water source such as a river, lake or the sea. After absorbing the heat from the steam, the water is returned at a higher temperature. In large bodies of water, such as lakes or the sea, the warmer water will disperse and be diluted into the large volume of cooler water so it has no significant effects. If the heated water goes into a relatively small body of water, such as a river or small lake, then it may cause a harmful temperature rise. In situations where this is likely to be the case, cooling towers are used to reduce the waste water temperature by dispersing the heat into the atmosphere, thereby returning cooler water to the source.

Cooling towers work by spraying the hot water from a shower floor in the lower part of a tall hollow tower. The air in the tower absorbs the heat from the water and rises up the tower, escaping into the open atmosphere. This causes an updraught which draws more air through the shower spray, aiding cooling.

A large (2000MW) power station uses 200 million litres of cooling water each hour which is returned at a temperature 5 to 8°C higher than its original temperature. The shower mixes the water with air so it is usually saturated with dissolved oxygen.

▲ Cooling towers that reduce the temperature of effluent water

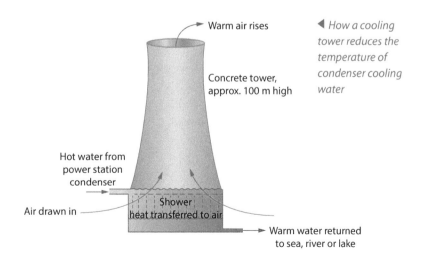

Warm air rises

Concrete tower, approx. 100 m high

Hot water from power station condenser

Air drawn in

Shower heat transferred to air

Warm water returned to sea, river or lake

◀ How a cooling tower reduces the temperature of condenser cooling water

Oil pollution

Oil pollution is caused by a variety of waste discharges and accidental releases. Some are point sources but most oil pollution comes from dispersed sources. Oil pollution harms living organisms directly, but it can also cause environmental changes that harm living organisms.

Causes of oil pollution

Waste lubricating oil
- Vehicle engine lubricating oil which leaks or is deliberately discarded into the environment.
- Industrial machine oil which is washed into drains, or mixed with other effluents.

Accidental releases
- Shipping accidents especially oil tankers.
- Oil rig accidents.
- Oil pipeline leaks.
- Leakage from storage tanks.
- Discharge of waste water from washing tanks on ship tankers.

▲ Wrecked cargo ships cause oil pollution from their fuel or the cargo on oil tankers

Oil exploration
Drilling. Drill pipes need to be lubricated to reduce friction as they bore through rock. This is usually done with fine clay suspended in water. Sometimes, oil-based clays are used, for example, where the rock would absorb the water and expand. The pollution risk with modern oil-based clay is reduced by using diesel and low toxicity oils rather than heavier oils.

Effects of oil pollution
- Some components of crude oil are toxic, such as benzene and xylene. Planktonic organisms that float near the water surface are most likely to be affected.
- Oil can cover aquatic life that lives on the seashore or at the sea surface. Animals such as molluscs and crustaceans can be asphyxiated. Algae on the seashore would be unable to absorb sunlight or carbon dioxide for photosynthesis.
- A severe covering of oil can cause birds to drown.
- Oil causes birds' feathers to stick together so they lose their insulating properties. The birds may die of hypothermia.

- Birds may be able to clean their feathers if they have a small amount of oil on them, but this may reduce the time available to find food for themselves or their young.
- Oil can form a very thin layer on the water surface which reduces the amount of oxygen that can dissolve from the atmosphere into the water. This can reduce the survival of aerobic organisms.
- Marine organisms which find mates or food using their sense of smell may have difficulties doing so because of the masking odour or narcotising effect of the oil.

Control of oil pollution

Prevention of oil releases

- **Recycling of waste lubrication oil:** used lubricating oil from vehicle engines, or engineering machinery, should not be treated as a waste material. Contaminants can be removed and chemical reforming and distillation can produce commercially valuable lubricants again. Waste oil that cannot be recycled can be burnt as fuel which reduces the demand for fuel from other sources.

▼ *A waste oil collection and recycling facility*

Improved oil tanker operation

- **Better shipping routes:** oil tankers may have to stay a greater distance away from the shore when possible. If a tanker has mechanical difficulties, such as engine failure, this would give more time to deal with it before it may be carried ashore by water currents or winds.
- **Better navigation systems:** new technologies such as GPS enable more accurate navigation. The Automatic Identification System (AIS) allows the positions of most ships to be monitored and coordinated to help avoid collisions.
- **Inert gas systems:** in the past when tankers unloaded their tanks at an oil terminal the space left by the oil used to fill up with air. This can produce an explosive mix of air and oil vapours which caused the loss of some tankers, causing pollution by the remaining oil in the tanks. Modern tankers use cooled exhaust gases from the engines to replace the oil. This has no oxygen in it so explosions are not possible.

- **Tank washing procedures:** oil tanks must be washed to prevent the build-up of tar sludges. Tanks used to be washed out with seawater then the oily water was discharged into the sea. This pollution is prevented by recirculating oil in the tanks during unloading so that the sludges are mixed up and removed with the cargo.
- **Oily waste water disposal:** any oily waste water that is produced can be unloaded at an oil terminal when the tanker docks. The oil and water can be separated, then the oil can be recycled, or incinerated, while the treated water is discharged.

▲ *Tankers unloading at an oil refinery*

Improved tanker design

- **Double hull:** tankers used to have a single layer of steel between the oil and the sea. Any damage to the steel hull could allow the release of oil into the sea. All large tankers now have twin hulls with a gap of up to 2m between the hulls so that damage to the outer hull does not necessarily cause the release of oil.

▼ **Twin engine/rudder/fuel tanks:** any mechanical failure on a tanker that affects propulsion or steering can be serious as the ship may be carried by currents or winds onto rocks or the coast. Having pairs of essential equipment can save the ship if one set breaks down.

❶ *A tanker with a single rudder*
❷ *A tanker with twin rudders*

▼ **Separate oil and ballast tanks:** when an oil tanker is not carrying oil it must carry ballast water so that the hull is kept down in the water and the propeller and rudder still work. In the past, the ballast water was carried in empty oil tanks. When the ballast water was pumped back into the sea it would carry some residual oil from the tanks. Modern tankers have separate oil and ballast water tanks so no pollution is caused by emptying the ballast tanks into the sea.

▶ *Features of oil tanker design that reduces the risk of oil pollution*

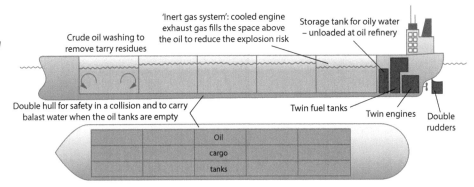

▶ *An oil interceptor*

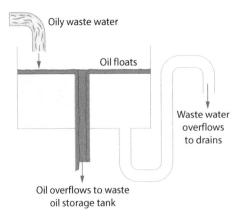

Oil interceptors: these separate oil from watery waste such as drainage water from major roads or car parks where there may be some floating oil. The water flows into the main drainage system or river but the oil is retained and can be removed later for treatment.

▼ **Bund walls:** oil storage tanks are built on impermeable bases surrounded by a bund wall which would contain the oil if the tank were to split. The volume enclosed by the bund wall is greater than that of the tank so it cannot overflow.

❶ *A bund wall that would enclose the oil if the tank split*
❷ *A bund wall around oil storage tanks*

Treatment of oil spills

In turbulent conditions in open water, most oil spills disperse in a few days or weeks. Lighter fractions such as petrol can evaporate and medium fractions will be digested gradually by bacteria, but heavier fractions may remain as tar balls for many years.

Oil pollution is most serious when it occurs inshore, or in an enclosed body of water, where dispersal is prevented, where there are more sensitive ecosystems or where there are more concentrated human activities to be affected.

Booms

Booms are inflatable tubes that restrict the movement of floating oil. A 'skirt' below the boom can retain oil if there is a water current. Booms do not work in open water where current or waves are too strong, so their main uses are in sheltered areas where they can reduce dispersal of oil from the pollution source or protect sensitive sites.

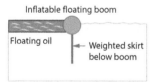

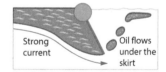

◀ *Oil booms reduce the dispersal of oil but they are not effective when water currents are strong*

❶ *Two oil rigs in a maintenance yard. Note the oil boom preventing the spread of any spilt oil.*
❷ *An oil boom on a refuelling tanker which can be deployed quickly if there is a spill*

261

Skimmers

Skimmers are rotating metal discs that pick up oil that can be scraped off and stored for later disposal by incineration or landfill.

Absorbent materials

High surface-area materials such as textile mops can help to absorb oil. The absorbent material and oil can be removed and disposed of by incineration or in landfill sites.

Detergents/dispersants

Detergents or dispersants break up the oil to produce an emulsion of oil droplets in water. They allow the oil to become more mobile and disperse, possibly to be broken down by bacteria but they do not reduce the amount of oil pollution themselves.

They can be spread at sea by aircraft and ships or using backpack sprayers on the shore.

Polymerising agents

Chemicals have been developed that cause the oil molecules to join together, producing more solid materials that can be collected more easily.

Steam washing

Oil on beaches can be washed off using sprays of steam and hot water. This does not destroy the oil, but it can remove it from particularly sensitive habitats. However, the steam jets may kill organisms deeper in the beach sediments that were not affected by the oil.

Bioremediation

Some bacteria break down hydrocarbons and help to remove the residual pollution left after other clean-up methods have been used. The rate of bacterial action depends on environmental conditions and is most rapid where temperatures, oxygen levels and nutrient levels are high. Bioremediation of soil may be accelerated by irrigation, the addition of nutrients and ploughing to aerate the soil.

▲ *Absorbent mops*

Pesticide pollution

Properties of pesticides that cause pollution

Pesticides are unusual pollutants because they are intended to be toxic and are deliberately spread into the environment. However, they do not just harm the target species.

❶ *Backpack pesticide sprayer* ❷ *Tractor spraying* ❸ *Aerial spraying: 'crop dusting'*

Specificity

No pesticides are so specific that they only kill the target organisms and are completely harmless to non-target organisms.

Harm to non-target species may be reduced by controlling the dose applied.

MDAF is the lowest dose that will kill every member of a population. It can be used to estimate the dose needed to control pests.

MDNF is the highest dose that can be used without killing any members of the population. Ideally, the pesticide dose would not exceed the MDNF of non-target species.

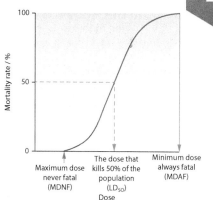

▲ LD_{50}, MDAF and MDNF are three important measures of the toxicity of a material

How the difference between MDAF and MDNF can affect the impact on non-target species

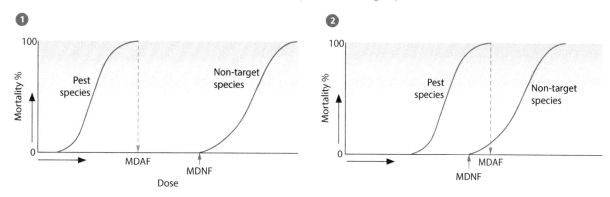

❶ The MDAF for the pest species is well below the MDNF of the non-target species so the dose that will kill all the pests will not kill any of the non-target species.

❷ The MDAF for the pest species is higher than the MDNF for the non-target species so killing all the pests may kill some of the non-target species. The impact on non-target species may be reduced by careful application such as spraying at night when bees are not flying.

Persistence

Persistent pesticides may remain in the environment long enough to disperse over larger areas and are more likely to have time to bioaccumulate and biomagnify.

Bioaccumulation

Liposoluble pesticides are those which dissolve into fats, for example, within the human body. If organisms are unable to excrete them or break them down fast enough some will accumulate in the body. Over a long period of time exposure, even to small doses, may eventually produce toxic concentrations.

Biomagnification

Pesticides which have bioaccumulated in one type of organism may become more concentrated when they are eaten by their predators.

Mobility

The mobility of a pesticide is controlled by other properties such as persistence, solubility and ease of vapourisation. Some pollutants may be transported within living organisms to new areas where they may be excreted.

Effects of pesticide pollution

Direct effects on living organisms

Pesticides cause harm to non-target species by being toxic. Doses which are not in themselves lethal may inhibit metabolic processes and cause ill health. Higher doses may kill. For example, DDT affected many birds by being concentrated within food chains. Low doses caused eggs to have thin shells which broke easily. Higher doses caused sterility. Much higher doses caused death. As a result, lower doses can still cause a species to die out as breeding success is reduced to below the rate needed to maintain the population.

Indirect effects on living organisms

A reduction in the population of one species can affect other inter-dependent species. Some species become rarer because they have lost a food supply or an ecosystem service such as pollination or seed dispersal. Other species may become more common because they have fewer competitors or predators.

The environmental impacts of selected insecticide groups

Organochlorines

Organochlorine insecticides were first used in the 1940s to control pests that transferred human pathogens such as the mosquitoes that carry malaria and the ticks, lice and fleas that carry typhus fever. This use of DDT saved many thousands of lives.

It was then used as an agricultural insecticide for which it had some ideal properties.

- ◤ High toxicity to insects
- ◤ Low toxicity to vertebrates including mammals, so farm workers were unlikely to suffer acute toxic effects.
- ◤ High persistence, so it continued to protect crops for some time after application.
- ◤ High liposolubility and low solubility in water so it was not easily washed off fields by heavy rain.

DDT was also used to control pests in homes by incorporating it in paint, wallpaper or in pest sprays.

However, its properties led to major environmental problems that were not initially understood.

The high toxicity to insects led to the deaths of many non-target insects such as bees, butterflies and beetles.

High persistence and liposolubility allowed DDT to bioaccumulate and biomagnify up food chains. The increase in concentration that occurred produced levels that are toxic to predatory vertebrates at the top of the food chain such as birds of prey, herons and otters. The use of organochlorines killed the top predators in many areas.

The rate of degradation of DDT depends upon environmental conditions but it can remain in the environment for decades.

Other major organochlorine insecticides include dieldrin, aldrin, and lindane.

The use of all organochlorine insecticides is now either banned or heavily restricted. DDT is still used to control malaria mosquitoes in houses. This is considered to be safe as it should not cause toxic exposure or lead to DDT entering the human food chain where it could biomagnify.

Organophosphates

Organophosphate pesticides are neurotoxins that inactivate the enzyme acetylcholinesterase so nerve function is damaged. The nerve gas Sarin is an organophosphate that was developed during the 2nd World War as a weapon. Other organophosphates were developed as insecticides, such as malathion and parathion.

Organophosphate use increased as the use of organochlorines declined.

They have low persistence and liposolubility so they do not bioaccumulate or biomagnify.

However, they have high mammalian toxicity so farm workers can be at risk of acute exposure to toxic doses, possibly causing death.

Chronic exposure to low doses is also associated with impaired memory, depression, behavioural changes, ADHD, Alzheimer's disease. Some organophosphates are suspected carcinogens.

Pyrethroids

Pyrethroids are synthetic insecticides that have been developed from natural pyrethrin insecticides extracted from plants.

They have high insect toxicity and low mammal toxicity. They are not persistent so they do not bioaccumulate or biomagnify.

Their use is generally safe for humans unless a very large dose is absorbed. Pyrethroids are the most commonly used domestic insecticides.

Pyrethroids are toxic to fish so should not be used near rivers or fish farms.

Neonicotinoids

These are the most widely used insecticides and are chemically similar to nicotine. They are neurotoxins, inhibiting the action of the neurotransmitter acetylcholine. They have high insect toxicity but lower toxicity to vertebrates as they cannot cross the blood-brain barrier of vertebrates.

They are relatively persistent and water soluble, so they remain in the soil long enough to be absorbed by roots and translocated within the crop plants which are then protected from insect pests.

Neonicotinoids are very toxic to bees and their use has been linked to the decline of many bee populations. They have neurotoxic effects, reducing their ability to navigate, and reducing their immunity to disease. Toxic effects are most likely when the neonicotinoids are sprayed onto the crop or when neonicotinoid dust is carried by the wind. Using neonicotinoids as a coated seed treatment minimises harmful impacts on non-target species.

The impact on non-target species appears to be increased by a synergist action with some fungicides that may be present at the same time.

Neonicotinoids are broken down most rapidly in the presence of sunlight and soil microbes. Some research suggests that neonicotinoids may build up in aquifers which may cause problems in the future.

Methods of reducing pesticide pollution

A range of methods can be used to reduce pesticide pollution. Some involve the ways that pesticides are used while others use alternative pest control methods.

Restrictions on use

Some pesticides have been banned, or their use has been restricted where they could cause problems, or when the benefit of use is greater than the disadvantages.

The use of the organochlorines DDT, dieldrin and aldrin is banned in most countries. DDT is still used in some countries for the control of malaria mosquitoes.

The organophosphate methyl parathion is still used as an agricultural insecticide, but its use is generally prohibited for control of garden or domestic pests.

Use of non-persistent pesticides

Pesticides which have low persistence will break down rapidly and cannot become more concentrated or travel long distances after application.

Organophosphate insecticides are less persistent than organochlorine insecticides.

Use of more specific pesticides

Pyrethroid and organochlorine insecticides are both toxic to insects but pyrethroids are less toxic to mammals.

Use of systemic pesticides

Systemic pesticides are absorbed by the crop and translocated within it. They do not need to be sprayed onto all surfaces, are not washed off after they have been absorbed, and will protect new growth.

As the systemic pesticides are present within the plant tissue, they may be eaten by humans if they are still present when the crop is eaten.

Application timing

Spraying on still days results in less spray drift onto surrounding habitats.

Spraying at night or when crops are not in flower will reduce the impact on bees.

Newer spraying techniques use smaller droplets to produce a more even coverage which reduces the amount required to adequately cover all areas of the crop leaves.

Non-pesticide techniques

For more details see page 314, Pest Control.

Inorganic nutrient pollution and cultural eutrophication

Nutrient enrichment of water bodies is a natural process as nutrients are washed in and accumulate, supporting increasingly rich food webs.

Sources of inorganic nutrients

▼ Phosphates in sewage effluent and eroded soil particles.

▼ Nitrates washed off farmland from manure and artificial fertilisers.

Effects of inorganic nutrient pollution

Cultural eutrophication

Eutrophication (Greek: eutrophia (from eu "well" + trephein "nourish".) is the enrichment of a water body with nutrients, usually with an excess amount of nutrients. As a result, plants and algae grow and may result in oxygen depletion of the water body. It can happen naturally over time, however it can also be a result of human activities such as the discharge of phosphate-containing detergents, fertilisers, or sewage, into an aquatic system. This 'cultural eutrophication' can also occur through clearing land and run-off, resulting in large quantities of nutrients that build up relatively rapidly. The main nutrients involved are nitrates and phosphates as these are often the limiting factors on plant growth in aquatic ecosystems.

▲ Cultural eutrophication in Lake Victoria, Africa

▼ Oligotrophic lakes – few nutrients, little plant growth, for example, mountain lakes.

▼ Eutrophic lakes – rich in nutrients, abundant plant growth, for example, lowland lakes.

▼ Algae and cyanobacteria absorb their nutrients directly from the water not from the sediments. This means that dissolved nutrients are used more easily although their levels may fluctuate rapidly. The growth of algae leads to a range of problems:

- cyanobacteria can release harmful toxins which can affect livestock, pets, and people who drink or are in contact with the water;
- floating algae shade the submerged or rooted macrophytes (larger plants) which cannot photosynthesise. The plants may die which disrupts food webs and their decay by aerobic bacteria may cause deoxygenation;
- algae are an unreliable food source and do not support rich food webs as they can die off rapidly if nutrients become depleted, or if other conditions are not ideal, for example, light or temperature.

At the end of summer, when warm temperatures cause dead vegetation to decay rapidly, the resulting deoxygenation kills off animal life. Deoxygenation is a particular problem at night when there is no photosynthesis to replace lost oxygen.

Effects of nitrates on human health

Nitrates are very soluble and may get into drinking water supplies. They may also be ingested in processed food.

① Unpolluted lake with rich foodwebs and high macrophyte (large plant) diversity

② Phosphates from sewage effluent and nitrates from farmland

Algae absorb nutrients and grow more rapidly than macrophytes

Algae shade macrophytes which reduces photosynthesis

③ Some algae (blue-green algae or cyanobacteria) release toxins

Livestock drink water and may die

Shaded macrophytes die, macrophyte-based food chains broken, higher trophic levels lose food

Decomposition of dead macrophytes reduces dissolved oxygen levels

④ Sediments formed of dead algae may be disturbed by storms, releasing nutrients and causing further algal blooms

Algae die when nutrients run out. Decomposition by bacteria depletes dissolved oxygen, killing fish, insect larvae and other aerobic organisms

▶ The processes involved in cultural eutrophication

Effect of nitrates on babies

Nitrates are not very toxic but bacteria in the gut convert them to nitrites. Nitrites react with haemoglobin in the blood and reduce its ability to carry oxygen. High levels may cause the disease methaemoglobinaemia or 'blue baby syndrome'. Infants are especially at risk as they have more of the necessary bacteria and their haemoglobin reacts more rapidly with nitrites. This is usually only a problem with water from shallow wells that receive drainage water from arable farmland. Nitrites are also ingested as food additives in meat, fish, and cheese products.

Nitrates and cancer

Gut bacteria convert nitrates to nitrites. These may then be converted in the gut to nitrosamines which are carcinogenic and may cause stomach cancer. Most research has been carried out on rats and the link between nitrates in water supplies and cancer in humans is not conclusive.

Control of inorganic nutrients

There are several ways that inorganic nutrients such as nitrates can be controlled through:

- reduced use of nitrate fertilisers;
- ploughing at times of heavy rain;
- use of soluble, rapid-release fertilisers;
- the depositing of waste manure where the nutrients could leach into the ground or be washed into a river;
- the cultivation of crops that have higher nitrogen requirements, for example, replacing wheat with triticale;
- the reliance on artificial fertilisers, for example, by growing more legume crops that have nitrogen-fixing root nodule bacteria.

These techniques are especially important in Nitrate Vulnerable Zones where aquifers may be exposed at the surface and can easily become contaminated.

Other ways to manage and limit the effects include:

- adding iron (III) sulfate to remove phosphates from liquid effluents released by sewage treatment works.. The phosphates are precipitated as a fine sediment of iron phosphate;
- dredging lakes and rivers that have phosphate-rich sediments from past pollution or adding iron (III) sulfur to reduce the solubility of the phosphates.

▶ Dredging phosphate-rich sediments from a lake in The Broads National Park.

Organic nutrient pollution

Source of organic nutrients

Many processes involving animal and plant products produce liquid effluents containing organic nutrients such as carbohydrates, lipids, and proteins. These processes include sewage works, manure disposal, silage storage, leather tanneries, paper mills, and food processing plants.

Effects of organic nutrient pollution

Deoxygenation

Untreated organic nutrients which flow into rivers or lakes provide food for microorganisms in the water. As a result, their aerobic digestion deoxygenates the water and may kill aerobic organisms such as fish and insects. The microorganisms can also cover the river or lake bed. This will prevent light reaching the normal water plants so that photosynthesis is inhibited, killing the plants and disrupting food webs. Eutrophication can also occur with organic nutrient pollution as microbial decay releases inorganic nutrients.

Pathogens

Sewage can contain pathogens from infected people. If other people come into contact with these pathogens, either directly or through contaminated food or water, the disease can spread. Diseases which spread via sewage and contaminated water include cholera, typhoid, and dysentery.

Inorganic nutrient release

Organic nutrients do not cause eutrophication directly as they provide nutrients for heterotrophs not nutrients for photoautotrophs. However, as they decay, they may release inorganic nutrients that cause eutrophication.

Treatment of organic effluents

It used to be common to discharge untreated sewage into rivers and the sea. This is now banned in many countries.

The main treatment processes used to treat organic nutrient effluents prevent deoxygenation of water bodies. Additional processes may be used to treat pathogens and inorganic nutrients.

Each sewage treatment works is designed to treat the specific effluent it receives to a satisfactory standard so the fluids can be discharged without causing unacceptable pollution. A higher standard may be required in more sensitive environments or where there are more people.

The effluent received by a sewage works is produced by a a range of activities such as toilet flushing water, water from washing clothes, dishes, personal hygiene; road drainage water; and non-toxic industrial waste. So, the actual concentration of sewage is actually very low (typically 250kg of water containing 2-3kg of liquid & solid sewage per person per day).

▲ *Untreated sewage being discharged into the Mediterranean Sea*

The main groups of treatment processes in activated sludge treatment

- ▰ pre-treatment – the removal of solid objects such as paper, plastic, road grit;
- ▰ primary treatment – the separation of most organic solids from fluids;
- ▰ secondary treatment – the digestion and breakdown of the remaining organic matter in the fluids;
- ▰ tertiary treatment – additional treatment to remove phosphates or bacteria;
- ▰ sludge treatment.

Pre-treatment methods

- ▰ Screens: metal grills or sieves are used to trap floating and suspended items such as plastic and paper items. These are then treated by incineration or disposed of in a landfill site.
- ▰ Grit traps for stones and road grit. Usually the channel widens out so that the effluent flows more slowly and the grit drops to the bottom as there is no longer enough kinetic energy to carry it along. The grit can later be removed from the tank then disposed of in a landfill site or by sterilisation and reuse.
- ▰ Comminutors chop up suspended faecal solids, increasing the exposed surface area and speeding up later processes.

❶ *Screens to trap non-biodegradable wastes*

❷ *A grit trap. The fluid flow slows down so road grit sinks to the bottom where it can be collected*

Primary treatment

Primary sedimentation is the most important process. The effluent is left to stand in large tanks where the faecal solids sink to the bottom so that they can be removed and treated separately. This results in over 95% of the organic matter being removed from the fluid effluent so the risk of deoxygenation in the river or lake is greatly reduced.

❶ *Primary sedimentation tank*

❷ *Anaerobic sludge digesters*

Sludge treatment

The sludge removed from the primary sedimentation tanks probably contains pathogens and its foul smell makes storage or disposal near urban areas difficult. To solve these problems anaerobic digestion is used. Anaerobic microbes digest the sludge in a warm digestion tank for about four weeks. This kills most pathogens and the odours are reduced. What remains after this process has a smaller volume which is disposed of in several ways:

- **landfill:** simple and relatively cheap but wastes their nutrient content;
- **dispersal in the sea:** relatively straightforward for coastal communities but most countries now ban this to reduce pollution;
- **incineration:** a lot of fuel (usually natural gas) is required and is therefore expensive. This also creates further waste in the form of gas and a small amount of ash which is deposited in landfill sites;
- **agricultural use:** the sludge can be used as an agricultural fertiliser. It has a better C:N ratio, has a lower volume and a lower odour than undigested sludge. It is important to time spreading carefully as application during the growing season would cover the crops, while application during the winter can cause damage to the damp soils as farm vehicles compact the soil. Heavy metals from urban wastes and road runoff may be present in the sludge and could be absorbed by crops and then be consumed with food. This can be reduced by adding lime to reduce the solubility of the heavy metals. Remaining pathogens can be destroyed by heat treatment of the sludge before use.

Anaerobic digestion also produces biogas which is mainly methane with some carbon dioxide. This can be used as a fuel, for example, to heat the digester, nearby buildings, or to generate electricity.

Secondary treatment

Secondary treatment destroys the small amount of organic matter that remains in the effluent from the primary sedimentation tank.

- **Aeration tanks/oxidation ponds:** the remaining organic matter in the fluid effluent is broken down by bacteria. Shortage of oxygen can be a limiting factor as it slows down this aerobic process. To prevent this happening, large amounts of air are mixed in by paddle wheels, or air stones. Pure oxygen may also be used.
- **Secondary sedimentation tanks:** the effluent from the aeration tanks contains suspended bacteria which must not be wasted. These are collected in the secondary sedimentation tank and returned to the aeration tank as 'activated sludge'. In most sewage works, the clear effluent from secondary treatment is discharged into the river, lake, or sea. It should contain no pathogens, or other organic materials, but it may contain some dissolved inorganic nutrients which could cause cultural eutrophication.

❶ Aeration tank
❷ Overflow from a secondary sedimentation tank

Trickling filter beds: these provide an alternative process to aeration tanks. It is an older technique that has been largely replaced by the use of aeration tanks in activated sludge treatment. Four rotating arms spray the liquid effluent over large cylindrical tanks containing lumps of a solid material such as gravel, coke, or blast furnace clinker. The surface area is maximised for bacteria, fungi, algae, worms, fly larvae, and other invertebrates to digest remaining organic matter. Nitrates may also be denitrified by bacteria so the liquid effluent will cause less eutrophication.

▲ *The effluent from sewage may pass over a weir to ensure the water is aerated to increase its dissolved oxygen concentration*

Tertiary treatment

Tertiary treatment is used if the discharge site for the treated effluent is particularly ecologically sensitive or important for humans.

▶ phosphates can be removed by adding a solution of iron(III) sulfate producing insoluble iron phosphate as a fine sediment which can be used as an agricultural fertiliser.

▶ the effluent can be strained through very fine sieves called micro-strainers. The remaining suspended bacteria are killed by UV light or by adding a sterilising chemical such as chlorine.

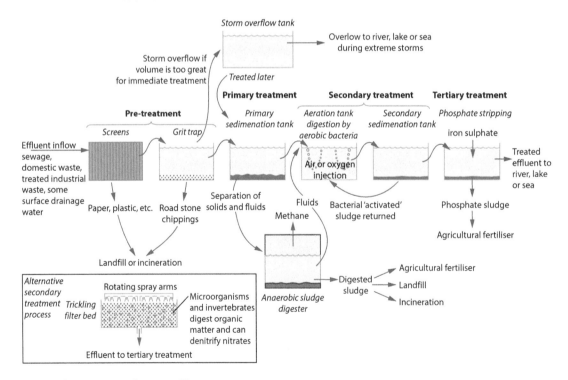

▲ *Processes in the treatment of sewage effluent*

Weather-related fluctuations in flow volume

While the volume of sewage remains relatively stable through the year the volume of effluent received by a treatment works can vary significantly with changes in weather, for example, as a result of a storm or a drought. Sewage works are designed to cope with some extra flow but not the maximum flow that is possible. To do this would incur great extra expense to allow for very rare extreme storm events. Most sewage works have storm overflow tanks that can be used to hold surplus effluent after a storm. This is treated later when the volume of effluent arriving returns to normal.

Types of sewage collection systems

In the UK, the majority of sewage systems were developed over the last 150 years. Underground pipes were laid to collect all solid and liquid effluents often including drainage water from roads and roofs. Originally these were discharged into the river or sea untreated, or onto fields in 'sewage farms'. Sewage treatment works were added later. This approach produces large volumes of dilute sewage effluent.

It is more efficient to have two separate waste collection systems. One collects only foul waste from toilets which requires full treatment but the smaller volume involved allows the construction of smaller, and therefore cheaper, sewage treatment works. It also means that the system is not affected by flow fluctuations caused by weather changes. The second system collects the larger volumes of cleaner water. This requires little treatment before discharge.

Acid mine drainage

Many igneous metal ores are sulfides. In spoil heaps chemical reactions take place between the small amounts of remaining sulfide ores and oxygen from air in the spaces between the waste particles. This may leave metal oxides and oxides of sulfur which dissolve in drainage water to produced sulfuric acid. This is known as acid mine drainage.

Effects of acid mine drainage

The acidic solutions that leach out of the spoil heap have similar effects to acid rain leaching through soil. See page 250, Acid rain. The pH of the solutions is often very low and may contain dissolved toxic metals if they were present in the mine waste.

Control of acid mine drainage

The pH of the drainage water can be increased by passing it through crushed limestone to neutralise the acids. This will also reduce the solubility of many toxic metals.

▲ *A spoil heap at an old lead mine on Dartmoor, Devon*

Monitoring water pollution

A wide range of physical, chemical and biological methods can be used to monitor water pollution. Most pollutants can be monitored using a chemical or physical method. Modern methods usually use a calibrated electronic meter. A number of factors determine which methods are selected:

- speed of data collection;
- level of expertise required;

- ▶ degree of accuracy;
- ▶ indication of long-term historical pollutant levels;
- ▶ methods that are specific to individual pollutants;
- ▶ measurement of the effects of pollution rather than the levels of the pollutant itself.

Some methods of pollution monitoring measure the impacts rather than the cause. This is usually done when a range of pollutants may be involved and it is difficult to distinguish between their individual effects or which direct measure should be used.

Biological or Biochemical Oxygen Demand (BOD)

Organic materials of plant or animal origin can provide food for bacteria and lead to deoxygenation as they respire anaerobically.

It is difficult to measure or forecast the levels of organic pollutants because there are so many that could be present and they have different potentials to cause deoxygenation. So, organic pollution is monitored through the level of deoxygenation that is caused. The amount of oxygen being used is measured under standardised conditions.

Standardised conditions for BOD measurement

Feature	Method of standardisation
Water volume	1 litre of water
Temperature	20°C
Time period	5 days
Light level	In the dark (to prevent oxygen replacement by photosynthesis if algae are present in the water)

Chemical Oxygen Demand (COD)

This is similar to BOD but measures the amount of oxygen needed to chemically oxidise all the organic and inorganic substances in a water sample.

Coliform count

One of the more common gut bacteria is *E. coli*. Its presence in water is taken as confirmation of faecal contamination. The health risk can be determined by measuring the number of coliform bacteria in a sample as this indicates how serious the contamination is. It is better to monitor this than the presence of pathogens such as typhoid as these will not always be present and whose absence would not confirm that the water is uncontaminated.

Biotic indices

A Biotic Index is a scale for showing the quality of an environment by indicating the types of organisms that are present.

Characteristics of species used in biotic indices:

- ▶ have different sensitivities to pollution;
- ▶ are easy to identify;
- ▶ are easy to find;
- ▶ are normally present;
- ▶ are usually common;
- ▶ are generally distributed.

Advantages and disadvantages of biotic indices

Advantages	Disadvantages
A rapid assessment of current and recent pollution can be made. Expensive equipment is not required.	Sorting samples can be time-consuming. Identification of different taxa involves some skill. Further tests are required using other techniques to detect the specific pollutants present.

Commonly used biotic indices

▼ Lichens to monitor atmospheric acidic pollution.

▼ Aquatic invertebrates to monitor water pollution.

Heavy metals

Key properties

Pollution caused by heavy metals is affected by properties such as liposolubility, synergism, and solubility.

Many heavy metals inhibit enzyme function, especially the enzymes of the nervous system.

Heavy metals that are liposoluble may be stored in fat droplets in living cells so that chronic exposure to small doses may eventually produce toxic concentrations. by bioaccumulation. Passage along a food chain may lead to biomagnification.

Some heavy metals cause more serious pollution if they act in conjunction with other pollutants such as synergism between cadmium and zinc.

Most heavy metals are more soluble at low pH. Therefore pollution caused by heavy metal wastes can be reduced by increasing the pH to reduce solubility.

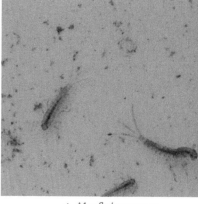

▲ *Mayfly larvae are indicator species for unpolluted water*

Lead

Lead has been used to make many products including car batteries, pipes, solder, paint, anti-knock petrol additives and flashing for roofs and windows on buildings. Some of these uses have been reduced or stopped because of the increasing awareness of the toxicity of lead.

Sources of lead pollution

The biggest uses of lead do not necessarily cause pollution because they may not cause the release of lead into the environment.

The uses of lead that cause pollution have been restricted but uses that do not cause pollution continue, for example, lead-acid batteries, lead flashing used in building construction.

❶ *A discarded lead-acid battery*
❷ *The rainwater flowing over this lead roof flashing inhibits the growth of moss and lichens*

Industrial workers may inhale lead dust or absorb it through the skin if it dissolves in sweat.

Acute exposure to large doses may cause severe symptoms including brain damage, paralysis and eventually death. Very high doses can kill by causing liver and kidney failure. These problems are only likely in industrial accidents and are prevented by good working practices, for example, wearing facemasks, using water sprays or remote operations.

Control of lead pollution

- **Water pipes:** lead has been used to make water pipes for over 4,500 years. Small amounts of lead dissolve into the water so people drinking the water may suffer chronic exposure. In the UK, most lead piping was replaced in the 20th century with copper pipes, although lead solder was still used to join copper pipes. Lead solder has now been replaced with solder based on tin, zinc, and copper. Water companies in the UK no longer use lead pipes, but some may remain in old buildings. In high risk areas, small amounts of phosphoric acid are added to the water supply. This produces an insoluble layer of lead phosphate in the pipes which prevents lead dissolving into the water.

- **Petrol additives:** anti-knock agents such as tetra ethyl lead (TEL) were added to petrol to smooth the explosion of combustion and reduce engine wear. However, lead particulates were released into the atmosphere which created a public health threat. Since the 1980s lead has been replaced with other chemicals such as benzene. Other fuels such as diesel, LPG, hydrogen, and alcohol do not need lead additives.

- **Electrical solder:** lead-based solder used in electrical connections is not a significant threat to public health during use. However, the lead can be vapourised and inhaled when it is melted during soldering, or if it is melted during recycling after use. Lead-free solder is now widely used and contains tin, silver, and copper.

- **Lead-based paint:** lead compounds have been added to paint to accelerate drying and increase durability. Paint layers that are intact on surfaces pose a small health risk but dusty, flaking old paint does pose a much greater health risk, especially to children who pick up particles under their fingernails and suck their fingers.
  The removal of old paint can be a health risk as dust or vapours produced may be inhaled. The use of lead-based paints has been phased out in many countries since the 1980s. Chemical paint strippers and hot air guns are safer paint removal methods as they do not produce dust or vapours containing lead.

- **Fishing weights:** lead weights that are used on fishing lines may be discarded or lost then swallowed by waterfowl such as swans who mistake them for snails. The swans may be killed by lead poisoning. Lead has been phased out in the UK for smaller fishing weights and replaced with metals such as tungsten which is less toxic.

- **Shotgun pellets:** most shotgun pellets miss their target and land on the ground. Water birds such as ducks and geese that feed on wetlands, where shooting has taken place, may swallow pellets and be poisoned. Some voluntary schemes use alternative materials such as tungsten steel for shotgun pellets that are used over wetlands.

Mercury

Sources of mercury pollution

Mercury is released into the environment in a number of ways:

- disposal of items containing mercury, for example, batteries, fluorescent lights, thermometers;

▼ chemical plants that produce chlorine using mercury electrodes;

▼ combustion of coal.

The effect of chemical form on the toxicity of mercury

The severity of mercury pollution depends upon its chemical form:

▼ liquid (elemental) mercury is not easily absorbed through the skin or gut, although vapours may be absorbed in the lungs if they are inhaled;

▼ inorganic mercury compounds such as mercury oxide are absorbed moderately well in the gut;

▼ organic mercury compounds such as methyl mercury are absorbed easily through the skin, by the gut, and as vapours if they are inhaled. Organic mercury compounds are liposoluble so they pass through cell membranes easily, including through the blood-brain barrier into the brain where the impacts can be more serious. It can also cross the placenta and harm unborn babies. Mercury also causes kidney damage.

In some situations, less toxic forms of mercury have been released but the pollution problems created have been very severe. Relatively low toxicity inorganic mercury compounds that enter anaerobic sediments in lakes or the sea may be changed into organic compounds such as methyl mercury by anaerobic microbes. The mercury then bioaccumulates and biomagnifies along foodchains, often reaching concentrations that are much higher than when it was released into the environment.

The biomagnification of mercury in a lake

Level in food chain	Mercury concentration / ppb	Concentration factor from level below	Concentration compared with water (approx.)
Fish eating birds	4 900	x 7	x 49 000 000
Large fish	700	x 7	x 7 000 000
Small fish	100	x 6.7	x 1 000 000
Invertebrates	15	x 7.5	x 150 000
Algae	2	x 20 000	x 20 000
Water	0.0001	-	-

Control of mercury pollution

Many uses of mercury and effluent disposal methods have been restricted as the understanding of mercury pollution problems have increased, for example:

▼ mercury thermometers have been replaced by alcohol or electronic thermometers;

▼ mercury can be removed from effluents by reverse osmosis, or by using activated carbon filters.

▼ ion exchange filters.

▼ disposal at high pH to reduce solubility.

Cadmium

Cadmium pollution is caused by:

▼ the disposal of old nickel-cadmium batteries;

▼ the incineration of wastes containing cadmium pigments, for example, some plastics and paints;

- drainage water from cadmium and zinc mines (cadmium and zinc are often found together).

One of the few new uses of cadmium is in cadmium-telluride photovoltaic solar panels. Manufacture and eventual disposal of old panels may cause pollution.

Effects of cadmium

Cadmium is liposoluble and bioaccumulates so chronic exposure can lead to toxic concentrations and it can biomagnify in food chains. Cadmium causes:

- brain damage and paralysis;
- lung cancer;
- kidney failure;
- skeletal collapse caused by bone decalcification.

Control of cadmium pollution

Most uses of cadmium have been restricted or banned, such as its use in pigments. Cadmium waste should be disposed of in a hazardous waste landfill site or may be recycled, for example, nickel-cadmium batteries.

Tin

▲ A boat being cleaned to remove marine growth

In the past, tin was used in antifouling paint on the bottom of boats to control the growth of marine organisms that create friction and slow boats down. The active chemical was tri-butyl tin (TBT) which is toxic to marine organisms such as molluscs and crustaceans and so prevented their growth.

It had been assumed that the small amount of TBT that dissolved into the sea would not be concentrated enough to cause problems. However, TBT is an endocrine disruptor that alters the growth and reproductive physiology of marine organisms such as oysters and whelks. It can then also pass into humans when such shellfish are eaten.

TBT is now prohibited in anti-fouling paint. It has been replaced with less toxic metals such as copper. Some countries also require paint residues produced by boat cleaning to be disposed of in a chemical waste landfill site rather than being washed into the sea.

Iron

Effects of iron pollution

Iron is not a toxic pollutant but it can cause deoxygenation when it is oxidised in water.

▶ Deoxygenation of a river caused by iron leached out of a spoil heap

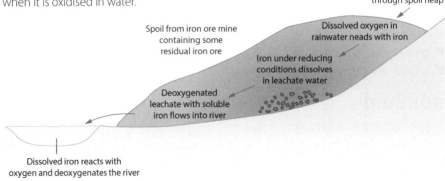

Rainware percolates through spoil heap

Spoil from iron ore mine containing some residual iron ore

Dissolved oxygen in rainwater reads with iron

Iron under reducing conditions dissolves in leachate water

Deoxygenated leachate with soluble iron flows into river

Dissolved iron reacts with oxygen and deoxygenates the river

Iron is soluble in its chemically reduced form (low oxygen conditions). Iron in mine spoil heaps, where there is little oxygen, is soluble and may be leached into a river by water draining through the spoil heap. In the river it will be oxidised and be deposited as an insoluble sediment of iron oxide. The process of oxidation may deoxygenate the river causing the death of aerobic organisms.

❶ Iron-rich leachate from an iron mine spoil heap is oxidised in the river

❷ Mesh screens on which iron is deposited before it could enter the river

Control of iron pollution

Spoil heap drainage water is collected and passed over mesh screens where the iron becomes oxidised and is deposited on the mesh so when the water flows into the river there is no longer a risk of deoxygenation. The solid iron is periodically removed from the mesh.

Solid wastes

Solid wastes are produced by many human activities. Their environmental impacts and the choice of disposal method depend upon the materials involved. Some are produced in large quantities but are relatively harmless while others are produced in small quantities but may be very hazardous.

Sources of solid wastes

Mining and construction wastes

Mining and the construction industry produce large quantities of waste. Most are non-hazardous but some can cause problems because they include particular hazardous materials.

- ▼ Mine overburden heaps – usually non-toxic.
- ▼ Mine spoil heaps – may contain toxic metals.
- ▼ Demolition waste – may contain hazardous materials such as asbestos.

Domestic and commercial municipal waste

Main categories

- ▼ Packaging and containers.
- ▼ Paper.
- ▼ Domestic appliances.
- ▼ Organic materials - food and garden waste.
- ▼ Clothing and other textiles.

Waste management problems:

- large quantities of waste are produced;
- every household across the country produces waste which makes collection labour intensive and expensive.
- the mix of waste varies through the year, for example, more garden waste during the summer;
- many different types of waste are mixed together.

Industrial waste

The majority of industries generate solid wastes. Disposal problems will depend on the properties of the specific waste involved and the amount produced.

Properties of solid wastes

Important properties of solid wastes that influence the choice of disposal methods include:

- degradability - how rapidly the waste breaks down;
- conditions that affect degradation, for example, oxygen, pH, temperature, presence of bacteria;
- flammability;
- release of radioactivity;
- toxicity.

Waste production and affluence

Affluence has a significant effect on the amount of waste generated as more affluent people are more likely to do the following:

- purchase more consumer goods.
- purchase more trivia.
- purchase disposable items.
- throw items away rather than repair them.

These activities also increase the wastes produced in the manufacture of goods and the mineral extraction required to make the items.

Manufacturing and retail industries may attempt to increase sales using strategies that also increase wastes, for example:

- **built-in obsolescence:** items are designed to have a short lifespan. For example, they are made to be non-durable or wear out. Or there may be changing fashions so that items become out-dated and are discarded. The customer can then 'upgrade' to the latest models;
- **disposable products:** items intended to have a limited usable life so they need to be replaced sooner such as disposable razors, cigarette lighters, ballpoint pens;
- **over-packaging:** items may be made more attractive with unnecessary packaging that is likely to be thrown away.

Some products have very large amounts of packaging to make them more attractive

Solid waste disposal

Large amounts of solid wastes are deliberately or accidentally dumped into the environment. Such waste including litter can harm wildlife that becomes caught in it or swallows it.

▼ *Litter washed up on a beach*

Plastic wastes can degrade to become small particles that can choke marine organisms or release chemicals that may be endocrine disruptors.

Factors affecting waste disposal methods

Many disposal methods are available for solid wastes. The method selected can be affected by the following factors:

- population density, for example, collection costs are higher where there are fewer people and the wastes are dispersed;
- mass of waste produced per capita;
- properties of the wastes, for example, toxicity, flammability;
- land availability;
- availability of recycling technology;
- degree of environmental awareness and willingness of people to recycle, reuse, repair;
- regulatory framework and legislation;
- household income;
- waste processing costs for labour or machinery.

Landfill

This is often the simplest option for disposal as it requires little or no treatment of the waste itself. However, early landfill sites were poorly managed, being used for mixed wastes with little attempt to prevent the escape of harmful fluids and gases.

Features of good landfill site management

- Separation of different waste types and recording of their composition and locations.
- Polymer liner to prevent the escape of leachate fluids.
- Perimeter fence to trap litter blown by winds.
- Regular covering with soil to reduce pest problems.
- Collection and treatment of leachate fluids.
- Collection of methane and its use as a fuel.
- Impermeable cap to prevent water entering once the site is complete: usually layers of clay and polymer.
- Deodorising spray to control odours.
- Dispersal of flammable materials rather than dumping large quantities in one place.
- Chemicals which may react with each other should not be dumped together.

❶ *An unregulated landfill site*
❷ *Waste gases being collected which will then be incinerated.*
❸ *A leachate sampling point at a landfill site*
❹ *Domestic waste being carried by barge on the River Thames*

Disadvantages of landfill

▼ The potential resource value is lost, such as metals , glass, plastics.

▼ Landfill sites use large areas of land.

▼ Organic matter decays anaerobically, releasing methane gas and carbon dioxide contributing to global warming.

▼ Toxic leachate may leak from poorly managed landfill sites.

▼ Wildlife habitats and farmland may be lost.

▼ Contaminants in the landfill site may prevent the later development of landfill sites for uses such as housing or agriculture.

▼ Transport delivering the waste to the site and the infrastructure around it generate noise and congestion in the local area.

▶ *Landfill site management*

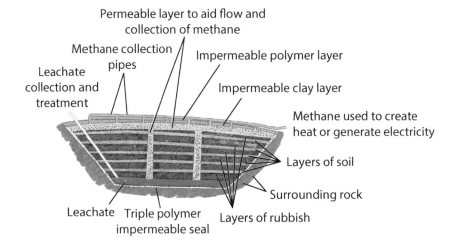

Spoil heaps

Industrial spoil usually involves large quantities of non-toxic solids so the main problem is the quantity, but it can also produce polluting leachate fluids.

A wide range of industrial activities produce spoil, such as:

▼ mining and quarrying, for example, coal, china clay, metal ores;

▼ coal-fired power stations and incinerators produce ash;

▼ iron blast furnaces produce slag.

Management, reclamation and remediation of spoil heaps

Spoil heaps need to be managed to minimise environmental problems. They can also be managed to make site reuse easier after site closure. To do this successfully a range of possible problems need to be solved.

▼ **Stability:** landslips are a danger. Surface erosion can be reduced by establishing vegetation so the roots hold the spoil together. Stability can be improved through compaction, either by compacting the spoil heap as it is built up, or by constructing buildings on concrete rafts to reduce uneven settling. This reduces the danger of subsidence.

- **Drainage:** natural or artificial drainage may be essential where spoil heaps are tall or on hillsides to reduce the risk of landslides following heavy rain.
- **Lack of nutrients:** some spoil contains low levels of plant nutrients, for example, the sand left after china clay extraction or shale spoil from coal mining. The addition of topsoil, sewage sludge and fertilisers are common techniques to improve the nutrient content and increase plant growth.
- **pH:** the addition of lime can reduce the acidity of spoil, for example, where sulphides in the spoil produce sulfuric acid. Spoil is rarely too alkaline to support plant growth. Old steel works can leave alkaline waste which can be valuable for uncommon plants such as cowslips.
- **Contamination:** Phytoremediation can be used where plants are used for the absorption and storage of pollutants such as heavy metals, mercury. Petrochemical waste such as oil can be treated by bioremediation. Certain species of bacteria will digest the oil if appropriate conditions of temperature, water supply, and aeration are maintained.
- **Topography:** spoil heaps can be unattractive with steep slopes and angular shapes. Landscaping can be used to reshape the heap, although this may require more land.
- **Toxic leachates:** these should be collected and treated to prevent them entering water courses. Deeper layers of soil should be applied during restoration so that plant roots cannot reach the layer containing toxic materials. This could bring toxins to the surface and cause their dispersal into the wider environment.
- **Heavy metals:** these are a problem when they are mobile in the environment. They can be inhaled or may be ingested in food or water. This can be prevented by disposing of them in solid form under alkaline conditions. This means the metals should remain insoluble as their solubility is usually reduced with increasing pH. To prevent dust particles, heavy metals should be covered so that the they cannot become airborne.
- **Flammable wastes:** Coal or shale oil production spoil can contain high proportions of hydrocarbons which can result in spontaneous combustion within the heap. This risk can be reduced with regular layers of fine-grained material to reduce air flow.

Incineration

This involves the destruction of wastes by high temperature oxidation.

❶ A domestic waste incinerator and energy recovery plant.
❷ Waste being stored and mixed before incineration.

Advantages of incineration

▶ The volume of ash produced is much less than the original waste.

▶ The heat produced may be used for district heating or the generation of electricity.

▶ No sorting or complicated management is needed.

▶ Flammable materials such as plastics and dirty paper & card can be separated and burnt in purpose-built power stations, or used for industrial heat such as cement manufacture. Large quantities of a single flammable waste can be used to produce a fuel for specific purposes.

Fuels can be created, for example, Refuse-Derived Fuel (RDF) pellets of shredded compacted flammable municipal waste and Tyre-Derived Fuel (TDF) made from shredded vehicle tyres, sometimes mixed with coal, wood or other fuels.

Disadvantages of incineration

▶ The resource value of recyclable materials is lost.

▶ Toxic dioxins may be produced by reaction of organic wastes and chlorine.

▶ The fuel used to maintain combustion of wet or non-flammable wastes is expensive.

▶ The wastes may need be separated to remove wet wastes, increasing processing costs.

▶ The treatment of atmospheric pollutants in the effluent gases increases costs.

Features of good domestic waste incinerators

▶ Recyclable wastes are removed before incineration.

▶ Wastes with a high water content are removed, for example, compostable waste.

▶ The combustion temperature is kept high and waste gases are cooled rapidly to reduce dioxin production.

▶ The heat produced is harnessed for use.

▶ Atmospheric pollution is controlled: SO_2, NOx, HCl, CO, smoke/PM10.

▶ Flammable organic wastes may be chemically broken down by incineration. The hydrocarbon component of the molecule will be converted to carbon dioxide and water. These are not serious problems as they will be produced in small quantities, compared with other sources such as vehicle fuel use.

▶ Some materials produced during the incineration process may need additional treatment.

▶ Chlorine atoms, for example, from CFCs, will react to create hydrogen chloride. This dissolves to form hydrochloric acid and causes acid pollution. A water spray 'scrubber' can be used to dissolve and remove it from gaseous emissions. The acid produced can then be neutralised by treating it with an alkali or crushed limestone.

▶ Heavy metals can be removed by scrubbing then stored in solid form at high pH, making them insoluble and less mobile.

Specialist wastes

If highly hazardous wastes are released into the environment they will cause serious pollution. Specialised storage or treatment techniques are likely to be required to avoid such pollution. Different techniques are used for different types of hazardous waste.

▶ **Asbestos:** asbestos is dangerous if it disintegrates and the fibres become airborne so they can be inhaled. The fibres can cause irritation and lead to asbestosis. Scar tissue produced in the lungs thickens the alveoli so gaseous exchange is slowed and breathing becomes more difficult. Asbestos can also cause a particular type of cancer:

mesothelioma. This is a cancer of the tissue that covers many internal organs, including the lungs. It can take decades to develop but it is not usually difficult to identify the cause as over 80% of mesothelioma cases are caused by asbestos.

◀ *Fly-tipped asbestos*

Asbestos has been used to strengthen cement roof panels. It can also be found in textured ceilings coverings. As long as the asbestos is encapsulated and remains intact it is not dangerous. Asbestos wastes require special handling. They need to be double wrapped in heavy-duty polythene bags in a specialised landfill site where the waste contents are recorded.

▛ **Cyanide wastes:** Cyanide compounds include triple bonds between carbon and nitrogen atoms. A fourth bond links the carbon atom to an element such as hydrogen or sodium Cyanide compounds are used in the manufacture of paper, textiles and plastics. Electroplating, metal cleaning and gold extraction all use salts of cyanide. Cyanide compounds can be very toxic enzyme inhibitors that may be inhaled or ingested. Incineration is the safest way to dispose of cyanide wastes so that the carbon and nitrogen are separated and oxidised. The carbon dioxide and oxides of nitrogen produced are a much smaller pollution problem.

Encapsulation and vitrification

Some wastes are so hazardous that they must be stored using a method where they become immobile and could not leak out in the future.

▛ **Encapsulation:** hazardous wastes containing heavy metals such as arsenic, mercury, nickel, and chromium residues and intermediate level radioactive waste are mixed with a cement slurry which is poured into containers made of an impermeable and unreactive material. The solid cement encapsulates the waste so it is immobilised.

▛ **Vitrification:** this is a specialist encapsulation technique used for the storage of high-level radioactive waste that has been extracted from used nuclear fuel. Powdered radioactive waste is mixed with molten glass and poured into stainless steel containers which are then sealed. The glass solidifies encapsulating the waste. Even if the glass were shattered, the waste would remain encapsulated in the fragments. The steel containers are placed in cylindrical passages inside a concrete building. The passages are ventilated to remove the heat generated within the waste.

Noise

Noise is sound that is unwanted because it is disturbing or causes damage. Noise pollution has limited impact on wildlife and the ability of the Earth to support life. However, it can have serious impacts on human quality of life and health.

The logarithmic nature of the dB scale

▶ *The exponential relationship between sound pressure and the decibel scale*

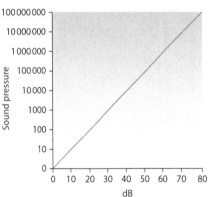

The human ear is sensitive to a very wide range of sound power levels so a logarithmic scale is used: the Bel. Each Bel is divided into ten decibels. An increase in volume of 10dB represents a ten-fold increase in sound volume. An increase of 3dB represents a doubling in volume.

0 dB does not mean there is no sound. It is set as the quietest sound that can be heard at 1000Hz and is called the threshold of human hearing.

The frequency range of human hearing

Sound vibrations passing through the air are detected in the cochlea of the inner ear by hair-like projections on sensitive nerve cells. Each group of cells is sensitive to a particular sound frequency. The typical range of hearing for young people is 20 – 20 000Hz. Older people generally have a reduced frequency range, especially at higher frequencies and require a higher volume for sounds to be detectable. Exposure to excessive noise and some health issues can also reduce sensitivity and range.

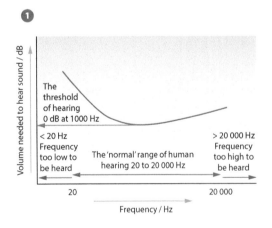

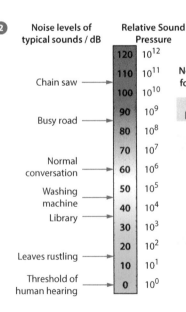

❶ *Frequency range and sensitivity of human hearing*
❷ *Relationship between noise levels, sound pressure and noise exposure limits*

Noise exposure limits for workers in the UK

Noise level / dB	Time limit
103	7½ mins
100	15 mins
97	30 mins
94	1 hr
91	2 hrs
88	4 hrs
85	8 hrs

Effects of noise

Effects of noise on non-living objects

▶ **Acoustic fatigue:** some objects have a frequency at which they will naturally vibrate: their natural resonant frequency. If they are exposed to sound at this frequency then they will vibrate. This may eventually cause stress cracking and structural failure called 'acoustic fatigue'. Acoustic fatigue in early aircraft jet engines led to improved designs to prevent cracking in the engine cowling.

▶ **Vibration damage:** repetitive vibration can cause structural damage to buildings, bridges, and underground pipes. This can be caused by the vibrations created by the wheels of heavy vehicles.

▶ **Shock impacts:** the force of the impact of a sudden very loud noise can cause damage, such as the 'sonic boom' of supersonic aircraft causing structural damage to buildings, for example, broken windows and dislodged masonry.

Effects of noise on living organisms

Effects on humans

▶ **Hearing damage:** this is usually caused by long-term occupational exposure to loud machinery, especially to high frequency sounds.

▶ **Stress-related health problems:** long-term exposure to high noise levels can cause ulcers, high blood pressure, and heart disease.

▶ **Behavioural changes:** noise can also cause behavioural changes such as irritability, aggression, or a lack of concentration, which may lead to accidents.

▶ **Communication problems:** high background noise levels can make it difficult to hear others talking. Children in schools beneath airport flight paths may underperform educationally.

Effects on other organisms

▶ **Livestock:** sudden noises such as low-flying aircraft may cause animals to panic, leading to injuries or breeding failure.

▶ **Disturbance of breeding birds:** birds that sing to establish their territories or attract mates may have difficulties in urban areas because of background noise levels. Birds scared by sudden noises may leave their nests, allowing predators to take eggs or chicks. Cliff-nesting birds may knock eggs or chicks into the sea if they are frightened by low-flying aircraft.

▶ **Reduced feeding success:** animals that use hearing to find food, for example, bats, owls, dolphins, may not be able to find food as easily if there is background noise.

▶ **Hearing damage/behavioural changes:** cetaceans such as whales and dolphins can be harmed by loud noises such as the military sonar used to detect submarines. If they are close to the source of the sonar they may suffer hearing damage. Mass-strandings of cetaceans may be linked to the use of sonar.

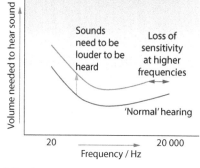

▼ *How a person's hearing may be affected by age or damage caused by exposure to noise*

▼ *Cliff-nesting seabirds are very vulnerable to disturbance by noise*

Aircraft noise: military aircraft

There are far fewer military aircraft flights than those of civil aircraft. Most military airfields are away from urban areas so there is limited annoyance to the public during take-off and landing. However, low-level training flights can cause annoyance over large areas. Where practical, some airforces plan low flying training flights to minimise noise nuisance problems using a range of methods:

- ◤ major urban areas are avoided, unless close to the airfield;
- ◤ in the UK there are 13 major avoidance areas that include major conurbations, civil airports, and certain key industrial and medical sites;
- ◤ flight paths are varied;
- ◤ the UK is divided into twenty Low Flying Areas (minimum flying height 250ft) of which three are Tactical Training Areas (minimum flying height 100ft at specific limited times);
- ◤ it is possible to request a temporary stop to low flying, for example, for an agricultural or horse show;
- ◤ low flying timetables may be published when practical;
- ◤ compensation may be paid for damage caused to property or harm to livestock;
- ◤ flights may avoid sensitive ecological sites such as seabird cliff breeding colonies.

❶ Military aircraft often train at low altitude
❷ Military flight zones in the UK.

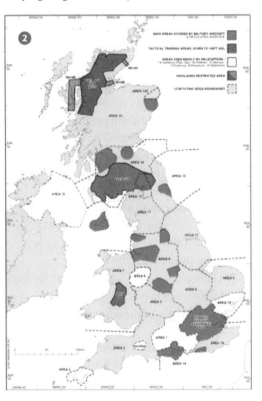

69 dB+
63 dB+
57 dB+

| 0 | 2 | 4 | 6 | 8 |

Distance / km

Runways

▲ Isolines of mean peak noise levels around the runways of a major airport

Aircraft noise: civil aircraft

- ◤ Civil airliners cruise at altitudes high enough that little or no sound reaches the ground, so noise nuisance is usually limited to the area around airports where aircraft are close to the ground.
- ◤ Many airports are located close to urban areas to reduce travel times to and from the airport for passengers. This increases the risk of noise causing annoyance in the urban area.
- ◤ The level of noise nuisance around an airport is affected by the timing and number of flights each day and by the sound level produced by each aircraft.

Airport design and location

▼ **Location away from major population centres:** new airport developments are located in areas with a low population density to minimise the number of people affected.

▼ **Taxi areas away from residential areas:** aircraft taxiing before take-off can increase noise levels for nearby residents. The layout of the airport can separate taxi areas and residential areas.

▼ **Engine test areas:** areas where engines are tested on the ground at high thrust are located away from residential area, are only used during the day, and are surrounded by acoustic screens.

▲ *An aircraft engine test area with acoustic walls to reduce noise pollution*

▼ **Acoustic insulation:** buildings affected by aircraft noise may have free acoustic insulation provided, for example, double glazing.

▼ **Land-use restrictions:** there may be restrictions on land-uses near airports, for example, allowing industry but not housing developments.

▼ **Noise deflection/absorption:** baffle mounds and acoustic barriers can deflect or absorb noise around an airport.

▼ **Multiple landing runways:** at a busy airport with a single runway for landing, aircraft may have to use noisy reverse thrusters to slow down so they can get off the runway before the next aircraft arrives. Having multiple runways allows more time for slowing down, so the wheel brakes can be used which are quieter than reverse thrusters.

▲ *An acoustic wall to reduce noise from taxi areas reaching nearby residential areas*

Aircraft Engine design

▼ **High bypass- ratio engines:** early jet engines had a single cowling (tube) around the jet with the turbulent exhaust gases providing thrust but also creating a lot of noise. Modern jet engines have a second cowling and a turbofan on front of the jet that forces 'bypass air' around the inner cowling. The bypass air smooths the flow of the exhaust air and reduces noise levels. The bypass ratio is the ratio of bypass air: jet exhaust gases. The higher the ratio, the quieter the engine.

Engine	Example of aircraft using the engine	Bypass ratio	First use	Comment on noise
RR Olympus	Concorde	0:1	Early 1950s	Noisiest
RR Conway	Boeing 707 Vickers VC10	0.25:1	Late 1960s	
P&W JT9D	Boeing 747	5:1	1969	
RR Trent 1000	Boeing 787	10:1	2011	Quietest

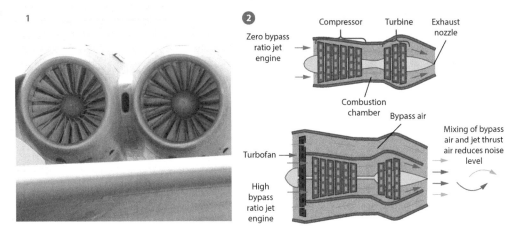

❶ Low bypass ratio engines

❷ The designs of low and high bypass ratio jet engines

1

2

Zero bypass ratio jet engine

Compressor   Turbine   Exhaust nozzle

Combustion chamber   Bypass air

Mixing of bypass air and jet thrust air reduces noise level

Turbofan

High bypass ratio jet engine

▲ A high bypass ratio engine with a chevron nozzle to reduce noise

▶ **Chevron nozzles:** these are used on high bypass engines to make them even quieter. A serrated trailing edge on the outer cowling mixes the bypass air with the surrounding air more smoothly.

▶ **Engine hush kits:** these work like chevron nozzles and can be fitted to low bypass ratio engines to make them quieter.

▶ **Engine acoustic liners:** acoustic liners are used inside the outer cowling and around the inner cowling to absorb noise.

Aircraft body design

▶ **Blended wing aircraft:** in this design the engines can be located on top of the aircraft so the body acts as a barrier reducing the noise that reaches the ground.

▶ **Aerodynamics:** fairings on the undercarriage reduce turbulence around the wheels and leg struts. Fairings covering wing flap hinges reduce turbulence. Riveted construction creates surface indentations which create turbulence and noise. Welded panels create less turbulence.

❶ An undercarriage fairing which reduces turbulence

❷ Wing flap hinge fairings

▶ **Lighter aircraft:** using composite materials, such as carbon fibre, makes aircraft lighter so less engine thrust is needed. For example, the Airbus A380 uses lightweight composite materials for 25% of its structure. The newer A350 uses 53% composite materials.

Aircraft operation

- ▼ **Take-off angle:** aircraft are noisier when taking off than landing because the engines are running at higher power and the take-off angle is steeper to allow the aircraft to climb rapidly to an altitude where it cannot be heard on the ground.
- ▼ **Flight path planning:** flight path routes are planned to avoid densely populated areas whenever possible.
- ▼ **Constant descent angle:** having a constant descent angle (usually 3°) for the final descent before landing makes the engine noise less intrusive. There are no periods of high thrust as there are with a stepped descent. A steeper descent angle allows aircraft to stay at greater altitudes for longer, so ground-level noise is further reduced.
- ▼ **Night flight restrictions:** most airports near large residential areas restrict the number of night flights, especially take-offs.

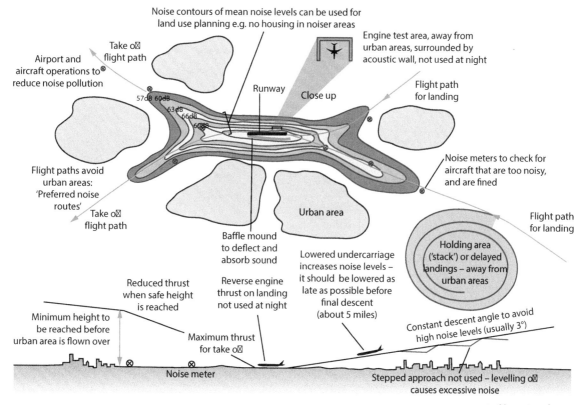

▲ *Airport and aircraft operations to reduce noise pollution*

Control of noisier aircraft

- ▼ **Noise limits:** Aircraft are categorised into groups according to whether they meet increasingly strict noise limits. Older noisiest 'Chapter 2' aircraft were banned from most major airports in 2002, when 'Chapter 3' limits were introduced (15dB reduction in maximum noise). All new aircraft since 2006 must meet 'Chapter 4' noise limits (10dB lower than Chapter 3). Chapter 3 aircraft are being phased out. New regulations being introduced from 2017 will make noise regulations stricter with a further 7dB reduction.
- ▼ **Charges for noisier aircraft:** aircraft pay charges for using airports. At many airports the charge is based on noise levels. At Heathrow, the noisiest aircraft pay 10 times as

much as similar sized quiet aircraft. Night flights cost nearly three times as much as day flights. There are fines for breaking flight noise limits. Fines in 2015 were £500 per dB above the limit for day flights and £4000 per dB above the limit for night flights.

▶ **Restricted flight times:** airports near high population density areas often restrict or ban night flights. Take-offs are controlled more than landings because they are noisier.

▶ **Quota Count System:** airports may encourage airlines to operate quieter aircraft by restricting flight times for noisier aircraft, or by using a points system. The Quota Count System is used at Heathrow, Gatwick, and Stansted airports. It has also been adapted for use at other airports. Aircraft types are allocated points depending on their noise levels. Each airline is allocated a certain number of points. The total point score of the actual flights must not exceed their allocation. It is easier to keep within the point total if new purchases are of quieter aircraft.

▶ *The quota count noise system*

Noise level / EPNdB	Quota Count
Below 84 EPNdB	Exempt
84–86.9 EPNdB	0.25
87–89.9 EPNdB	0.5
90–92.9 EPNdB	1
93–95.9 EPNdB	2
96–98.9 EPNdB	4
99–101.9 EPNdB	8
Greater than 101.9 EPNdB	16

Aircraft type	QC Departure	QC Arrival
Airbus A320 family	0.5–1	0.25–0.5
Airbus A380	2	0.5
Boeing 737 Classic	0.25–0.5	1
Boeing 747-400	4	2
Boeing 747-8	2	1
Boeing 757-200	0.5	0.25
Boeing 767-300	1–2	1
Boeing 777-200ER	2	1
Embraer 145	0.25	0.25

Annual movement limit – 5800
Noise quota – 9180

▶ **Control of supersonic flights:** there are no longer any supersonic civil airliners. Concorde ceased commercial flights in 2003. Concorde was banned from almost all airports and was not allowed to fly supersonic over most countries.

Railway noise

Railway noise pollution affects a small proportion of the population but it can be a serious local problem. High speed passenger trains are noisiest but freight trains are often very long and travel slowly, so they can take a long time to pass.

Controlling train noise

Source	Control
Wheel vibration	Track polishing, sound-absorbing ballast
Engine noise	Sound-absorbing suspension
Pantograph turbulence	Aerodynamic fairing
Wheel squeal on corners	Lubrication of wheels/track
Braking squeal	Use of composite material brakes
Wheel noise	Good carriage suspension

Road traffic noise

Road traffic noise affects more people than any other form of noise pollution.

Controlling road noise

Source	Control
Wheel noise	Sound absorbing road materials such as porous asphalt or asphalt that includes shredded rubber from old vehicle tyres.
Vehicle air turbulence	Improved vehicle aerodynamics.
Engine noise	Acoustic insulation around the engine; quieter exhaust pipes.
General road vehicle noise	Traffic may be rerouted to avoid more sensitive (usually residential) areas.
	Traffic management to produce free-flow of the traffic reduces the louder noise produced during acceleration.
	Fences, embankments, walls, and dense tree planting can help to absorb noise around roads.
	Double glazing can reduce noise levels within buildings.

▶ *A permanent acoustic fence on the M25*

Industrial noise

Most industrial noise is produced within industrial buildings so the noise pollution is only likely to affect workers. However, some industrial activities can affect the public and wildlife.

Sources and control of industrial noise

Source	Control methods
Air compressors and pumps	Silencers to reduce the explosive expansion of air.
Stamping machines	Use of an alternative process, for example, pressing or moulding.
Metal conveyors (metal on metal contact)	Use of nylon bearings, wheels, or rollers.
Mine blasting	Regular timing to reduce public concerns.
	Baffle mounds.
Pile-driving on land	Drilling instead of pile-driving.
Pile driving at sea for the foundations of bridges or wind turbines	Air bubble curtains around the pile driver absorbs noise and reduces the impact on dolphins and whales.
Marine seismic surveys and military sonar harming whales and dolphins (cetaceans)	Acoustic survey to detect cetaceans before use. High noise activities are delayed if they are present. Increase volume gradually so cetaceans can leave if they are present.

General methods used to control industrial noise

▼ Sound absorbing surfaces in the room.
▼ Sound absorbing materials around the equipment – acoustic curtain.
▼ Machinery placed on an acoustic mat.
▼ Sound absorbing materials as part of the equipment.
▼ Remote machinery operation.
▼ Worker ear protection.

▶ *Baffle mounds are used around mines, landfill sites, airports and motor sport tracks*

Domestic noise

Domestic noise pollution is mainly caused by domestic appliances such as washing machines, music equipment, garden machinery, DIY power tools, and barking dogs. These are not technically complex but they can have serious impacts on quality of life.

Control of domestic noise

▼ Domestic appliances with acoustic absorbers, for example, washing machines, vacuum cleaners.
▼ Wearing ear defenders when using power tools.
▼ Volume limiters on music equipment.
▼ Selection of quieter domestic appliances. This requires the availability of good information to help in making choices.
▼ Control of pet dogs.

Measuring noise pollution

The loudness of sound is measured using the decibel scale. This can be modified for specific applications. Other scales derived from the dB scale are used to give an overall measure of how noise levels change over time or for events where the loudness is not constant, for example, an aircraft takeoff.

Modifications to the dB scale

The dB(A) scale is used for human hearing. It takes into account the sensitivity of human hearing by 'weighting' sounds between 1000 and 4000Hz. This is because the nerve cells in the ear are more sensitive to sounds in this frequency range so they are heard more easily.

Measuring road traffic noise levels

LA10 measures noise exceeded for 10% in any set period. It is a good measure of the noisiest periods.

LA90 measures the noise level exceeded for 90% in any set period. It is a good measure of the quietest periods.

Traffic Noise Index (TNI): this produces a representative measure of traffic noise using LA10 and LA90.

L10(18h): this measure assumes that traffic noise is only a problem during the 18 hours between 6am and midnight. The noise level that is exceeded during the noisiest 10% of each of these 18 hours is measured. The mean of these 18 levels is then calculated.

Measuring aircraft noise levels

Effective Perceived Noise Levels (EPNL): this is an estimate of the relative loudness of a particular type of aircraft during takeoff, overflight, and landing. It is calculated from many observations, recorded at 450m to the side of the flight path.

Noise and Number Index (NNI): this combines the number of flights and the noise levels of aircraft above 80dB as it is presumed that aircraft below 80dB do not cause serious annoyance. It has been replaced with the Leq 57dB.

Leq 57dB: leq is an average sound level over a particular period. For UK airports, an average of 57dB between 7am and 11pm in the summer is used. Levels above this are considered annoying. Areas with noise above this level will experience 'significant community annoyance'.

Ionising radiation

Ionising radiation is a naturally occurring phenomenon which has been used in a wide range of applications. However, it does present a threat to health and radioactive materials need to be managed. Pollution caused by radioactive materials has resulted from past nuclear weapons testing, nuclear waste disposal, accidents at nuclear power plants, as well as from transportation, processing and storage of radioactive materials.

Uses of ionising radiation and nuclear power

Radioactive materials and ionising radiation are used in many ways.

Industry

- Measuring the thickness of rolled metals and paper.
- Testing aircraft jet engine turbines.
- Strengthening polymers. Radiation can create cross-links in molecules. This is used to improve the properties of latex rubber for surgical gloves, balloons used in heart surgery and vehicle tyres.
- In oil and gas exploration to test rock porosity.

Healthcare

- Sterilising heat-sensitive surgical equipment.
- Cancer treatment.
- X-ray photography and CT scans.

Agriculture

- Pest control: stored food sterilisation.
- Sterile male insect pest control.
- Production of mutations in crop breeding programmes.

Scientific research

- Radio-labelled tracers to track the movement of materials within organisms or the environment.

Nuclear fission and fusion

- Nuclear weapons use nuclear fission and fusion. About 500 nuclear test explosions took place in the atmosphere up to 1980.
- Nuclear electricity: nuclear fission using uranium and plutonium is used in nuclear reactors to generate electricity.
- Ship propulsion: the high energy density of nuclear fuel means that ships propelled by nuclear reactors rarely need to be refuelled and don't need air for combustion which is very useful in submarines.

▶ *How ionising radiation is used to check the thickness of rolled materials*

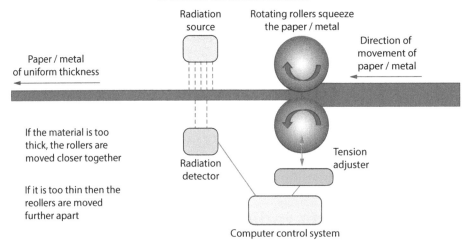

The amount of radiation passing through the rolled material is used to measure the material thickness

Paper / metal of uniform thickness

Radiation source

Rotating rollers squeeze the paper / metal

Direction of movement of paper / metal

If the material is too thick, the rollers are moved closer together

If it is too thin then the reollers are moved further apart

Radiation detector

Tension adjuster

Computer control system

❶ *Surgical equipment is sterilised using X-rays or gamma rays*

❷ *Smoke detectors use a small source of Americium 241.*

❸ *Heysham nuclear power station*

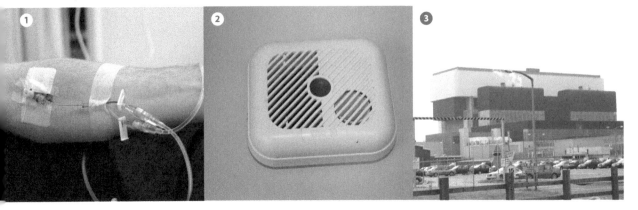

Risk: Benefit analysis

No activity is completely safe. The risks of engaging in the activity must be compared with the benefits to decide whether the benefits outweigh the risks and whether the risks can be reduced. The benefits are often obvious in the new activities that become possible, but the risks can be much more difficult to assess.

Assessing the risks and benefits of using ionising radiation can be difficult for example:

- ▀ symptoms may take a long time to develop, especially those caused by the chronic exposure to low doses;
- ▀ some effects of exposure to ionising radiation may be difficult to identify as there may be alternative causes of the same symptoms;
- ▀ accurate data on the impacts on humans is often not available;
- ▀ accurate data on exposure is often not available following accidental releases;
- ▀ the people who benefit from the use of ionising radiation and those who take risks may not be in the same place, for example, the people who benefit from nuclear electricity may live in a different country from the miners who extract the uranium fuel used in the power station;
- ▀ the risks associated with using radioactive materials may be offset by the reduction of other risks, for example, the risks of using X-ray photography must be offset by the reduced risks of invasive surgery.

Sources of radiation exposure

Average annual dose of ionising radiation dose received in the UK

Source of radiation	% of average annual dose
Natural sources	
Cosmic radiation from the sun	10
Gamma rays from the lithosphere	14
Internal sources in the body	11
Radon from the ground	50
Human activities	
Medical exposure	14
Occupational exposure	0.3
Weapons fallout	0.2
Consumer products	<0.1
Industrial effluent discharges	<0.1

These are average values. The dose received by an individual depends upon factors such as where they live, their occupation, lifestyle, and state of health.

Cosmic radiation

Large amounts of charged sub-atomic particles are released by the natural processes that occur in the Sun. When the particles reach the Earth's atmosphere they are absorbed, releasing high-energy electromagnetic radiation, including gamma rays.

Gamma rays from the lithosphere

There are many radioactive isotopes in the lithosphere. They release different types of radiation when their atoms decay. However, it is only gamma rays that penetrate well enough to travel from underground to reach people on the Earth's surface.

Internal radiation from the body

Activation products from the upper atmosphere and radioisotopes from the ground can enter the body via food and water or by being inhaled. These can decay inside the body and release radiation.

Radon from the ground

When radioisotopes in underground rocks decay, the radiation released is usually absorbed by the surrounding rocks. When some uranium atoms decay the gaseous radionuclide, radon, is produced. Radon is unstable and releases alpha radiation. It travels up cracks in the overlying rocks and escapes into the atmosphere. It can pass through the foundations of buildings above uranium-bearing rocks, and become concentrated inside buildings. Some parts of the UK such as Devon and Cornwall have relatively high radon levels as a result of the type of underground rocks found in the region. Ventilating building foundations can be used to blow out the radon before it enters the building.

Medical exposure

Ionising radiation is used in a number of medical procedures. Medical uses of ionising radiation have benefits but involve risks. A risk:benefit analysis should be considered to ensure the benefits outweigh the risks.

These medical procedures include:

- X-ray photography to gain information about the inside of the body, for example, broken bones, or dental X-rays to find decay;
- X-ray radiography, after injecting radio-opaque dyes, can be used to find blockages such as kidney stones in ureters or blocked arteries;
- high doses of radiation to kill cancerous tissue;
- the use of radio-labelled substances to track the passage of that substance in the body and assess any blockages.

Occupational exposure

Working in a number of industries can increase exposure to radiation. The industries involved include:

- nuclear electricity generation;
- manufacturing industry which makes items containing radioactive materials;
- mining;
- medical radiographers and radiologists;
- dentists and dental technicians;
- workers who use radioactive sources to test the thickness of paper or steel;
- research scientists who use radio-labelled tracer substances;
- aircraft flight crews

Atomic weapons fallout

Atmospheric testing and use of nuclear explosives released radioactive material. This was carried by winds and contaminated all parts of the Earth's surface although the degree of contamination varied greatly. No nuclear weapon tests have been conducted in the atmosphere since 1980.

Consumer products

Common consumer products, including smoke detectors and some camping gas mantles, contain radionuclides. Small amounts of radioactive materials may be present in ceramics, granite worktops, and fertilisers. These result in a small increased dose to the public.

Industrial radiation discharges

Most industries that use radionuclides release some radioactive wastes into the environment. The majority comes from nuclear electricity generation and nuclear weapons manufacture. Improved processes, such as the use of filters on gaseous emissions and ion-exchange sands in liquid releases, have reduced the amount of radioactive materials released.

Background radiation, for example, from the sun, rocks, and food is the radiation exposure which cannot be avoided.

▲ *Radioactive paint used to be used in clocks with luminous dials.*

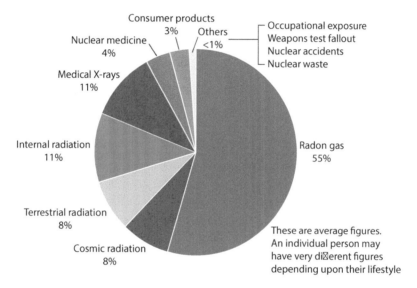

Consumer products
3% Others
Nuclear medicine   <1%
4%

Medical X-rays
11%

Occupational exposure
Weapons test fallout
Nuclear accidents
Nuclear waste

Internal radiation
11%

Radon gas
55%

Terrestrial radiation
8%

These are average figures.
An individual person may
have very different figures
depending upon their lifestyle

Cosmic radiation
8%

◀ *The average exposure to ionising radiation and sources of exposure*

Factors that affect the impact of ionising radiation

Properties of different types of ionising radiation

The effect of ionising radiation is determined by the properties of different types of ionising radiation such as their power to penetrate other materials, the distance they can travel, and the ease with which they can be absorbed.

Ionising radiation that has poor penetrating power is more easily absorbed. This means that workers can be protected relatively easily. However, if the ionising radiation penetrates living cells then the energy from a less penetrating type will be absorbed in a smaller amount of tissue and so can cause more serious local damage.

Relative Biological Effectiveness (RBE) is a measure of the comparative effects of different types of ionising radiation on living tissues. More damaging forms of radiation have higher RBEs.

Properties and health risks of different types of ionising radiation

Type of radiation	Ease of absorption/ distance travelled	RBE	Comparative health risks
Alpha	Very easily absorbed Travels short distances	20	Alpha particles are absorbed by clothing and dead skin so alpha emitters outside the body are usually safe Ingested alpha emitters are very dangerous as the particles are all absorbed in a small mass of tissue, creating more concentrated damage and increasing the risk of free radical interactions
Beta	Moderately easily absorbed Travels medium distances	1	Moderately dangerous. Sources near to the body still pose a risk.
Gamma and X rays	Not easily absorbed Travel long distances	1	Lower danger Longer distance of travel means distant sources are still a risk
Neutrons	Moderately easily absorbed Travel medium distances	2 - 10	Very dangerous Ionising radiation neutrons still pose a risk after they have been absorbed. Some atoms are changed when bombarded by neutrons so they become activation products. A stable nucleus becomes a radionuclide when bombarded by neutrons and may later decay and release ionising radiation.

The density of the material through which the ionising radiation passes determines how far it will actually travel. The denser the material is, the more easily the radiation will be absorbed by the material.

Half-life and health risks

All atoms of an unstable isotope have the same probability of decaying during a specific time period. The likelihood of an atom decaying is not affected by the number of atoms present. For a mass of an individual isotope there is a predictable rate at which the atoms will spontaneously decay and emit ionising radiation. This rate is usually expressed as its half-life. This is the length of time it takes for half of the original isotope to decay. So, if a mass is observed for several half-lives then the remaining proportion will be ½, ¼, ⅛ , ¹⁄₁₆, ¹⁄₃₂, ¹⁄₆₄, etc. of the original amount.

Isotopes

Isotope	Half-life	Source
Uranium-238	4.5 x 109 years	Occurs naturally in rocks
Iodine-131	8 days	Fission in nuclear reactors
Caesium-137	30 years	Fission in nuclear reactors
Plutonium-239	24 400 years	Produced in reactors by neutron bombardment of uranium-238
Strontium-90	29 years	Fission in nuclear reactors

� with short half-lives release all their radiation quickly. They are dangerous but they do not pose a danger for long. Therefore short-term precautions may be sufficient to protect workers and the public.

- Isotopes with long half-lives pose a danger for a long time. They emit small amounts of radiation in any given time period so the level of danger may be quite low.
- Isotopes with half-lives of several decades generate concern because the rate of radiation release is quite high. People can be exposed for most or all of their lives and short-term protection measures are inadequate.

Effects of ionising radiation on living tissue

When ionising radiation is absorbed by living tissue, unusual ions called 'free radicals' are produced. These have unpaired electrons, are highly reactive, and can cause biologically damaging reactions. The most common molecule in cells is water so it is most likely to be affected by the radiation. The free radicals produced are often short lived but they may produce more stable molecules which can cause damage within the cell.

- **Damage to the nucleus of the cell:** this is most likely to be observed as it affects the existing cell and all future cells produced from its chromosomes when it divides. Such a change in the DNA is called a mutation. Rapidly dividing cells such as the skin and gut are more easily affected because their cells are more genetically active.
- **Damage to other parts of the cell:** this may mean the cell cannot function properly and may die. Lower levels of damage may cause no long-term effects as the intact nucleus can co-ordinate the repair of the damage.
- **Somatic effects:** damage to general body cells and organs;
- **Gonadic effects:** damage to cells in ovaries or testes.
- **Chronic effects:** effects which appear slowly and in proportion to the radiation doses received;
- **Acute effects:** these are a collection of health effects which appear quickly. If radiation is received over a shorter period of time then more damage is likely as there may be more damaging free-radical interactions and the cells have less time to repair themselves.

  If a person receives very large doses of radiation, for example, in a nuclear power accident, the impact will be severe and can cause rapid death as a result of damage to the bone marrow, immune system, and the gut causing haemorrhage and blood loss.

Exposure and contamination

- **Exposure** involves the absorption of ionising radiation. For exposure to occur, the person must be close enough to the source for the radiation to reach them.
- **Contamination** refers to physically carrying radioactive materials which, when they release radiation, may cause exposure. If someone is contaminated, then exposure will continue as long as they carry the source on or in them.

Sources of ionising radiation which are sealed inside a container may expose people nearby to radiation but they cannot become contaminated.

Activation products

Exposure to most types of radiation does not cause the material that absorbs it to become radioactive because the nuclei are unaltered. However, exposure to neutrons can cause previously stable nuclei to become radioactive as the absorption of a neutron will convert it into a new isotope. Activation products are most often found in the structures of nuclear reactors.

Control of exposure to ionising radiation

Principles of control

There are two basic principles for managing safety and radioactive material:

- ▼ **ALARA:** the situation should be managed such that the exposure should be: 'As Low As Reasonably Achievable' (ALARA);
- ▼ **BATNEEC:** the low exposure can be achieved by using the Best Available Technology Not Entailing Excessive Cost (BATNEEC). The assessment of 'excessive cost' depends upon the level of risk and the ease with which adequate safety can be achieved.

Strategies to reduce exposure

- ▼ **Closed sources:** prevent workers from coming into direct contact with the source by enclosing a radioactive source in a container. Workers are not contaminated by picking up radioactive material which would have continued their exposure when they moved away from that location. A closed source of alpha-emitters may reduce exposure to zero as the container will probably absorb all the radiation. Remote handling techniques can be used to minimise contamination. If the source cannot be enclosed then the worker can wear a sealed suit with a separate air source.
- ▼ **Materials to absorb the radiation:** if possible, materials should be used as barriers to prevent the radiation from reaching the workers. The choice and thickness of the material used will depend upon the type of radiation involved and the space available.
- ▼ **Protective clothing** can be used to minimise contamination.

▲ *Nuclear waste transport flasks have thick metal walls to absorb radiation and are sealed to prevent the escape of radioactive materials*

- ▼ **Distance from the source:** radiation follows the Inverse Square Law so when the distance from the source is increased there is a more than proportional drop in exposure. So, doubling the distance from the source reduces the exposure to one quarter of its previous level.

$$\text{Dose received} = \frac{1}{\text{Distance}^2}$$

- ▼ **Reducing the period of exposure:** working arrangements should minimise the time a worker is close to the source.
- ▼ **Decontamination:** washing, scrubbing and exfoliating scrubs remove surface contamination. Swallowing stable potassium iodide tablets prevents uptake of radioactive iodine.

Good waste management

The nuclear electricity industry creates the largest quantities of concentrated radioactive waste materials.

Category of radioactive waste	Origin of the waste	Storage method
High level waste	Used uranium fuel rods - split nuclei form highly radioactive isotopes	Vitrification - dried powdered solid waste mixed with molten glass and allowed to solidify in stainless steel containers, surrounded by concrete to absorb radiation. Air cooling removes the heat of radioactive decay. In the UK it is stored at Sellafield, Cumbria
Intermediate level waste	The metal tubes that surrounded the fuel rods become radioactive in the reactor. Filters from waste reprocessing	Mixed with cement and stored in stainless steel drums. In the UK it is stored at Sellafield
Low level waste - solid	General equipment and clothing that become contaminated by coming in contact with radioactive material	Sealed in thick polythene bags, inside steel drums, inside steel truck containers in a concrete-lined landfill site. In the UK it is stored at Drigg near Sellafield
Low level waste - liquid	Waste solutions from used fuel reprocessing and storage	Filtered, including ion exchange, then discharged.
Low level waste - gases	Gases released from used fuel during storage and reprocessing	Filtered then released.

Monitoring radioactive materials

Units used to measure ionising radiation

▼ The Becquerel is used to measure the activity of the source.

▼ The Gray is a measure of absorbed dose. 1 Gy is the absorption of one joule of radiation energy per kilogram of matter.

▼ The Sievert is a measure of effective dose that allows for the differing effects of the different types of radiation.

No. of Sieverts = No of Grays x a radiation weighting factor for the type of radiation.

The weighting factor for alpha radiation is 20, for gamma and beta radiation it is 1.

Worker monitoring

Monitoring the work environment and testing the workers themselves can be used to ensure exposure is kept low. A range of monitors may be used:

▼ personal dosemeters which give a reading of current exposure;

▼ photographic film badges which measure long-term measure exposure;

▼ air monitors to detect atmospheric particles, including alpha-emitters;

▼ contamination monitors which monitor workers as they leave the premises and detect any contamination.

Critical Pathway Analysis (CPA)

Normal discharges from nuclear establishments release very small amounts of radioactive materials. However, it cannot be assumed that they will be dispersed and diluted so that the risks drop to an insignificant level. It is possible that natural processes may concentrate them in locations where they could be hazardous.

Critical Pathway Analysis identifies the possible environmental routes that radioactive materials may take in the environment after release. The analysis makes it possible to predict where discharges could cause problems by becoming more concentrated. CPA involves the following factors:

- ▼ the physical state of the effluent – solid/liquid/gas/solution;
- ▼ density;
- ▼ meteorological conditions that determine atmospheric dispersion including wind speed and direction;
- ▼ river flow and ocean currents;
- ▼ the physical nature of the environment including its geology – porous/permeable, vegetation cover;
- ▼ effect of pH and oxygen availability on solubility;
- ▼ bioaccumulation and food-chain concentration;
- ▼ food sources and consumption by local people;
- ▼ half-lives of isotopes involved.

▶ *Some of the pathways that may be included in a Critical Pathway Analysis*

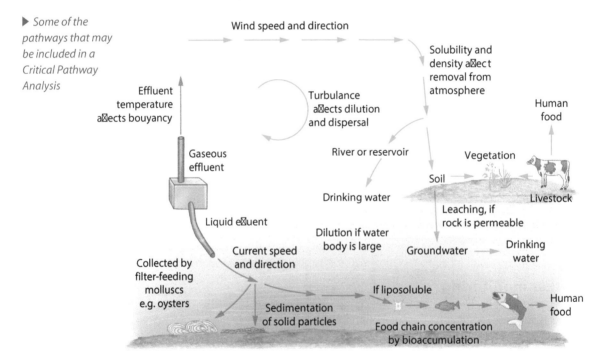

Critical Group Monitoring (CGM)

If there is concern about radioactive contamination it is important to determine the level of risk to people. The effective way to do this is to review the risk to the Critical Group. This group is comprised of those members of the public who are most at risk because of where they live, where their water comes from, what they eat, what they do in their spare time, and where they work. If the Critical Group is found to be safe then all other members of the public should be safe as well. There is no need to monitor all members of the public. The Critical Group does not include occupational workers who are monitored in other ways.

Factors that would be considered in identifying the critical group:

▼ where individuals live in relation to the source;

▼ time spent outside, for example, farmers, dog walkers, anglers, walkers;

▼ sources of food, for example, local food: milk, seafood, vegetables;

▼ source of water, for example, a local well.

The Critical Group near one nuclear establishment was identified as livestock farmers who lived downwind of the establishment, who worked outside, grew their own vegetables, ate meat and milk from their own farms, and obtained their water from a local well.

Environmental monitoring

If places in the environment, where radioactive materials are likely to be most concentrated, are identified and monitored and it is established that levels are found to be acceptable, then it is assumed that everywhere else is safe. However, it is important to recognise that this assumes that the pathways have been predicted correctly. Atmospheric dust, soil, water, grass, milk, meat, fish and vegetables should be assessed as they are the materials that are most likely to be contaminated and those that indicate direct risk to humans.

◀ *Tacky shades collect atmospheric dust samples in monitoring programmes for radioactive materials*

Key principles

▼ The properties of a substance or energy form that will cause pollution.

▼ An understanding of the properties of the potential pollutants can be used to predict the possible problems.

▼ Features of the environment affect the way pollutants behave and the severity of the pollution they cause.

▼ Pollutants can affect living organisms directly, or indirectly, by altering other environmental factors that are damaging.

▼ Many pollution problems are caused by a lack of knowledge of the problems being caused, or an unwillingness to implement control methods that are available.

▼ Many pollution problems are caused by linear human systems that do not involve dynamic equilibria: resources become depleted and wastes accumulate.

Agriculture

Chapter topics

- ▼ Factors that affect agriculture
- ▼ Abiotic factors and their control
- ▼ Biotic factors and their control
- ▼ Manipulation of the food species
- ▼ Environmental impacts of agriculture
- ▼ Social factors that affect agriculture
- ▼ The availability of technology
- ▼ Economic and political influences on agriculture
- ▼ Strategies to increase agricultural sustainability

Farmland covers a large proportion of the Earth's land area with about 10% being cultivated and a further 25% used as permanent pasture. With a growing human population, it is important to ensure that future agriculture is sustainable. Agriculture affects large areas of natural habitats and affects many important natural processes.

The principles of agriculture

Agriculture involves the control of terrestrial ecosystems to divert energy and nutrients into the human food chain. Key principles are:

- ▼ selection of species;
- ▼ control of abiotic and biotic environmental factors to control production;
- ▼ manipulation of the food species to improve productivity.

The selection of species for agriculture

The choice of which species and varieties of crop or livestock are selected for cultivation depends upon three basic factors:

- ▼ market demand and access;
- ▼ whether environmental conditions are within the range of tolerance of the food species;
- ▼ whether environmental conditions or the species' adaptations can be controlled to improve productivity.

Abiotic factors and their control

For every abiotic factor, each species has its own range of tolerance within which it can survive.

Factors that affect agriculture

Part of that range will be the optimum for survival and growth. Maintaining conditions within this optimum range will maximise productivity.

Temperature

The importance of suitable temperatures

- ▶ **Length of the thermal growing season:** it is not just necessary for temperatures to be warm enough for survival, it must be warm enough for growth. For example, grass can survive very low temperatures but does not grow at temperatures below 5°C.
- ▶ **Frost-free period:** some crops are damaged by frost, for example, maize, so it cannot be grown in areas where late frosts are likely. The blossom of many fruit crops is damaged by frosts.
- ▶ **Impact on evaporation:** higher temperatures increase the rate of evapotranspiration which increases crop water requirements.
- ▶ **Biochemical reactions:** the rate of biochemical reactions, including those involved in photosynthesis and plant growth, are generally increased by higher temperatures.
- ▶ **Thermoregulation:** mammal and birds use food energy to maintain a constant internal body temperature. Keeping the animals warm reduces heat losses and increases the amount of food energy put into growth.

Control of temperature

The selected field location can affect the temperature.

- ▶ Low lying areas such as valley bottoms are more likely to have frosts as cold dense air collects there.
- ▶ South-facing slopes in the northern hemisphere (and north-facing slopes in the southern hemisphere) receive more solar insolation and tend to be warmer. Where the crop is sufficiently valuable, temperatures may be raised with more intensive methods:
    - greenhouses achieve higher temperatures from solar heating;
    - greenhouses may be heated in cold weather by burning fuel, for example, gas or paraffin;
    - greenhouse overheating can be prevented by ventilation.
- ▶ Frosts in orchards during the flowering period can destroy the flowers and prevent any crop from being produced. This can be prevented by burning gas, oil, or candles in the orchards, or by dispersing cold air with large fans.
- ▶ Transparent woven plastic cloth over fields helps to retain warm air close to the ground and protect crop seedlings.
- ▶ Livestock can be kept warm by providing shelter or buildings that may be heated. In hot weather, buildings may need to be ventilated to prevent overheating.

1 *Greenhouses*

2 *Polythene cloches can keep individual crop rows warm*

Light

The importance of light

The intensity of light affects the rate of photosynthesis, brighter light producing more rapid photosynthesis.

Photoperiodism (daylength) affects the growth and development of crops. Some plants require longer periods of light each day for flowering, for example, oats, while others require shorter days, for example, maize. Day length can affect the reproductive function of some livestock species.

- Long day length increases milk production.
- Poultry grow best with short days while egg production is greatest when days are long.
- Some livestock, such as sheep, mate when days are getting shorter in the autumn, with the lambs being born in spring.

Control of light

Artificial lighting can be used to extend the growing season, for example, for salad crops in greenhouses. The artificial production of autumn lighting conditions in spring will produce another mating season for sheep, with a second lambing season in the autumn.

Water

Plants need water for many reasons.

- Physiological functions: water is the general physiological solvent in all living cells.
- Nutrient absorption. Nutrients are absorbed from soil as ions dissolved in water.
  - Nitrogen is absorbed as nitrate ions: NO_3^{1-}
  - Phosphorus is absorbed as phosphate ions: PO_4^{3-}
  - Potassium is absorbed as potassium ions: K^{1+}
- Cell water produces cell turgidity which provides support, especially in seedlings.
- Water is used to transport materials such as glucose, oxygen, and mineral nutrients.
- Water is needed to replace the water that is lost during transpiration. Transpiration causes water to be drawn upwards to the leaves, carrying nutrients from the roots with it.
- Gaseous exchange. Stomata are the pores in leaves where carbon dioxide dissolves and is absorbed, so it can be used during photosynthesis. Water is lost during this process by evaporation from the cells in the stomata. If there is a shortage of water, the stomata close to prevent dehydration and death. The plant may survive, but gaseous exchange and growth will stop.

How water supply affects crops

Some crops have a high water requirement, for example, most rice varieties must be flooded during early growth. Some cereal crops have a low water requirement, for example, wheat. Irregular water supplies can cause some crops to expand and split, for example, tomatoes. Humid conditions can increase the risk of fungal diseases.

- **Amount**: the amount of water available to plants is affected by precipitation rates and soil properties such as permeability and water retention. The 'hydrological growing season' is the time during the year that there is sufficient water to sustain growth.
- **Reliability**: it is difficult for farmers to plan activities if they do not know how much water will be available. This is a particular problem in areas with unreliable seasonal rainfall or where there are no alternative water supplies for irrigation.
- **Quality**: substances dissolved in irrigation water can cause problems, especially if groundwater or polluted river water is used.
  A high salt content can cause salinisation, leading to osmotic dehydration of the crop.
  Heavy metals may bioaccumulate in crops and be a threat to the health of people who eat the harvested crop.

Problems caused by waterlogged soils

- higher risk of fungal diseases;
- soils become anaerobic and create ideal conditions for denitrifying bacteria, but not nitrifying bacteria. This reduces soil fertility as nitrates are lost from the soil more rapidly and replaced more slowly.

Methods used to reduce soil water levels

- excavation of drainage ditches or installation of drainage pipes;
- deep ploughing;
- avoidance of soil compaction by machinery or livestock;
- provision of conditions to encourage worms, for example, soil organic matter.

▲ A drainage ditch that increases soil aeration in the surrounding feilds

Problems caused by water shortages

Crops:

- plants lose water by transpiration during dry weather but this is reduced by closure of the stomata in their leaves. This also stops the absorption of carbon dioxide so photosynthesis and growth stop. Even a moderate water shortage reduces crop productivity.
  A severe water shortage will kill plants as cell dehydration inhibits cellular biochemical reactions.

Livestock:

- livestock in semi-arid areas may die if there is a water shortage. Shortages can increase trampling damage if animals have to regularly walk longer distances to reach water. This can increase the risk of erosion and desertification.

Methods used to increase water availability

- crop irrigation;
- soil mulching to reduce evaporation losses from the soil surface;
- provision of suitable conditions for worms to increase infiltration and reduce runoff losses;
- reducing soil compaction by machinery and livestock to increase infiltration and reduce runoff losses;
- adding soil organic matter to increase water retention.

Soil fertility

Soil fertility is a measure of the ability of the soil to support plant growth. It is the combination of soil properties such as the availability of nutrients and water, aeration, texture, and structure. See page 158, Soil.

Soil nutrients

Plants need a range of nutrients for growth and good health. Nutrients that are needed in large amounts are called macronutrients. Those needed in smaller amounts are called micronutrients.

Nutrients must be added to soil to replace the nutrients removed when the crop is harvested, to replace nutrients lost due to natural processes or if the soil is naturally deficient in that nutrient.

Nutrient category			Nutrient	Form absorbed	Function	Commonly applied to fields as fertiliser?
Macronutrients	Primary macronutrients		Nitrogen	Nitrate ions NO_3^{1-}	Protein manufacture	Yes
			Phosphorus	Phosphate ions PO_4^{3-}	Root growth and ATP manufacture	Yes
			Potassium	Potassium ions K^{1+}	Ion transport and seed development	Yes
	Secondary macronutrients		Calcium	Calcium ions Ca^{2+}	Cell walls	If soil is nutrient-deficient or in intensive systems such as hydroponics
			Magnesium	Magnesium ions Mg^{2+}	Chlorophyll synthesis	
			Sulfur	Sulfate ions SO_3^{2-}	Protein synthesis	
Micronutrients			Iron	Iron ions $Fe^{2+},\ Fe^{3+}$	Chlorophyll manufacture	
			Zinc	Zn^{2+}	Enzyme activation	
			Copper	Cu^{2+}	Enzyme activation	

Nutrients may be made available by natural processes in the soil.

▼ Legumes have symbiotic nitrogen-fixing bacteria in root nodules, for example, *Rhizobium*.

- Some free-living soil bacteria also fix nitrogen, for example, *Azotobacter*.
- Crop rotation gives time for weathering to release more nutrients and to even out the demands for particular nutrients by different crops.

Fertiliser application

Organic fertilisers are animal and plant materials that release nutrients as they decompose. They include:

- faecal material: manure/sewage sludge;
- animal food production wastes: bone meal/fish meal/dried blood;
- plant food production wastes: crop harvest wastes/composted plant waste.

Advantages & disadvantages of fertilisers

Fertiliser	Advantages	Disadvantages
Organic fertiliser	Many are waste products and may be locally available They increase the soil humus content They increase soil biota populations	The nutrient composition cannot be controlled. Nutrients are released slowly as the material decomposes, so they must be used as part of a long-term cultivation plan. Many are bulky with a high water content so transport is expensive. They usually cannot be added to a growing crop.
Inorganic nutrient	The nutrient composition can be controlled to meet specific crop requirements. The nutrients are released rapidly.	Some require large amounts of energy during manufacture by the chemical industry. They do not add organic matter to the soil, so humus levels and soil biota populations may decline. Some are toxic to worms. Some have high solubility and may be leached after application. Raw material supplies for manufacture may be limited, for example, phosphate rocks

Nutrient application methods include:

- cultural methods using natural processes such as bacterial fixation and weathering release the nutrients in the soil. A crop rotation cycle that includes livestock will add manure to the soil;
- mechanical application is normally used to spread organic and inorganic fertilisers.

❶ *Spreading inorganic nitrate fertiliser*
❷ *Spreading manure*

Hydroponics

Hydroponics involves the growth of crops in a nutrient solution rather than a solid growth medium. It is usually carried out in greenhouses as part of an intensive system. Productivity is maximised by controlling limiting factors as much as possible.

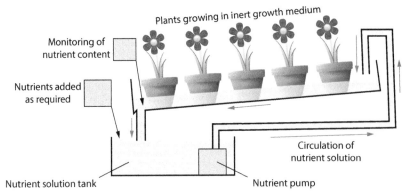

Advantages of hydroponic production.

- ◤ Nutrient supply is optimal so this is not a limiting factor for growth.
- ◤ All the roots are in contact with the nutrient medium, so the roots are smaller and more growth is directed into the harvestable crop.
- ◤ There is no soil to hold pathogens.
- ◤ There are no weeds.
- ◤ The harvested crop still has roots so it stays fresh longer.
- ◤ The harvested crop is attractive for consumers as it has no soil on it.

Disadvantages of hydroponic production.

- ◤ Intensive production involves high inputs of nutrients and energy.
- ◤ A high level of technical knowledge is needed.

Aeration

An uncompacted soil has larger spaces between the soil particles which increases aeration. This is important because many important soil processes are aerobic such as root respiration, nitrogen fixation, decomposition. The force of gravity naturally causes soil particles to become compacted. This is counteracted by the tunneling action of detritivores such as worms and the growth of plant roots, especially of larger plants whose larger roots create drainage channels when they die and decompose.

Some farming practices increase soil compaction, for example:

- ◤ soil compaction is increased by the weight of farm machinery or livestock trampling;
- ◤ farming methods often reduce soil organic matter content and therefore worm populations;
- ◤ natural communities have deep-rooted plants, such as forests, but most crops have shallow roots;
- ◤ ploughing can kill soil organisms by moving them to depths at which they cannot survive.

Control of aeration

- Ploughing turns over and aerates surface soil layers but not deeper layers.
- Adding organic matter provides food for the soil biota that increase aeration.
- Low tillage methods prevent the disturbance to soil and the killing of soil organisms during ploughing.
- Removing livestock from fields when the soil is very wet reduces the compaction caused by trampling.

Soil salinity

Dissolved salts in soil water are essential for plant growth as they include soil nutrients but excessive salinity can kill plants by osmotic dehydration of their roots.

The main method to control salinity is to avoid farming methods that increase salinity, especially irrigating with groundwater that has a high salt content. The salt concentration of the soil increases as the salts are left in the soil when water evaporates from the soil.

Extra water can be used to wash the salts out of the soil but this greatly increases water consumption and can cause ecological problems by increasing the salinity of the local river.

Soil pH

All plant species have their own range of tolerance for pH, usually between pH5 and pH7. A high pH can inhibit nutrient solubility. A low pH can increase the leaching of nutrients and inhibit nutrient uptake. It can also mobilise toxic ions in the soil such as aluminium and lead.

Soil pH can be increased by:

- adding crushed lime (calcium carbonate or hydroxide);

Soil pH can be reduced by:

- spreading powdered sulfur.

Carbon dioxide

Carbon dioxide concentration can be the limiting factor on the rate of photosynthesis.

It is not practical to increase the carbon dioxide concentrations for crops grown in fields. However, crop growth rates in greenhouses may be increased by burning carbon-based fuel such as gas or paraffin. The carbon dioxide is kept in the greenhouse rather than being lost and the increased costs may be justified by the high market value of greenhouse crops.

Topography

The undulations of the land surface can affect its suitability for particular crops and the methods that are used.

- **Aspect:** undulations, such as valleys, produce some areas which are more exposed to sunlight and tend to be warmer.
- **Frost pockets:** cold dense air may collect in low-lying areas, making crop frost damage more likely.
- **Runoff rate:** steeper gradients make soil erosion by surface runoff more likely. Gentle or flat gradients make flooding more likely.
- **Use of machinery:** it may be difficult to operate large machinery on land that undulates a lot or where gradients are very steep.

Control of topography

It is not practical to alter the topography of large areas of land but it may be possible in some areas. An area of steep gradient may be changed to a series of flat fields by terracing. This is usually done to retain irrigation water and reduce soil erosion.

Areas that are nearly flat may be levelled by machinery so that water drains slowly. This can reduce irrigation needs and can help produce flooded fields for rice cultivation.

Relief

The altitude of an area controls other factors that affect the choice of species for cultivation, for example:

- **crops:** temperatures are often colder at higher altitudes. The low atmospheric pressure increases the evaporation rate;
- **livestock:** some species are adapted to high altitudes such as goats, sheep, and llamas. They can survive lower temperatures and low atmospheric pressures. Cattle do not thrive at high altitude because the low atmospheric pressure causes 'high altitude disease' where pulmonary arteries thicken.

It is not possible to control the relief of an area.

Wind velocity

High wind velocities cause several problems

- Increased soil erosion, especially in dry areas.
- Increased evaporation rates and the drying of soils.
- Crop damage, for example the 'lodging' of cereal crops when they are flattened by strong winds.

Wind velocity can be controlled by windbreaks such as hedgerows or rows of trees.

Biotic factors and their control

Agriculture removes most of the previous natural ecosystem and replaces it with a simpler agricultural ecosystem, dominated by the crops and livestock. Some wildlife species take advantage of the new community of species and may become pests, especially if their natural predators are no longer present.

Other species that provided important services may become less common, such as crop pollinators and the soil organisms that recycle nutrients.

Pest control

Pests are organisms that reduce agricultural productivity or the quality of the product. They can do this in a range of ways. They may:

- be predators that eat the crop or livestock;
- compete for resources such as water or nutrients;
- be pathogens that cause disease;
- carry pathogens;
- reduce marketability, for example, spoiling the appearance of fruit or by weed seeds mixing with the cereal harvest.

Pest groups and their effects

Pest group	Problems caused	Examples
Weeds	Competition for nutrients, water, light Harvested with the crop, reducing quality or spoiling taste Provide food for other pests	Wild oats compete for light, water and nutrients in cereal crops
	Parasitism of crop roots	*Striga* parasitises maize crops
Insects	Eat the crop, destroy the crop, or reduce harvests Spoil the appearance of the harvested crop	Aphids (for example, greenfly and blackfly) suck the sap and reduce the growth of many crops, for example, cotton, sugarcane, fruit, cereals Locusts eat almost any plants Termites attack tree crops such as fruit trees
	Act as vectors and spread pathogens	Aphids carry many pathogenic diseases, for example, potato blight
Fungi	Cause the growing plants or harvested crop to rot	Leaf smut (of rice) Leaf blight (of sugarcane)
Bacteria	Reduce harvests by causing disease	Bacterial wilt (of potatoes) Bacterial leaf blight (of wheat)
Molluscs	Eat the crop, reduce harvests, or spoil appearance	Many snails and slugs
Nematode worms	Damage roots and reduce water and nutrient uptake Increase the risks of fungal and bacterial disease	Potato cyst nematode Soybean cyst nematode
Vertebrates	Eat the growing or harvested crop	Mammals e.g. mice, rats, deer, rabbits. Birds, for example, sparrows, quelea

Endemic and epidemic pests

Endemic pests are always present, usually in small or moderate numbers.

Epidemic pests are not normally present but there may be 'outbreaks' where they rapidly become a major problem. This is a different use of the word endemic than that used in wildlife conservation.

Indigenous and introduced pests

Indigenous species are native to the area where they are found. Many pests have been introduced from other areas.. These are often more of a problem as they may not have any predators in the new areas.

Cultural pest control

Cultural pest control involves non-pesticide methods where crops or livestock are cultivated in a way that reduces the risk of pest damage, often by using natural ecosystem services.

Crop rotation

Different crops often have their own unique pest species. If the same crop is grown in the same place in consecutive years then pests from the first year may survive until the second year so pests are already present and do not need to colonise from elsewhere. This allows the pest population to increase earlier in the year and cause more damage. Crop rotation involves the cultivation of a different crop each year, usually on a four or five year cycle. The pests remaining at the end of one year will have died off before that crop is grown again.

▲ *Striga is a parasite of crops such as maize, rice, and sugar cane. It reduces crop growth by absorbing nutrients from the crop roots.*

Companion crops

These are crops which, if grown together, will be more productive. Sometimes both crops will produce a harvestable crop. In other cases, one of the plants is only grown because the harvest of the other one will be increased.

There are a number of different inter-species relationships between companion crops:

- ◤ nutrient supply – legumes can be intercropped among other crops to increase nitrate availability in the soil;
- ◤ barrier crops – the smell of onions can mask the smell of carrots and reduce damage caused by carrot root flies;
- ◤ pest attraction to protect the other plants – nasturtiums attract blackfly pests that could damage bean crops;
- ◤ support of pollinators – flowering plants that support bees which are important in pollinating fruit crops.

▼ hedgerows provide important habitats for the predators of crop pests

Predator habitats

The populations of natural pest predators can be increased by providing suitable habitats. Beetle banks and hedgerows provide habitats and hibernation sites for pest predators such as black ground beetles and ladybirds that eat aphids such as greenfly and blackfly.

Biological control

Predator or pathogen species may be introduced to control pests. This is especially important if the pest is a non-indigenous species that has been introduced and has no indigenous predators. Biological control species should be selected carefully. They should be specialist feeders that will eat the pest species. If they have a wider diet then they may eat beneficial and other non-target species.

Case studies of biological control

Successful biological control	Biological control that went wrong
The Prickly Pear Cactus was introduced from South America to Australia where it had no predators and spread rapidly over large areas of farmland. It was controlled by introducing the *Cactoblastis* moth from South America. The cactus and moth are now both rare. Whiteflies in greenhouses have been successfully controlled by the introduction of parasitic *Encarsia* wasps.	Cane toads were introduced to Australia to control beetle pests of sugar cane but they have eaten a wide range of other species. They are toxic so they have few predators and have colonised a huge area. The African Land Snail was introduced to islands of Polynesia in the Pacific Ocean as a source of human food but it spread and ate farmers' crops. The predatory Florida Rosy Wolfsnail was introduced to control the African Land Snails but they also ate the indigenous Partulid snails. 48 species of Partulid snails are now extinct, 11 only survive in zoos and 15 are critically endangered. Harlequin ladybirds were introduced to Europe from Asia in 2004 to control agricultural insect pests. They also predate indigenous insect species including natural predators of crop pests such as native ladybird species. Within 10 years of their introduction they had colonised most of the UK and have caused the decline of seven indigenous ladybird species.

❶ Prickly pear cactus
❷ A Cane Toad

Sterile male techniques

In many insect species, the females only mate once then store sperm for all future egg laying. If a female mates with a sterile male then she will never produce any offspring.

This method of cultural pest control involves producing many sterile males by exposing them to gamma radiation. They are then released. If enough sterile males are released then the number of fertile matings will be reduced to a level below that needed to produce enough young to compensate for mortality, so the population would decline.

Pests that have been controlled by sterile male techniques include:

- Screw Worm Fly which is an important parasitic pest of livestock in Central America;
- Mediterranean Fruit Fly;
- Sweet Potato Weevil in Japan.

It is species-specific so it does not affect non-target species. It is only successful if the sterilised males behave normally and succeed in finding mates. In some projects, such as those with mosquitoes, the process of sterilisation of the males with radiation alters their behaviour so that females reject them and still mate with wild fertile males.

Re-colonisation from nearby areas that have not been cleared may require regular re-treatment.

Pheromone traps

In many insect species, mates are attracted by a scent called a pheromone. Pheromone traps release an artificial scent that attracts the pests: either males or females, depending upon the species. They can be used in two ways:

- to show that the pest is present so that pesticides can be used to protect the crop;
- to kill all the pest individuals or enough of one gender of the pest so that there are not enough fertile matings to maintain the pest population. This normally only works in enclosed areas such as greenhouses.

Pheromone traps are used for a wide range of pest taxa including moths, weevils, and flies.

▲ *A pheromone trap*

Genetic resistance to disease

Within any species there is a range of genetic characteristics for every environmental adaptation. Selective breeding may enhance the resistance of a variety to pests or disease.

Pathogens evolve to overcome crop disease resistance so it is necessary to regularly introduce new characteristics to maintain resistance. Commercially cultivated crops often have little genetic diversity so the search for new characteristics must focus on wild varieties and CWR (Crop Wild Relative) species, or on traditional crop varieties which are often grown by subsistence farmers. All these genetic resources are threatened by habitat loss and the spread of commercial crop varieties with small gene pools. For example, Boran cattle in East Africa are more resistant to the protozoan disease East Coast Fever than most other cattle breeds.

GM crops and pest control

The DNA of a crop can be modified to control pests more effectively by reducing susceptibility to pests..

Pest control using chemical pesticides

The properties of pesticides influence their effectiveness and environmental impacts.

▶ **Toxicity:** pesticides which have high toxicity require the use of smaller volumes. Most pesticides act by inhibiting enzyme action.

▶ **Specificity:** a measure of the range of taxa affected by the pesticide. More specific pesticides are less likely to harm non-target species.

▶ **Persistence:** persistent pesticides are chemically more stable and degrade slowly. This reduces the frequency of re-application but can increase the likelihood of a pesticide dispersing more widely in the environment and may extend the time period that it may harm non-target species.

▶ **Solubility in water/lipids:** pesticides that are water soluble are more likely to be washed off a crop, requiring re-application. Liposoluble pesticides may be absorbed and stored within the crop, possibly entering the human food chain.

▶ **Mode of action:** there are two main modes of action by which chemical pesticides kill pests

- **Contact action:** contact herbicides kill plants by damaging the tissues they are sprayed onto. Contact insecticides kill insects that are sprayed directly or come in contact with the pesticide that was sprayed onto the crop that is being protected. The pesticide only protects the crop surfaces that are sprayed. Unsprayed surfaces are not protected, such as the undersides of many leaves or new growth. They may also be washed off by rain.

- **Systemic action:** systemic pesticides are absorbed by the crop and translocated throughout the plant. This protects all of the plant and will also protect new growth. The pesticide cannot be washed off by rain but can be retained in the harvested crop and be eaten by humans.

Washing food such as fruit or vegetables may remove contact pesticides but not systemic ones. Public safety is increased if a sufficient time period is left between application and harvest for the pesticides to degrade..

See Pollution for more details on the impacts of organochlorine, organophosphate, pyrethroid and neonicotinoid pesticides.

Antibiotics

Antibiotics are chemicals that kill microbes such as pathogenic bacteria. They can be used in livestock farming for several reasons:

- to treat infections: a course of antibiotics may kill the pathogenic bacteria;
- to prevent infection: regular large doses of antibiotics may prevent livestock from becoming infected with pathogenic bacteria. This may be done as a precaution, especially where the livestock stocking density is high, such as in intensive production units;
- to promote growth: antibiotics can be used to increase the Gross Growth Efficiency of livestock. Regular small doses of antibiotics reduce the population of non-pathogenic gut bacteria. This can increase the amount of the animal's food that is used for growth, therefore increasing productivity and farm income.

The use of antibiotics in agriculture is greater than the amount used in human healthcare.

Exposure to a high dose of an antibiotic may kill all of a pathogen population. Exposure to a lower dose may only kill the most sensitive individuals so the surviving population will be less easily controlled by the antibiotic. The large scale use of antibiotics as growth promoters increases the risks of producing antibiotic resistant bacteria. Some of these may be zoonoses which cause disease if they are transferred to humans, for example *E. coli, Salmonella, and Campylobacter.*

Hormone pesticides

These kill pests through their biochemical action. However, they don't kill through toxic action but by increasing or starting natural processes in a way that is harmful to the pests. Insect hormone pest control chemicals control development in a way that causes death.

Some hormones cause insects to metamorphose into adults before they are large enough to function properly so they die. Others prevent the formation of the chitin skeleton when they moult.

Hormone pesticides have low persistence and are more specific than most pesticides.

Integrated control

Each pest control technique has its own particular advantages and disadvantages. The use of a combination of techniques can maximise effective pest control while minimising environmental impacts. Integrated control often has an order in which the techniques are used based on cost and ease of use, effectiveness, and environmental impacts.

The principles of integrated control:

- use of cultural techniques which make the growth environment less suitable for the pests, for example, maintaining habitats for indigenous predators;
- use of cultural techniques that prevent the build-up of a pest population, for example, crop rotation;
- cultivating species and varieties that are less likely to suffer pest attack;
- use of other appropriate non-pesticide techniques;
- use of pesticides when essential – carefully timed applications of specific, non-persistent pesticides.

Pollinators

Many crops are pollinated by species of bees, moths, beetles, and other taxa. Their services can be aided in several ways:

- provision of food supplies by growing plants that provide nectar, for example, a mix of flowering plants alongside the crop;
- restricting the use of pesticides that harm pollinators;
- introduction of bee hives.

Maintenance of soil biota

▶ *Worms are important in nutrient recycling and soil aeration*

Soil biota are important for soil fertility and crop productivity, especially detritivores and decomposers. They increase nutrient availability through the breakdown of dead organic matter and nitrogen fixation. Organic acids produced by decomposition increase the weathering of rocks that releases nutrients into the soil.

Earthworms increase aeration and drainage which aid aerobic processes and water retention.

Manipulation of food species

The crops and livestock cultivated can be manipulated through their population structure, population density, and their genetics.

Population control

Optimum livestock/crop density

Increasing the population density can increase the total yield, although yield per individual may be reduced due to inter-species competition. A high population density can increase the risk of the rapid spread of disease.

Monocultures

A monoculture involves cultivating a single species, often over a large area. This can make cultivation easier by allowing the use of larger machinery but pests and diseases can spread rapidly if they colonise the field.

▲ *These machines were all used to prepare and plant a potato field on the same day*

The removal of hedgerows and other habitats to create larger fields can also increase pest damage as natural predator habitats are lost.

Control of genetics

Asexual reproduction

Plants

In natural asexual reproduction, the offspring develop from the parent plant rather than from seeds, for example, strawberry plant 'runners'. Artificial asexual reproduction involves cuttings where new plants are produced from sections of leaf, stem or root tissue from the parent plant.

▶ Advantages: offspring are genetically identical to the parent plant, so their characteristics are predictable. The survival rate is high.

▶ Disadvantages: There is no genetic variation in the offspring so their characteristics cannot be improved. Fewer offspring are produced than by sexual reproduction.

Animals

Cloning is an artificial asexual reproduction technique for livestock that is still being developed. The aim is to produce offspring that are genetically identical to a selected individual with desirable characteristics: the 'donor'.

▶ Method: Cells are removed from the donor and grown in culture.

An egg is removed from a female. The nucleus of the egg is removed and replaced by the nucleus from one of the donor cells.

The egg is implanted into a surrogate female where it develops during a normal pregnancy. When it is born it has the characteristics of the donor.

Potential applications of asexual reproduction to agriculture

▶ Valuable animals that die can be replaced by genetically identical individuals.

▶ Herds that are culled during a disease outbreak can be replaced with genetically identical individuals.

▶ Large numbers of individuals with desirable characteristics could be produced.

Sexual reproduction

Offspring combine the genes from two parents, so their characteristics cannot be predicted accurately. Producing a variety or breed with particular characteristics, but without undesirable characteristics, can take many generations.

Selective breeding

This involves the production of offspring from parents that were chosen because of their genetic characteristics. Breeding between genetically similar individuals may produce offspring with similar characteristics, but there is an increased risk of inbreeding.

Examples of livestock breeds with desirable characteristics

Livestock	Breed & its characteristics
Cattle	Limousin – high muscle growth efficiency Belted Galloway – high milk yield, rapid growth Highland – even temper, few stress problems, hardy
Pigs	Large white – hardy, good quality bacon, large litters Saddleback – good milkers, large litters Tamworth – very active, good foragers, very high quality bacon
Sheep	Merino – very high quality wool Cheviot – very hardy, rapid maturity, good quality wool, resistant to foot rot and parasitic worms, wool-free face so less wool-blindness

▶ *Highland cattle can survive a harsh climate*

Crossbreeding

Cross-breeding between two different parental breeds may produce a combination of desirable characteristics with 'hybrid vigour' and a lower risk of inbreeding. An example of crossbreeding is Zebu cattle which are reared in areas with a hot climate. They tolerate the heat well but give a low milk yield. Ayrshire cattle from Scotland give a very high milk yield but they are not heat tolerant. Crossbreeding between Zebu and Ayrshire cattle has produced cattle that can tolerate the heat and have a high milk yield.

Crossbreeding also reduces the problems caused by homozygous recessive genes that are often found in inbred varieties. This is called 'hybrid vigour' or heterosis.

Improved breeding techniques:

- ▼ artificial insemination (AI): semen collected from a male who has desirable characteristics is used to impregnate females. Many more young can be produced than by natural mating. Frozen semen samples can be transported much more easily than parents and can be stored so offspring can be produced long after the male has died;
- ▼ embryo transfer: the hormone FSH is used to stimulate ovulation and the release of many eggs by the female. The eggs are washed out of the uterus and collected. The eggs are fertilised by sperms collected from a male with desirable characteristics (IVF). Each fertilised embryo is implanted into a different surrogate female. The donor female can produce multiple embryos more frequently than she could produce offspring through normal pregnancies.

Genetic engineering/transgenics/Genetic Modification (GM)

These are alternative names for the same procedures. The potential benefits are very large but there are concerns about environmental impacts.

Conventional selective breeding programmes can only introduce characteristics that exist within the gene pool of the species or other species that are very closely related and can produce fertile hybrid offspring.

GM allows the introduction of single characteristics from one species to another, or between varieties or breeds of the same species.

A range of new GM varieties has been developed but concerns over environmental and human health impacts have prevented many of them entering commercial cultivation.

GM case studies

Crop variety	Characteristics
Roundup Ready Soya	A strain of the bacterium *Agrobacterium* is resistant to the herbicide glyphosate (trade name: Roundup). The gene that produces this resistance has been introduced into soya beans. Weed problems are reduced because the soya crop is unaffected by the spraying of Roundup so higher spraying rates can be used if necessary.
Bt crops	The bacterium *Bacillus thuringiensis* naturally produces a toxin that kills insects. The gene that controls the production of the toxin has been transferred into crops such as corn, cotton and maize so that the toxin protects the crops from insect pests.
Golden rice	A diet that is deficient in Vitamin A causes about 500 000 new cases of blindness each year, especially in India and sub-Saharan Africa. Rice contains vitamin A, but it is in the husk that is often removed so that the rice grains can be stored. Genes have been transferred from the daffodil and a soil bacterium (***Erwinia uredovora***) so that vitamin A is produced within the rice grains. The rice grains have a yellowish colour, hence the name Golden Rice.
Oilseed rape omega-3 fatty acids	Omega-3 fatty acids can be a component of a healthy diet. It is found in many seafood species but many people have inadequate supplies. The gene for omega-3 production has been transferred from a marine alga (*Thalassiosira pseudonona*) into oilseed rape which could make supplies of omega-3 fatty acids more available.

Advantages of GM production

- Individual desirable characteristics can be introduced without associated unwanted characteristics, as can occur in normal selective breeding.
- Genes may be introduced from other species that could never have been achieved by by normal selective breeding.

GM techniques can increase resistance to specific insects reducing the amount of pesticides used to protect a crop;

GM techniques can increase pathogen resistance reducing disease in a crop.

Disadvantages of GM production

The use of transgenics is a relatively new technology and concerns over potential problems have delayed the general use of GM crops. More evidence is needed before the risks can be fully assessed.

Potential risks claimed for the use of GM crops.

- It has been claimed that GM food can increase food allergies.
- Potential gene transfer from GM foods to cells of the body or to bacteria in the gastrointestinal tract.
- The migration of genes from GM plants into conventional crops and plants. For example, pollen from GM crops may contaminate organic crops. Pollen from GM crops may spread to closely related wild varieties that could have ecological impacts, for example, if the Bt gene entered the gene pool of wild plants then insects that feed on them may be killed.
- Transfer through the food chain, for example, GM crops approved for animal feed or industrial use being detected at low levels in products for human consumption.
- Genes that provide resistance to antibiotics are often inserted with the desired genes. They act as 'markers' and are used to check whether the gene transfer has been successful. Cells into which the genes have been transferred successfully will not be harmed by the antibiotic. There is some concern that the antibiotic resistance gene present in food may transfer from GM crops to pathogenic bacteria, making the disease harder to treat.
- Increased costs to farmers especially in LEDCs as many GM crops require new seeds to be purchased each year rather than harvesting seeds from an existing crop. The Intellectual Property rights and patents for specific GM crops are owned by specific companies who control the prices and availability of the seeds.
- Concerns in LEDCs that GM crops will reduce the local indigenous crop diversity including the successful seed saving practices.

Agricultural energetics

Intensive and extensive agriculture

A major aim of agriculture is to produce more food than would be produced by the previous natural ecosystem but this requires inputs of materials and energy. The intensity of agriculture is a measure of the amount of artificial inputs and the extra yield that is produced.

In extensive agriculture, the aim is to maximise the total yield by spreading the available inputs over a large area of available land. Intensive agriculture is practised where large inputs are available but there may be a shortage of land. Yields per unit area may be very high but the extra yield per unit of input may not be. So, although intensive agriculture may be very productive, it is not necessarily very efficient.

The link between the intensity of farming, efficiency and productivity is demonstrated by the law of diminishing returns.

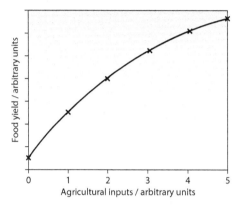

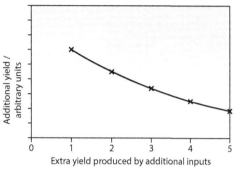

◀ The law of diminishing returns and agricultural output

Each extra unit of input causes the yield to increase, but by a smaller amount than previous inputs

Each extra unit of input results in an increase in yield but the size of each successive increase gets smaller. If enough suitable land were available, then spreading the inputs evenly over the total area would produce a greater overall yield than concentrating all the inputs onto a small area.

This principle could be applied to the global food production system. The total yield would be increased if the intensity of agriculture were reduced in some areas, with the unused inputs being used on land that is currently farmed extensively. The uneven investment of inputs may be sensible in some situations, such as where one area has the potential to be much more productive. However, sometimes the uneven use of inputs is purely economic, with more affluent societies having the ability to buy more while poorer communities that could benefit greatly from access to more inputs cannot afford them

Energy subsidies

An energy subsidy in an agricultural system is any input that aids productivity but requires the use of energy.

Major agricultural energy subsidies include:

- manufacture of nitrate fertilisers;
- manufacture of pesticides;
- pumping of irrigation water;
- fuel for machinery for ploughing, spraying, harvesting;
- energy for the manufacture of machinery and equipment;
- heat for drying harvested grain;
- processing of food for consumers;
- transport of food to consumers.

As agricultural systems have become more productive and more intensive, they have become increasingly dependent on energy subsidies, especially energy from fossil fuels. It may be difficult to maintain or increase food production if abundant energy supplies cannot be maintained.

▲ *A grain store*

Energy ratios

The energy ratio is a measure of efficiency by comparing energy inputs and outputs and then expressing this as the number of units of food energy produced per unit of energy input. Systems that give the highest yields per unit of energy input have higher energy ratio values.

Energy ratio is not the same as productivity per unit area. A system with a high productivity may require high energy subsidies and therefore have a low energy ratio.

Product energy ratios

Product	Energy ratio (typical values)	
	Extensive system	Intensive system
Wheat	11	5
Rice	16	4
Beef	0.3	0.1
Milk	1.2	0.4

Food conversion ratios (FCR)

The food conversion ratio is a measure of the mass of food needed to produce a given mass of livestock growth. The lower the ratio, the better the conversion of food into animal biomass.

Livestock Food Conversion Ratios

Livestock	FCR (typical value)
Salmon (aquaculture)	1.1
Chicken	1.7
Pork	3.1
Sheep	6.0
Beef	7.0

Control of food chain energy losses

An understanding of energy flow in food chains can help in developing more efficient ways of using farmland.

Autotrophic nutrition

All living organisms need chemical energy to drive biological metabolic processes.

The chemicals that are broken down to release this energy are not generally available in the environment but can be built up from simpler molecules by some living organisms called autotrophs ('self-feeders'). To build up high-energy molecules the autotrophs need a source of energy. They use this energy to make carbohydrates such as glucose, starch and cellulose, and lipids such as fats and oils. Most of these organisms are photo-autotrophs, such as plants, algae and photosynthetic bacteria, which capture sunlight during photosynthesis. Some are chemo-autotrophs, such as the bacteria that harness energy by oxidising substances such as hydrogen sulfide, methane, and ions of ammonium and nitrite.

Autotrophs have a big advantage for survival because they do not rely on other organisms for their energy supplies. All other organisms rely on autotrophs for their energy supplies.

Heterotrophic nutrition

Organisms that cannot produce their own high-energy molecules must gain their energy from other living organisms. These are heterotrophs ('different-feeders') which include all animals, fungi, and many bacteria.

Much of the energy captured by autotrophs is used in their metabolic processes and released back to the environment as low energy-density heat. So, the amount of energy available to the heterotrophs is much less than was harnessed by the autotrophs. In a food chain with several trophic levels, less energy is passed on to the next trophic level than was received from the previous one. This is why few food chains have more than four trophic levels.

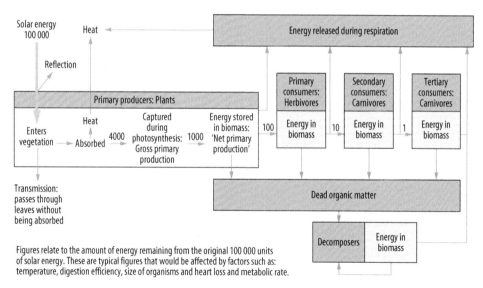

◀ *Energy flow in an agro-ecosystem*

Because the amount of energy in a food chain declines with each progressive trophic level, the amount of food that can be produced by an agricultural system depends upon which trophic level produces the food. So, in general, the greatest possible amount of food produced by an area would be plant material rather than meat.

If an area of land can grow crops that can be eaten by people then this would be the most productive system. In some areas this is not possible, such as upland or semi-arid areas where permanent grassland is a more sustainable land use than arable farmland. In such areas, the best option for food production is to raise grazing animals that can digest grass, such as sheep or cattle. They have symbiotic bacteria in their stomachs that produce the enzyme cellulose which is needed to digest the cellulose in plant material.

▶ Sheep grazing on land that is too poor to be cultivated for crops

Omnivores such as pigs can produce edible meat from food wastes that were not wanted by people, such as the wastes from producing cheese and butter or leftover food from the catering industry.

Environmental impacts of agriculture

Habitat impacts

Large areas of land have been cleared to produce farmland. In general, these are areas where the climate is favourable and the soil is fertile. These are often areas where the natural biomes are forest or grassland.

In some cases, the change to farming does not destroy the habitat, but it may change it so that the indigenous species cannot survive.

- ▶ **Drainage:** farmland is often drained to produce more aerobic soils, for example, the drainage of waterlogged grassland to increase grass growth. Wetland plant species and the animals they support may not be able to survive the changes.
- ▶ **Nutrient enrichment:** using fertilisers increases nutrient availability and plant growth rates. Species that respond by growing taller such as grasses may out-compete smaller plants such as many wildflower species.
- ▶ **Reduced biodiversity:** natural ecosystems often have small-scale local variations in abiotic factors producing differences in the composition of the community of species found there. Agroecosystems often replace diverse communities of indigenous species with a community of species that has fewer species, many of which may not be indigenous. Many indigenous species will not be able to survive the new conditions or may be removed because they are predators or competitors.

Agriculture does not just destroy habitats. It can also create new habitats which may be gradually colonised by wildlife species. Some areas that have been farmed in the same way for long periods of time have become plagioclimax habitats that are valuable to wildlife.

Examples of habitats created by farming that support important wildlife communities:

- hedgerows;
- hay meadows;
- grazed moorland and heathland;
- chalk grassland.

Introduced species

Agricultural systems often introduce species into areas where they are not normally found. Sometimes this causes problems.

Introduced pests

Farming has introduced many species into new areas where they would not naturally be found. Some are crop or livestock species that have colonised the surrounding area and become pests, others are pests that have been introduced accidentally such as the late blight fungus of potato and tomato crops.

Biological control species

Biological control can be used to control pests instead of using pesticides, which should reduce environmental damage. However, introducing non-indigenous species can cause problems. Introduced predators may eat other species as well as the pests.

Pollution

Agriculture involves several activities that have caused serious pollution, especially the use of agrochemicals such as pesticides and fertilisers. Agriculture also contributes to climate change by the release of greenhouse gases. See Chapter 10 Pollution.

▲ *Pesticde spraying*

Pesticides

Pesticides are deliberately used because they are toxic and are intended to kill pests. Because pesticides are not species-specific, sensitive non-target species may also be killed. Species may also be affected if inter-species relationships are affected such as the death of food species, pollinators, or pollution that favours competitor species.

Nutrient pollution

The nutrients that were intended to stimulate crop growth, or are digestive wastes from livestock, can stimulate the growth of undesirable organisms.

Leached inorganic nutrients cause eutrophication, for example, nitrate fertilisers.

Organic nutrients such as manure can cause deoxygenation of rivers and lakes because of the aerobic respiration of bacteria.

Nitrate toxicity

Nitrates can be leached from farmland into water bodies that are used as sources of potable water for human consumption. High nitrate levels can cause blue baby syndrome (methaemoglobinaemia) and nitrates may be a human carcinogen.

Climate change

Several farming activities release greenhouse gases.

Greenhouse gases produced by agricultural activities

Greenhouse gas (GHG)	Sources
Carbon dioxide	Fossil fuel use Ploughing increases soil aerobic respiration
Methane	Bacterial anaerobic digestion: livestock intestines rice padi fields
Oxides of nitrogen (nitrous oxide)	From livestock manure and nitrogen fertilisers

Embodied energy

The manufacture of materials, especially nitrate fertilisers, and machinery, usually involves the use of fossil fuels and causes the release of GHGs, mainly carbon dioxide.

Changes in the hydrological cycle

Agriculture has several important impacts on the hydrological cycle.

- ⚑ Irrigation water can deplete the sources of the water, such as aquifers or rivers.
- ⚑ Soil erosion caused by agriculture can reduce the effect that soil has on the hydrological cycle such as water retention and the moderation of extremes in river flow.
- ⚑ Soil compaction can increase runoff rates and cause more rapid fluctuations in river flow.
- ⚑ Agriculture changes evapotranspiration rates but the actual change depends on the ecosystem that was present before farming started. Evapotranspiration is increased in arid areas but may be reduced in areas where forests were removed.

Soil erosion

Soil is the growing medium in almost all agricultural systems. Soil erosion is a natural process but poor soil management can lead to the rate of erosion exceeding the rate of formation, so the amount of soil present declines. For more details on soil erosion see page 162.

Social factors that affect agriculture

Personal choices about food affect market demand and may affect the methods used in food production.

- ⚑ **Cultural factors:** horsemeat is not popular in the UK but is widely eaten in other European countries.
- ⚑ **Religious factors:** people with religious convictions may avoid certain foods. Jews and Muslims do not eat pork while Hindus do not eat beef.
- ⚑ **Ethical issues:** a desire to reduce the environmental or social impact of food production can influence food choices.
  - • **Local food/food miles:** buying food that was produced nearby reduces the energy involved in transport and the pollution that would have caused.
  - • **Seasonal food:** choosing food that is grown when the local weather is suitable has

a lower environmental impact than eating out-of-season food that needs heating, lighting, or transporting from another area with a suitable climate.

- **Free-range livestock:** some consumers choose to buy eggs and meat from animals that are kept under conditions close to their natural conditions, especially having the freedom to move around and search for food. They often consider the conditions of intensive rearing to be cruel.

❶ Free range pigs
❷ intensively reared pigs

- **Organic food**: some consumers choose to buy food that was produced using natural processes wherever possible rather than those using artificial processes for pest control and nutrient supply.
- **Fairtrade food**: fairtrade food is produced in a way that provides an income for producers which means that they can afford basic human rights such as water, education, health care and food.

Availability of technology

Productive agriculture benefits from the development and availability of a wide range of technologies. These are usually more available in more affluent societies.

These include:

- ⬧ Machinery and equipment for activities such as ploughing, sowing, spraying, harvesting, spreading agrochechemicals, and irrigation.
- ⬧ Pesticides.
- ⬧ Fertilisers.
- ⬧ Genetic improvements through breeding programmes.
- ⬧ Support infrastructure such as transport systems, refrigeration, food processing.

Survey technology

A range of new technologies provide better information that can be used to inform better decision making. GPS mapping and the use of drone and satellite surveys are used to monitor a wide range of factors:

- ⬧ rates of photosynthesis;
- ⬧ biomass estimation;

- soil water content;
- the spread of pests and diseases;
- the cropped area of the fields, area of cover for wild birds, tree plantations etc.

Computer-based monitoring of the yields produced in different areas of a field can be used to better control fertiliser application in each area for future crops. This maximizes yields while avoiding wastage and minimising environmental impacts.

Economic and political influences on agriculture

Economic and political strategies are often used to influence the foods produced and methods used by agriculture. This can produce benefits but problems may also be created. These issues can be illustrated by looking at the changes in food production in Europe since the Second World War ended in 1945.

Food aid

After the war, Europe could not produce enough food to feed everyone. Without a major change in food availability there would have been serious food shortages, possibly famine and social and political problems. Food aid from the USA helped to reduce these problems.

Grants

At that time, farmers in Europe could not afford to invest in more productive methods because they were not sure they would earn enough to repay the loans they would have had to take out. To solve this, grants were made available so farmers could get financial assistance for a wide range of projects to increase food production such as:

- hedgerow removal to increase field size;
- purchase of machinery;
- drainage of wet fields;
- improved livestock;
- liming to neutralise acidic soils.

These changes increased food production but had environmental impacts such as the loss of hedgerows and wetlands.

Guaranteed market

Increasing production eventually created a new problem. If output exceeded demand then the market price would drop and the farmers could make a loss, despite the high yield. To solve this problem greater financial security was given to farmers by providing a 'guaranteed market' with a price-support system.

If there was a surplus harvest the government would buy some of the harvest from farmers to create an artificial market shortage and raise the price to an agreed level that had been set earlier in the year. Where possible, the surplus would be stored, for example, grain, milk powder, cheese, meat. Surplus food that could not be stored was often destroyed, for example, fruit and vegetables.

If there was a poor harvest then the shortages in supply could have caused prices to rise. The government prevented this by selling just enough food that had been stored from previous years to bring the market price down to the agreed level.

This system created more financial stability for farmers and consumers and helped to raise food production.

Food surpluses

By the 1970s, food production had increased to the level where there were more surpluses than shortages in MEDCs. Farmers continued to grow more food as they had the guarantee that the government would buy their produce even if the consumers did not want to buy it. The government could not sell the surplus food in the normal consumer markets as there were not enough years with poor harvests. Finding alternative markets was difficult due to competition with other food exporters or a lack of consumers to buy the surpluses.

The surpluses could not be sold to other MEDCs like the USA, Canada, or Australia as these countries also produced surpluses. Japan was an MEDC that imported food but already had established suppliers such as the USA and Australia. The countries of Eastern Europe and the USSR needed food but could not afford to pay the full price. Selling the surplus food in LEDCs would undercut local producers, put them out of business, and reduce long-term food production.

The only real solution to surpluses was to avoid producing them but this involved big changes in the way agriculture was supported by the EU and national governments.

Reducing food surpluses

Governments have used a range of methods to reduce excessive food production while, hopefully, maintaining farm incomes and therefore confidence in the industry.

- **Quotas:** farmers are given limits on what they are allowed to produce, for example, dairy farmers are given a limit on the amount of milk they can sell.
- **Farm diversification:** farmers have been encouraged to concentrate less on products that were being over-produced and more on new products and non-food production activities such as recreation, public visits to working farms and specialised dairy production such as cheese and ice cream.
- **Alternative crops and livestock:** biofuels, pharmaceutical crops, for example, poppies, llamas, bees for honey, and deer.
- **Set-aside:** farmers of crops in surplus have been paid for taking farmland out of production and keeping it in a condition where it could be farmed again if needed.
- **Agri-environmental schemes:** a range of schemes have given farmers a contribution to their income for farming in ways that benefit the environment, for example:
  - Environmentally Sensitive Areas (ESAs);
  - Countryside Stewardship Scheme (CSS);
  - Environmental Stewardship Scheme (ESS);
  - Countryside Stewardship (CS);

Aspects of many agri-environmental schemes

Feature	Requirements	Purpose
Hedgerows	Must be at least 1.5m tall No fertilisers or pesticides to be applied within 2m At least 2 year interval between cutting No cutting during the bird breeding season	To maintain habitats for birds and insects To restore traditional patchwork of fields
Ditches	No cultivation within 2m No fertilisers or pesticides applied within 1m of the bank top Ditches may only be cleared once in a 5 year period	Farmland ditches are an important habitat for many wetland invertebrate and plant species
Dry stone walls	Protection of dry-stone walls	Important as landscape features and for stock management
Trees	Conservation of in-field trees	To conserve soil, energy, water, wildlife, and the atmosphere To protect ancient indigenous trees
Beetle banks	At least 2m wide Sown with tussocky grasses, for example, Timothy	To provide habitats for natural pest predators
Livestock density	Control of livestock stocking density	To reduce soil compaction
Planting	Planting selected plants for nectar and seeds.	To support pollinating insects To provide winter food for seed-eating birds
Nesting plots	Provision of skylark nesting plots in fields	To maintain and increase skylark populations
Woodland planting and management	Rhododendron control Removal of diseased trees, for example, ash trees with *Chalara* dieback.	To reduce non-indigenous trees To ensure healthy and sustainable woodlands

Agri-environment schemes vary a great deal between countries even within the EU. The main objectives include reducing nutrient and pesticide emissions, protecting biodiversity, restoring landscapes and preventing rural depopulation.

❶ *An uncultivated field margin*
❷ *A drainage ditch with an unculivated buffer strip*
❸ *In-field trees*
❹ *A skylark nesting plot*

Strategies to increase agricultural sustainability

Food is a basic requirement for survival. With a growing human population, it is increasingly important that food supplies also increase.

The population size of most species is controlled by density-dependant factors such as disease and food supply. If the population rises above the carrying capacity of the environment then the death rate increases and the population is reduced.

Only humans can consciously manipulate the environment to produce more food and allow the population to rise above the natural carrying-capacity.

▼ *The human food chain*

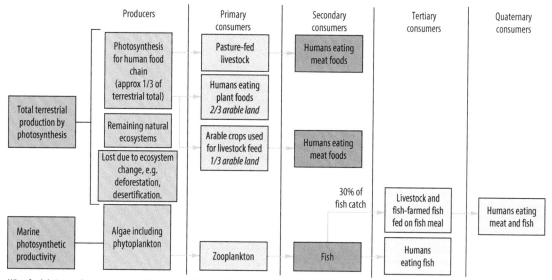

When food choices put humans in later torphic levels, the efficiency of food production goes down

It would not be possible to support the huge global human population without directing more of the energy captured by photosynthesis into the human food chain and therefore artificially raise the food output of the agricultural system. The growing human population will probably reach at least 12 billion during this century. This will make the sustainable management of food production even more important.

Sustainable agriculture

The development of sustainable agricultural systems can be guided by learning from past mistakes.

Agriculture first developed about 12,000 years ago in the 'fertile crescent'. This is an area of the Middle East, largely in the modern countries of Iraq and Syria. It was an area with diverse habitats. It included forested areas with a good climate and fertile soils which made it suitable for food production as well as more fragile grassland and semi-desert areas. Natural climate change and the way in which the land was exploited has gradually reduced the capacity of the land to produce food. Similar reductions in productivity have occurred in many areas such as the mid-west of the USA, parts of the UK, deforested rainforest areas, and large areas of Africa.

The key features of land degradation are often soil erosion, combined with a reduction in soil nutrient and water levels. The reduction of natural biodiversity often makes pest problems worse. The response to these problems has often involved strategies that increase productivity but may be unsustainable in the long term:

- ▼ reliance on artificial fertilisers for nutrient supplies;
- ▼ reliance on chemical pesticides for pest control;
- ▼ irrigation using water from groundwater resources that are not being recharged.

If food production falls, then the supply of food can only be maintained if more land is farmed or food is imported but each of these strategies has its own difficulties.

About 10% of the Earth's land area is cultivated for crops, with another 25% being grazed with livestock. The potential for cultivating new areas is limited as much of the remaining land is too dry, wet, cold, hot, steep, is covered in ice, or has no soil.

Food may be imported from other areas but that may reduce food availability in the area in which the food has been produced. Food may become even less available to people with less money as the land they used to farm becomes too expensive to rent and the land is used to grow food that will be exported to supply more affluent societies.

The strategies needed to develop sustainable agricultural methods are a combination of new approaches applied to ecological principles.

Organic agriculture is often described by the practices that are not done, for example, not using pesticides and artificial fertilisers. This misses the point. Organic agriculture uses natural processes to provide nutrients, control pests, and provide ecological services so that the use of pesticides and artificial fertilisers is unnecessary.

A lot of progress has been made in developing and implementing sustainable strategies but it has not always been easy to gain support for change and the introduction of new techniques.

This section provides a brief overview of unsustainable features of agriculture and changes that may help to achieve sustainability. More details are found in earlier sections of this chapter.

Key issues in agricultural sustainability

Issue	Sustainability problem	Selected sustainability strategies	Page ref
Pest control	A reliance on chemical pesticides may be unsustainable Use of some pesticides has been banned or restricted due to their impacts on non-target species many pests have developed resistance to pesticides	Cultural pest control: weeding, mulching, crop rotation, barrier crops, culling, biological control, predator habitats, polyculture/companion crops Integrated control Reduced use of antibiotics	
Nutrient supplies	Current supplies of rock phosphates to produce phosphate fertilisers are non-renewable	Increased use of natural processes to supply nutrients Recycling of organic matter Crop rotation Cultivation of legumes Conservation of soil biota	
Energy inputs	Manufacture of nitrate fertilisers requires large energy inputs from fossil fuels	Reduced use of artificial fertilisers, especially nitrates Low tillage techniques Low food miles	

Gene pool for breeding programmes	Gene pools of Crop Wild Relative (CWR) plants include genes that will be important in future breeding programmes	Conservation of habitats that protect CWRs. Seed banks to conserve biodiversity.
Water supplies	Over-exploitation of rivers and groundwater reserves Soil salinisation caused by using saline irrigation water	Cultivation of low water-use crops Maintenance of soil and soil organic matter Use of reservoirs and aquifer recharge Drip irrigation rather than overhead sprays
Carbon dioxide emissions	Loss of soil organic matter increases atmospheric CO_2 levels CO_2 released by fossil fuel use	Low-tillage farming to reduce the decomposition of soil organic matter Maintain or increase soil organic matter Reduced use of machinery Use of renewable energy resources
Methane releases	Methane produced by anaerobic microbes in rice padi fields and the digestive systems of livestock	Cultivation of rice varieties that can tolerate drier conditions so fields can be drained earlier Feeding cattle a high carbohydrate diet and grinding their food first reduces methane production
Wildlife biodiversity	Loss of species that provide important ecosystem-services such as pest control, nutrient provision, and pollination	Retain natural and semi-natural ecosystems such as hedgerows, ditches, ponds, woodlands. Maintenance of soil biota

Key principles
- Food supplies are essential in supporting a growing human population.
- A range of factors controls the crops and livestock species that are cultivated.
- The control of abiotic and biotic factors increases food production.
- Food species can be manipulated to increase food production.
- Agriculture has important environmental impacts but many of these can be reduced by good management.
- Agriculture is affected by economic and political decisions.
- A range of strategies are being developed to produce sustainable agricultural systems.

Aquatic food resources

Chapter topics
▼ Marine productivity
▼ Fishing
▼ Aquaculture

Marine productivity

Oceans cover over 70% of the Earth's surface but only a small proportion is biologically productive as limiting factors restrict the growth of the most important photosynthetic organisms which are algae.

Variations in light levels

Little light penetrates water to a greater depth than 100m, less if the water is turbid, so photosynthesis is limited to the surface water layers, called the photic zone. Moat life at greater depths, in the aphotic zone, relies on food produced near the surface, for example, planktonic algae that is carried down by water currents, or the bodies of dead organisms that sink.

How nutrient movements in the sea affect productivity

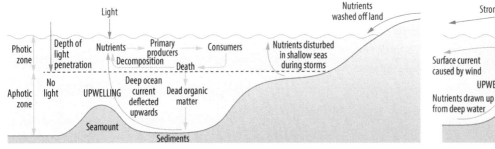

How upwellings caused by a seamount and storms over shallow water affect nutrient movements.

Coastal upwelling caused by an offshore wind

▲ *How nutrient movements in the sea affect productivity*

Nutrient availability

Algae absorb nutrients directly from the water because there is no soil and they don't have roots. Some nutrients are readily available, such as carbon dioxide. Others are often the limiting factor on biological productivity when they are not sufficiently abundant, for example, phosphates.

The low solubility of phosphates causes the oceans to be deficient in phosphates except where there are processes that cause phosphates to be added.

Phosphate levels in the photic zone are increased by runoff from rivers and in areas in which deep, cold water rises towards the ocean surface, a process known as upwelling, but these are not found in most areas of open ocean. In open areas the nutrients contained in planktonic organisms are carried to the seabed when they die. This may reduce nutrient availability in the surface photic layer so future biological productivity is reduced.

▼ *Variations in the factors that affect productivity in different oceans*

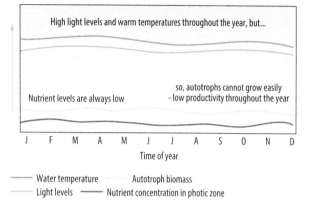

Tropical oceans

High light levels and warm temperatures throughout the year, but...

so, autotrophs cannot grow easily - low productivity throughout the year

Nutrient levels are always low

Time of year

—— Water temperature —— Autotroph biomass
—— Light levels —— Nutrient concentration in photic zone

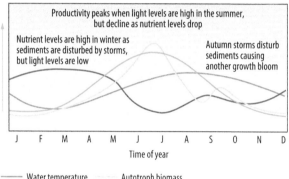

Temperate oceans (northern hemisphere)

Productivity peaks when light levels are high in the summer, but decline as nutrient levels drop

Nutrient levels are high in winter as sediments are disturbed by storms, but light levels are low

Autumn storms disturb sediments causing another growth bloom

Time of year

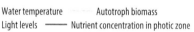

—— Water temperature —— Autotroph biomass
—— Light levels —— Nutrient concentration in photic zone

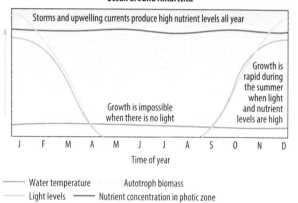

Ocean around Antarctica

Storms and upwelling currents produce high nutrient levels all year

Growth is rapid during the summer when light and nutrient levels are high

Growth is impossible when there is no light

Time of year

—— Water temperature —— Autotroph biomass
—— Light levels —— Nutrient concentration in photic zone

Freshwater productivity

Water bodies on land are often very productive as they receive nutrient runoff from the land and receive high light levels because they are relatively shallow. Total productivity is limited by the relatively small total area of rivers and lakes.

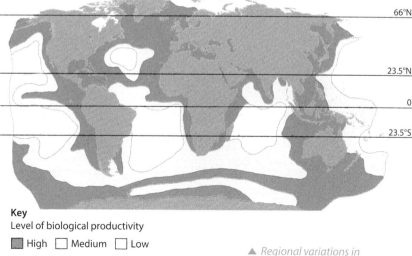

66°N

23.5°N

0

23.5°S

Key
Level of biological productivity

■ High ☐ Medium ☐ Low

▲ *Regional variations in marine productivity*

Fishing

Many different methods are used to catch different aquatic species. Large-scale methods are used mainly in the sea and some large lakes. The word 'fishing' includes the capture of a wide range of species of different taxa, including fish and shellfish (crustaceans and molluscs).

Purposes, advantages and disadvantages of the main fishing methods

Demersal fishing

Demersal fishing includes fishing for species that live on the seabed.

Demersal trawling is used for species on the seabed such as cod, hadddock, plaice, shrimps, and scampi.

Demersal long lines use a line of baited hooks to catch species such as cod and haddock.

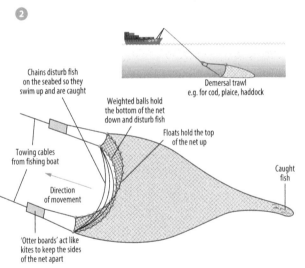

Chains disturb fish on the seabed so they swim up and are caught

Weighted balls hold the bottom of the net down and disturb fish

Floats hold the top of the net up

Towing cables from fishing boat

Direction of movement

'Otter boards' act like kites to keep the sides of the net apart

Demersal trawl e.g. for cod, plaice, haddock

Caught fish

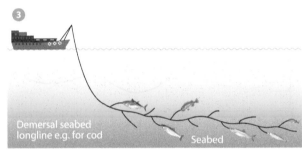

Demersal seabed longline e.g. for cod

Seabed

❶ The chains on this trawl disturb the seabed to catch scallops buried in the sediments. This causes a lot of damage to the demersal ecosystem
❷ Demersal trawling
❸ Demersal longlining

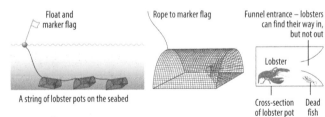

Float and marker flag

Rope to marker flag

Funnel entrance – lobsters can find their way in, but not out

Lobster

A string of lobster pots on the seabed

Cross-section of lobster pot

Dead fish bait

❶ Lobster traps ❷ Shellfish traps

Shellfish traps

These are baited traps that catch crustaceans such as crabs, crayfish, and lobsters.

Pelagic fishing

Pelagic fishing includes fishing for species that live in open water above the seabed, often near the water surface.

Pelagic trawling

This is used for species that form shoals in mid-water or near the surface such as bass, anchovies, herring, and mackerel. Pelagic fish often form single-species shoals so the catch of non-target species is usually low but predator species may also be caught accidentally, for example, porpoises and dolphins.

Drift nets

Drift nets are long curtain-like nets that are supported by floats and catch pelagic species near the surface such as tuna and herring.

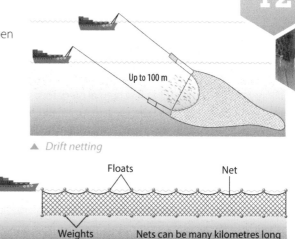

▲ *Drift netting*

▲ *Pelagic long line and hooks*

Purse seining

Purse seining uses a net that is laid around a shoal of fish. The top is held up by floats while the bottom is held down by weights then pulled tight underneath the shoal. It is used for species such as tuna, sardines, herring, and anchovies.

Pelagic long lines

These use a line of baited hooks which can be many kilometres in length. Pelagic longlines catch species such as tuna and squid.

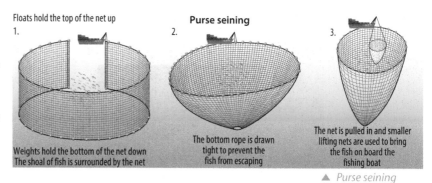

▲ *Purse seining*

▲ *Pelagic longlining*

Environmental impacts of fishing

Fishing can have major impacts on the target species by reducing their populations but it can also have impacts on non-target species. Some of these impacts are direct, while others are caused indirectly by other ecological effects of fishing.

Population decline caused by overfishing

The population of any species will decline if mortality exceeds the birth rate but some species are more likely to be overfished than others. k-selected species are more vulnerable to overfishing because they produce fewer young and start breeding at an older age, for example, Orange Roughy, Blue Fin Tuna, and all shark species.

These species may reach a catchable size before they are sexually mature, so overfishing could remove the entire breeding population. The survival of the population then relies on the immature fish which may be caught before their first chance to breed.

r-selected species breed at a young age and produce more young. Their populations recover more rapidly after over-fishing, for example, Herring, Atlantic Mackerel, Yellow Fin Tuna.

The 'common' skate is the biggest skate species reaching a size of 1.9m across its 'wings'. It has few natural predators, starts breeding around 11 years old, produces few young, and can live to be over 100. It is not a commercially important species but it is caught in demersal trawls. Its range includes the NE Atlantic, Mediterranean Sea, and Baltic Sea. It is now extinct in the Baltic Sea and Critically Endangered in the Mediterranean Sea and the NE Atlantic. The commercial value of demersal trawling makes it likely that fishing will continue and the Common Skate will become extinct. It has been renamed the Blue Skate or Flapper Skate.

The Greenland Shark was fished commercially for lamp and lubricating oil until the 1960s. Its main threat now is bycatch from commercial deep-water trawling. It is a cold-water species but little is known about its range or populations size. It can live to be over 400 years old but does not start breeding until it is 100-150 and produces few young so it is very vulnerable to overfishing.

❶ Six-gilled shark steaks for sale in a fish market
❷ Scallops have been overfished around the UK. These came from Patagonia, South America

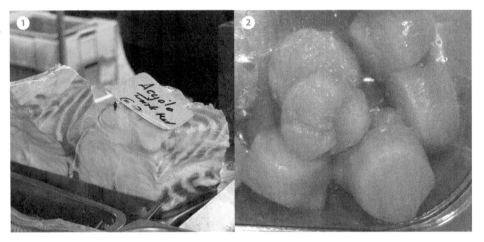

As local fisheries are over-exploited, seafood supplies in countries like the UK are often maintained by exploiting fisheries at increasing distances from the UK.

By-catch

By-catch is the catch that is not wanted. It is usually the catch of non-target species but it can also include the catch of the target species where the individuals are too small to be legally landed or sold. By-catch may be unwanted for several reasons:

- ▶ immature fish of the target species that are too small to sell. This may reduce future catches by killing the fish that would have grown to reach a saleable size;
- ▶ individuals of species which would be saleable but the catch quota has already been reached, so they must be discarded. If these species are still being killed during fishing for other species, then having a catch quota will fail to protect them;
- ▶ species with no commercial value.

Many of the by-catch organisms will be dead or injured and will not survive when thrown back into the sea.

The amount of by-catch varies greatly between different fishing methods. More species-selective methods such as purse-seine nets or pelagic trawling tend to have lower by-catch rates. Demersal trawling usually exploits mixed fisheries where the by-catch rates can be high.

Bycatch from different fishing methods.

▲ *A dead Finetooth Shark unintentionally caught in a trawl net*

- ▗ **Drift net bycatch**: driftnets are non-selective and will catch any animals swimming near the surface including whales, dolphins, turtles, and sharks.

- ▗ **Pelagic long line bycatch**: Albatross are large seabirds that feed over large areas of the open ocean in the southern hemisphere and North Pacific. Most species cannot dive deep into the water so they collect food such as squid, krill, and fish near the water surface. Large numbers are caught by long-line fishing where they drown after being caught on the lures put out for squid or fish. Albatrosses are long-lived birds, living up to 50 years, and do not normally start breeding until they are 7 – 10 years old. Most species have a low reproduction rate, laying one egg every second year so their populations are seriously affected by any increase in mortality. Other bycatch taxa caught on long lines include sharks and turtles.

- ▗ **Pelagic trawling bycatch**: pelagic pair trawls for seabass can kill porpoises. The porpoises are trying to catch the bass but become trapped in the nets where they drown.

- ▗ **Demersal trawling bycatch**: seabed fish often live in mixed-species shoals so the chance of catching a mixture of species is high.

- ▗ **Shrimp bycatch**: shrimp trawling uses nets with a very small mesh size so few by-catch animals can escape. These include crabs, sea urchins, molluscs, and starfish. The by-catch of shrimp trawling can make up as much as 99% of the catch.

Ghost fishing

Fishing gear that has been discarded or lost may continue to trap and kill marine organisms. The dead organisms caught in the fishing gear often act as bait and attract more individuals which also become trapped and die.

▶ *Discarded fishing net*

Habitat damage

- ▶ **Seabed damage**: to be effective, demersal trawls need to disturb organisms so that they swim upwards and are caught in the net, especially if they normally live in the sediments on the seabed, for example, shrimps and scampi (Norway Lobsters). Trawl nets often have chains or metal balls to disturb the seabed. This mixes the shallow aerobic surface layer of the seabed with deeper anaerobic layers. The nets also destroy slow-growing organisms such as sea fans and deep water corals.

- ▶ **Coral reef impact**: coral polyps are sensitive to physical damage as they can be killed if they are pressed against the sharp coralite cup to which they are attached. Nets, traps, ropes and discarded gear can all cause physical damage.

- ▶ **Seagrass beds:** grass-like flowering plants that grow on shallow sandy areas of relatively protected tropical seas. They are important nursery grounds for many species of fish that may live on coral reefs or in deep water as adults. Disturbance by trawling kills the plants so their roots no longer hold the sand grains together. Currents and waves move the sand around, making it more difficult for new plants to colonise and become established.

- ▶ **Dynamite fishing**: the pressure waves released by underwater explosions can stun fish and make them easy to catch. The use of dynamite is illegal in most countries but it is still carried out in remote areas, especially where subsistence fishermen are finding it difficult to catch fish with other methods. It is a particularly common method on coral reefs where nets cannot be used to catch the fish that live among the coral heads. The explosions destroy coral and kill many other organisms.

- ▶ **Food web impacts**: reducing the numbers of any species will affect the other organisms that are in the same food web, for example:
  - competitors may become more common;
  - their prey may become more common;
  - their predators may become rarer.

Methods of reducing the environmental impacts of fishing

Catch quotas

A catch quota sets a limit on the total weight of fish that can be landed. This quota may be divided up amongst all the fishing boats in the fleet.

Quotas work best when fish are found in single-species shoals where fishing will stop if the quota for that species has already been reached. In mixed fisheries, many species may be caught in the same net. If the quota for one species has been reached then any surplus must be thrown back even though they are probably dead, while fishing for other species continues.

Fishing equipment design and use

Fishing equipment can be designed so that it continues to be effective while environmental damage is minimised.

- ▶ **Mesh size**: net mesh size can be set so that fish below a certain size can escape.

- ▶ **Mesh design**: fishing nets are designed so that the mesh direction is diagonal to the direction of movement. This gives the net elasticity as it is pulled through the water but the mesh closes as it fills with fish and drag increases, so smaller fish cannot escape through the shrinking gaps. Panels in the net with the mesh at right angles to the direction of movement do not close up so small fish can still escape.

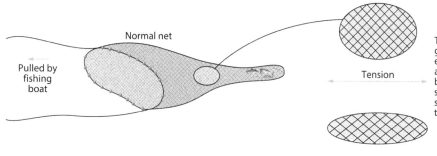

Normal net

Pulled by fishing boat

Tension

The diagonal arrangement gives the net greater elasticity so it stretches as the speed of the fishing boat changes. This increases safety for the boat. However small fish cannot escape through the stretched mesh.

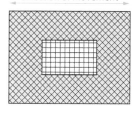

Direction of movement

Having a square mesh panel allows small fish to escape because the mesh does not close up when it is pulled. The rest of the net retains its elasticity.

◀ *Square mesh escape panels*

- **Escape panels**: Turtle Exclusion Devices (TEDs) are large spring loaded escape panels in the nets which allow turtles to escape.
- **Acoustic deterrent devices** ('dolphin pingers'): these produce high frequency sounds that warn dolphins about the presence of the net.
- **Hook shape**: longline hooks with curved points still catch tuna but are less likely to catch albatrosses.
- **Decoys**: these attract and distract birds so that they do not get caught on longline hooks.
- **Sinkers**: weights attached to pelagic longlines hold the hooks down in the water so that they still catch fish but don't catch albatrosses.
- **Night fishing**: using longlines at night when birds are not feeding.
- **Biodegradable & radio tracked equipment:** to reduce ghost fishing. If traps for crabs and lobsters are lost, they may continue to catch more crabs and lobsters as the dead trapped individuals act as the bait for more to be caught. Traps that are held together by biodegradable rope will fall apart if they are lost. In the USA traps have radio-transmitters that activate if the traps are lost so they can be recovered.

Restricted fishing effort:

In some areas around the UK there are limits on the size of fishing boats and the power of their engines. Fishing boats have limits on the number of days each year that a boat may spend fishing. Where the number of fishing boats is so large that overfishing is unavoidable, boat owners may receive compensation for their boats to be de-commissioned.

Restricted fishing methods

- **Ban drift nets**: in some areas, drift nets may be banned or their length restricted.
- **Bans on demersal trawling**: in areas where the seabed ecosystem is particularly sensitive or important demersal trawling may be banned. Demersal trawling is banned on the NW Rockall Bank and Hatton Bank which are large deep water coral reefs off the NW coast of Scotland.

- **No-take zones (NTZs):** NTZs are areas where fishing and other activities that exploit wildlife or damage the habitat are not permitted. This protects the breeding populations of breeding adults, especially larger individuals. They produce a lot of offspring which can colonise surrounding areas where fishing may have reduced the populations of breeding adults. The communities of wildlife species that live within the NTZ can recover once damaging activities stop.
- **Turtle bycatch:** In tropical fishing areas with large numbers of turtles, reducing the time that the net is towed can reduce by-catch mortality. The survival rate of turtles caught in shrimp trawls depends on the length of time they were in the net. If it is less than 10 minutes the survival rate is over 99%. If the trawls are towed for an hour then 50 – 100% drown.

Existing and proposed NTZs

Name	Location	Area /km²
Lamlash Bay	Isle of Arran, Scotland	2.6
Lundy Island	Bristol Channel, SW UK	3.3
Great Barrier Reef (1/3 of the national park)	East coast of Australia	110,000
Ascension Island	Atlantic Ocean	235,000
Palau	Pacific Ocean	500,000
Easter Island	Pacific Ocean	600,000
Chagos Archipelago	Indian Ocean	640,000
Pitcairn Island	Pacific Ocean	834,000

▼ *Exe Estuary bass nursery area*

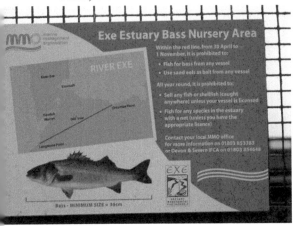

- **Closed-seasons:** a ban on fishing for part of the year allows the fish to grow to a larger size. Ideally, the closed-season should include the breeding season to protect future generations, however, many fish species congregate in shoals to breed which makes them easier to catch, so fishermen may oppose this restriction.
- **Minimum catchable size:** banning the capture of small fish may not reduce the mass of the catch by much but it may allow large numbers of small fish to grow to a larger size and live long enough to breed.

Fishing size limits around the UK (may vary between areas and change over time)

Fish	Size limit
Cod	35cm
Plaice	27cm
Mackerel	30cm
Edible crab	130mm (carapace width)
Lobster	90mm (carapace length) - minimum catchable size for lobster in the UK is larger than the first time they breed, so overfishing cannot destroy the breeding population

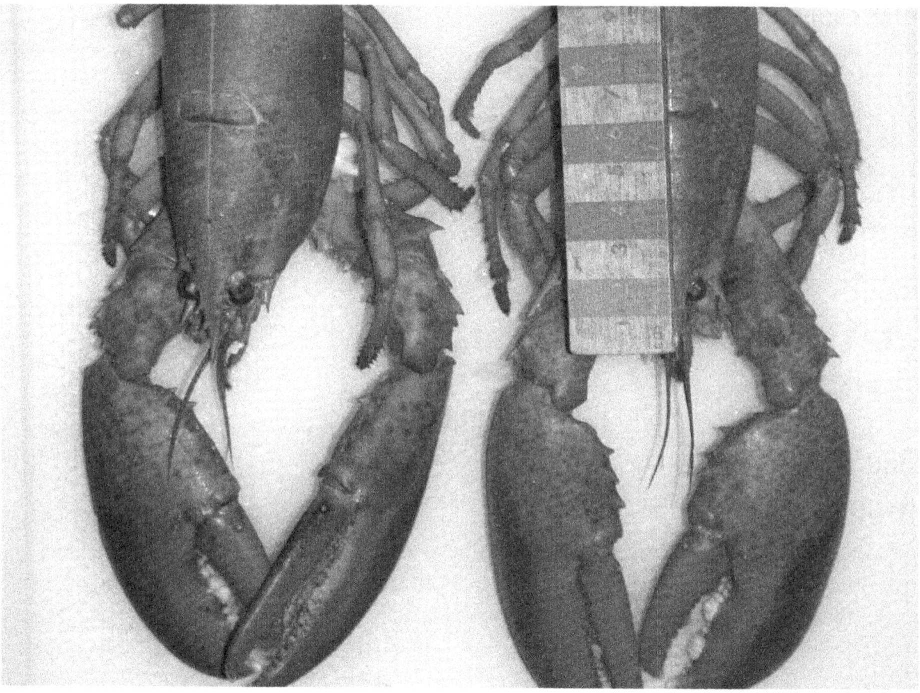

Lobster carapace being measured

- **Maximum catchable size:** protecting large individuals may ensure there is a surviving population of breeding adults. Each individual, being large, may produce many young, for example:
    - female lobsters around the Outer Hebrides of NW Scotland may not be caught if the carapace (shell) is longer than 145mm;
    - larger Nassau Grouper in some areas of the coral reefs of Belize in Central America are protected to conserve the population of good breeding individuals.
- **Protected individuals:** the future production of young can be increased if adults that are known to breed are protected. Female lobsters that are caught and are found to be carrying eggs must be released. A V-notch is cut in the tail so if it is caught again it will be released. Female velvet crab around Orkney must be released if they are carrying eggs.

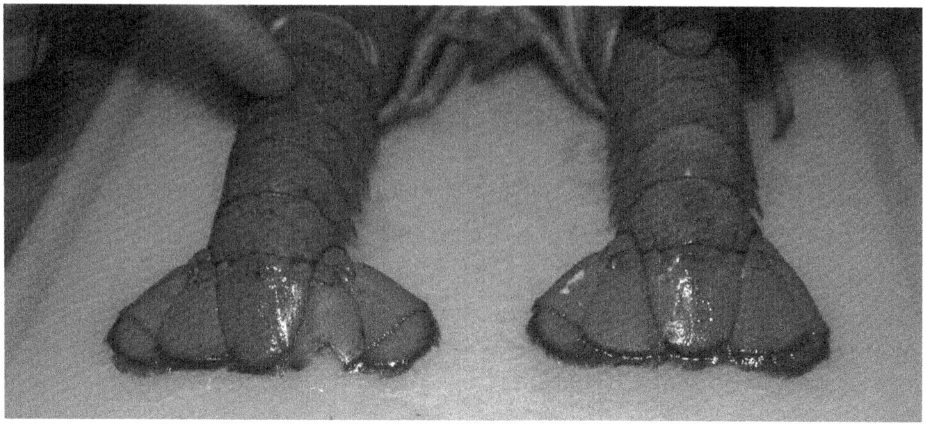

A female lobster with a v-notch in its tail

▶ **Captive rearing and release:** this is also called 'population seeding'. The wild populations of some species may be increased by releasing individuals that have been raised in captivity. They are usually raised from eggs or larvae until their chances of survival in the wild are good so they should increase the size of the adult population, for example, lobsters, oysters. Most marine species spend their first few weeks drifting in the plankton before they settle to the seabed where they may colonise a suitable habitat. Most individuals are either eaten while they are drifting in the plankton or fail to find a suitable habitat. Population seeding increases the chances of surviving this period.

Population dynamics and monitoring fish populations

Fish are a renewable resource as they naturally replace themselves by breeding to produce offspring that replace the adults that have died.

Breeding rates

All species are adapted through evolution to have a natural breeding rate which exceeds the rate that is necessary to sustain the population. This breeding surplus will not increase the long-term adult population as the carrying capacity of the environment will have been exceeded and the surplus individuals will die. In any population which exceeds the carrying capacity, density-dependant factors will increase the mortality rate, especially intra-specific competition for food.

If the adult mortality rate increases (for example, due to fishing) then more juvenile fish will survive and be recruited to the adult population as more food will be available and intra-specific competition will have reduced. This will maintain the population.

If an excessive number of adults is caught then the adult population may decline because there are not enough young to replace them. A reduced adult population will produce fewer young which may further reduce the ability of the population to recover and lead to a rapid population decline.

So, catching fish does not always reduce the total population, as long as the catch does not exceed the population's ability to replace the losses.

Overfishing

Overfishing is not necessarily evident in reduced catches as the total catch weight may be maintained by catching a larger number of smaller fish. If such fishing continues then the adult breeding population may be reduced to the point that very few young fish are produced. This may result in a complete population collapse.

If a fish species reaches a catchable size after it has started breeding then there will always be an adult breeding population, although overfishing may remove all the larger fish.

If a fish species reaches a catchable size before it is large enough to breed then it is possible to catch all the breeding adults and destroy the entire population.

Maximum Sustainable Yield (MSY)

The MSY for a fish population is the greatest biomass that can be removed from the population each year without the population suffering a long-term decline. It is important that the fishing rate does not exceed the MSY as that would cause over-fishing and a population decline.

Examples of fish that have been exploited above the MSY

▼ **Orange Roughy:** the Orange Roughy is a deep water fish species found off many coasts such as New Zealand, SE Australia, west of Ireland, and NW Scotland. It was first exploited in the late 1970s but many populations were soon overfished. The Orange Roughy is a k-selected species so it is very vulnerable to overfishing. The fish live to an age of 150 but do not start breeding until they are 30 years old and produce few eggs.

▶ *Orange Roughy*

▼ **Atlantic Cod:** cod reach a catchable size at age two but most do not reach maturity until age four, so excessive fishing can remove the majority of the breeding population.

▼ **Tuna:** tuna start breeding after they have become large enough to be caught so excessive fishing can remove most of the breeding population.

◀ *Atlantic cod*

Estimating the MSY

Reliable data are needed in order to estimate the MSY. Biomass can be estimated if the following information is available to use in the Russell formula:

S1 = biomass of stock at beginning of year
S2 = biomass of stock at end of year
A = biomass of young fish added to stock
G = biomass added by growth of all fish in the stock
C = biomass caught by fishing
M = biomass lost through natural mortality

Russell Formula

S2 = S1 + (A + G) - (C + M)

Collecting data

The only one of these factors that is easy to measure is the biomass caught by fishing as the catch is landed at ports and the mass caught can be recorded. The other factors require data about the fish in the sea which may be difficult to collect because:

▼ fish populations are often mobile and can move long distances, often between the territories of different countries;

▼ the distribution of fish populations is often very uneven;

▼ collecting representative data of a large enough proportion of the total area occupied by the population may be impractical.

▶ *An unexploited
population
A population
fished sustainably
at the Maximum
Sustainable Yield
An overexploited
population*

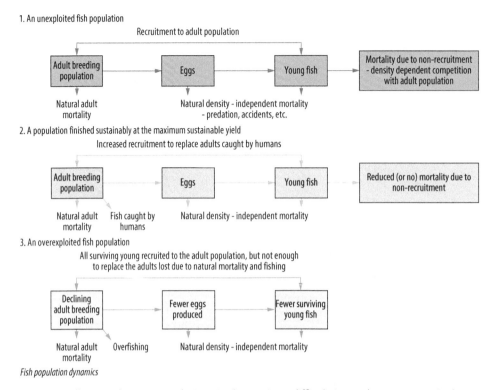

1. An unexploited fish population

Recruitment to adult population

| Adult breeding population | → | Eggs | → | Young fish | → | Mortality due to non-recruitment - density dependent competition with adult population |

Natural adult mortality   Natural density - independent mortality - predation, accidents, etc.

2. A population finished sustainably at the maximum sustainable yield

Increased recruitment to replace adults caught by humans

| Adult breeding population | → | Eggs | → | Young fish | → | Reduced (or no) mortality due to non-recruitment |

Natural adult mortality   Fish caught by humans   Natural density - independent mortality

3. An overexploited fish population

All surviving young recruited to the adult population, but not enough to replace the adults lost due to natural mortality and fishing

| Declining adult breeding population | → | Fewer eggs produced | → | Fewer surviving young fish |

Natural adult mortality   Overfishing   Natural density - independent mortality

Fish population dynamics

Because collecting data on populations in the sea is so difficult, it may be more practical to collect data from the fish that are caught which indicates whether the structure of the population is changing. This may indicate whether fishing is taking place above or below the maximum sustainable yield.

Data from fishing catches

▶ **Catch size:** the total landed catch each year is not always a good measure of the biomass or population size of the species being exploited. Technological changes may make it possible to maintain catches while the population is declining at an increasing rate, for example, bigger boats with bigger nets, improved fish detection equipment such as sonar. The final, sudden population collapse may come as a surprise.

▶ **Catch per unit fishing effort:** this is more difficult to measure but it is a better measure of fishing sustainability than the actual catch. If it is becoming harder to maintain catches then the population is being overfished.

▶ **Mean fish size:** the catch biomass may be maintained but this can hide the fact that it includes an increasing number of smaller fish. However, a reducing mean fish size may indicate that the older adults are being caught faster than they are being replaced.

▶ **Mean age:** in many species, the age of fish can be determined by the growth rings on the scales that grow on their skin or from otoliths which are bones in their ears. If the mean age is declining then overfishing is taking place.

Data from research

The people fishing generally only have knowledge of fish in the population that are large enough to be caught in their nets. If data on catches are collected then the current catchable population can be estimated. The fish in younger year groups are very important as they will be recruited to the adult population in the future and would replace those that have been caught or died. If there are too few fish in the younger year groups, then the adult population could suddenly collapse. If the adult population declines but fish catches are not reduced then the population decline will accelerate as a greater proportion of the population is being removed. With fewer adult fish, fewer young will be produced.

Most fish eggs and larvae die in the first few weeks of life when they are planktonic. They are eaten by predators, fail to find food, or suffer accidental deaths during storms or by being carried into unsuitable areas by currents. Survival rates in different years can vary greatly so knowing the population of breeding adults is not an accurate predictor of the number of young fish that will be produced.

Collecting data on planktonic fish egg and larval populations can help to predict the number of young fish that are likely to be recruited to the adult population in future years.

If this data is not collected then it is possible that several years of poor survival of eggs and larvae may lead to poor recruitment and a sudden population collapse because fishing rates were not reduced to anticipate the lowering in the MSY.

Because the information about breeding success and the survival of juvenile fish is not available to those fishing, it must be collected by scientific research programmes.

▼ *A quantitative plankton net*

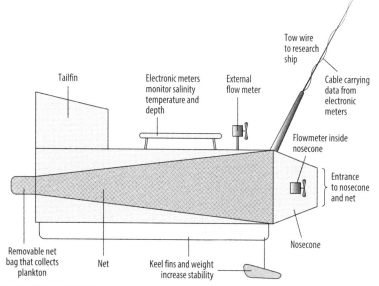

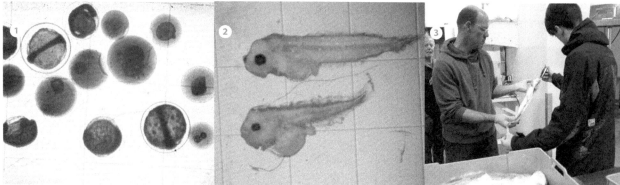

❶ *Planktonic fish eggs seen under a microscope (2mm grid). The species can be identified from the egg diameter and the presence and distribution of oil droplets*
❷ *Planktonic fish larvae seen under a microscope (plaice, sole, and turbot)*
❸ *Monitoring fish catches (part of a study run by Sharklab, Malta)*

Aquaculture

Aquaculture is to fishing what agriculture is to hunting and gathering. It aims to control aquatic ecosystems so that more food enters the human food chain.

Principles of aquaculture

The intensity of aquaculture varies greatly. Extensive aquaculture involves minimal inputs which may simply involve a pond where fish have been introduced to feed on the wild food naturally present before being caught when they have grown. Greater inputs may involve feeding with wastes, adding nutrients, or the control of competitors and predators. Extensive aquaculture may be for subsistence or commercial purposes. At the other extreme, intensive aquaculture may involve artificial control of all abiotic and biotic limiting factors to maximise productivity and profitability for commercial purposes.

Species selection

The main species raised by aquaculture

Food group	Examples	Proportion of total production / %
Fish	Carp, salmon, *Tilapia*, catfish	50%
Algae	Seaweeds for food and food products such as gelling agents	25%
Molluscs	Oysters, mussels, clams	15%
Crustaceans	Shrimps	10%
Others	Sea cucumbers, sea urchins, amphibians	1%

NB. Values are rounded and do not total 100%.

Factors that affect the choice of aquaculture species:

- ▼ **local conditions and species' adaptations:** local conditions will control the species that can survive, especially temperature and water quality. Salmon and trout are important in cooler temperate regions while Tilapia thrive in warmer tropical regions. Marine species are kept in coastal areas.
- ▼ **market demand:** in MEDCs the main species raised by aquaculture are carnivores such as salmon and trout because of their better flavour and popularity with customers. In LEDCs the traditional species raised by aquaculture are herbivores or omnivores, for example, carp and tilapia because they can feed on naturally occurring vegetation, phytoplankton, and wastes. They require low food inputs, although productivity is increased if more food is provided. As international transport has become easier, the demand for seafood in MEDCs has stimulated a big expansion in tropical aquaculture.

Selection of adults for breeding

Adult fish with desirable characteristics are selected for breeding. Desirable characteristics may include:

- ▼ disease resistance;
- ▼ rapid growth rate;
- ▼ good appearance, for example, bright colour.

Eggs and milt (sperm) are collected from mature individuals. Hormone injections may be used to induce spawning.

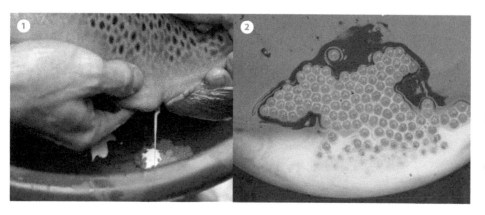

❶ *Collecting milt (semen) from a male trout*
❷ *Fertilising eggs with the milt*

Gender control

The gender of fish can be controlled hormonally regardless of their genetics. Young fish with two X chromosomes normally become female, while fish with one X chromosome and one Y chromosome normally become male.

However, if young fish are given female hormones they will develop into female adults. If they are given male hormones they will all develop into male adults. Which gender is considered to be desirable depends upon the species being cultivated, for example:

�Rainbow trout: the meat from female trout has a better flavour than meat from males. Some female fish are given the male hormone testosterone. They are still genetically female but they are functional males and produce sperm, all of which carry an X chromosome. When they are used to fertilise eggs with X chromosomes, only female fish are produced.

❶ *Rainbow trout*
❷ *The production of all-female fish*

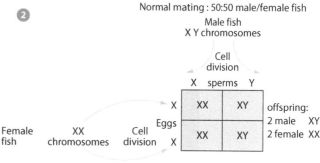

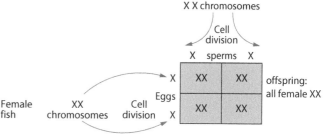

The production of all-female fish

Normal mating : 50:50 male/female fish

Male fish
X Y chromosomes

Cell division

X sperms Y

	X	Y	
X	XX	XY	offspring:
X	XX	XY	2 male XY 2 female XX

Female fish — XX chromosomes — Cell division — Eggs

Mating between normal female and a testosterone-treated female

Testosterone-treated female fish
X X chromosomes

Cell division

X sperms X

	X	X	
X	XX	XX	offspring:
X	XX	XX	all female XX

Female fish — XX chromosomes — Cell division — Eggs

- **Tilapia:** male *Tilapia* are more energy efficient than females and grow larger. Treating the young fish with the male hormone testosterone produces all male fish so a bigger and more marketable harvest is produced.
- **Triploid fish:** fish that escape from fish farms may prey on local wildlife and compete with other fish but the ecological impacts of fish that escape from fish farms are not serious if they cannot reproduce. Triploid fish have three sets of chromosomes and are infertile. This is achieved by heat or pressure-treating the eggs soon after fertilisation has taken place.

Control of pests and disease

Keeping fish at high stocking densities increases the risk of the spread of disease between individuals. Where water flows between tanks with fish of different ages, the flow is from tanks with younger fish to tanks with older fish. This reduces the risk of the continual spread of disease from older fish to new stock.

High stocking densities increase contact and collisions between fish. This increases the risk of the spread of pathogens and parasites. Injuries that may lead to infections are also more likely. A lower stocking density reduces these risks. Pesticides may be used or biological control such as wrasse that eat the lice that carry disease.

Tanks with circulating water currents encourage all the fish to swim in the same direction so there is less contact between them which could have transferred pathogens.

▶ *Circulating tank*

Competition and predation

Other species that are competitors or predators are rarely a problem in closely controlled intensive systems but outdoor large-scale systems are harder to protect. Fencing, netting and bird scarers can be used to exclude problem species. Culling may be used to reduce populations of pest species. Some licences are granted in the UK for the killing of seals and cormorants.

Nutrition

Herbivorous fish are more likely to find natural food in their lagoons, such as phytoplankton or water weeds. Carnivorous fish are more likely to require artificial feeding. Artificial control of the food supply is more important with intensive production systems.

Control of abiotic factors

▌ **Temperature**: temperature requirements depend upon the species that are being kept and their natural adaptations. Warmer temperatures increase metabolic rates and growth but can reduce levels of dissolved oxygen which may be unsuitable for some species.

▌ **Dissolved oxygen**: fish with a high oxygen requirement such as trout must have well aerated tanks, especially if the stocking density is high. Food waste and faecal matter must be removed as this can cause deoxygenation.

Fish that are adapted to feeding in sediments with a high dead organic matter content can usually survive with a lower dissolved oxygen level, for example, carp. Catfish live in water but breathe air. Low dissolved oxygen levels do not harm them so they can be kept at very high stocking densities.

▲ *Tank aeration*

▌ **Daylength**: as with many terrestrial livestock species, reproduction is affected by the length of the day. This is a natural adaptation to match the annual reproductive cycle to seasonal changes in abiotic climatic factors and food availability. Salmon stop growing when they become sexually mature. Having a long daylength delays maturation and increases the size they reach so some fish farms extend the length of the day with artificial lighting to produce larger fish.

▌ **Water flow**: fish often swim against the flow of water. This can be used to get all the fish swimming in the same direction in circular or oval tanks. This reduces collision damage between fish which improves the appearance of the saleable fish. It also reduces the risk of injuries and allows a higher stocking density in the tanks.

A comparison of extensive and intensive aquaculture systems

Extensive oyster aquaculture

Most oyster farms use extensive systems with low inputs. Oysters filter planktonic organisms from seawater.

In some systems, young oysters are bred from selected adults. In other systems, oyster 'spat' (planktonic larvae) settle onto cleared areas of seabed and are collected. The young oysters are spaced out on the seabed where they grow until they are large enough to harvest. Predators such as crabs may be removed.

Shrimp aquaculture

Most shrimp farms are in tropical areas: SE Asia and Latin America. The most important species are Giant Tiger Prawn and Pacific White Shrimp. 10% of the world's mangroves have been destroyed to create coastal shrimp farms.

Females in hatcheries lay up to 500,000 eggs each. Ovary development and egg production are increased by eyestalk ablation where one or both eyestalks are broken off which simulates the low light levels that stimulate breeding, because they are blind. The eggs hatch to produce shrimp larvae that are fed on algae and zookplankton. As they grow, the shrimps are moved to outdoor lagoons up to 100ha in size.

In extensive systems, the shrimps feed on plankton naturally produced in the lagoons.

In intensive systems, nutrients are added to increase the growth of algae. Food pellets may also be added.

- Water may be exchanged to remove wastes.
- Aeration may be needed to prevent deoxygenation as wastes decompose.

Salmon aquaculture

Most salmon farms are intensive with the control of many factors to maximise productivity.

Breeding

- Fish are chosen with desirable characteristics such as fast growth rate, shape, and brightly coloured scales.
- Adult fish in breeding condition are stripped of their eggs (roe) and milt (sperms). These are mixed to allow fertilisation to take place.
- The fertilised eggs are raised in aerated freshwater tanks. Dead or diseased eggs are removed daily.
- After hatching, the young fish are moved through a series of tanks as they grow, being fed on fish meal pellets.
- After 12 – 18 months they become 'smolts' and are ready to move to seawater tanks. They continue to be fed on fish and plant meal pellets until they are ready for harvest, usually at 3 – 5 kg.

Control of limiting factors:

- Salmon are sensitive to low dissolved oxygen levels, so the water temperature must not be too high. Most salmon farms are in countries with cooler climates such as Scotland and Norway.
- Dissolved oxygen levels are kept high with water sprays or weirs which aerate the water.
- The water flow rate is kept fairly high to produce more muscular fish as they swim against the current.
- The water flow direction is constant, often around circular tanks. This keeps the fish swimming in the same direction so there are fewer injuries.
- Pests, parasites and diseases are controlled by removing diseased fish and selective use of antibiotics and pesticides. Predators may be excluded or killed.
- Light levels are controlled to induce the smoltification of the young fish as they mature.
- The food chain is controlled to increase its efficiency. Like most fish raised in aquaculture systems, salmon are carnivores. Fishmeal pellets made from low value fish such as sandeels, herring, anchovy and sardines are similar to their natural food. Food chain efficiency is increased by adding food from lower trophic levels such as plant foods and vegetable oils.

▼ A salmon farm in a sea loch in Scotland

Polyculture

Some aquaculture systems produce food from more than one species. Total productivity may be increased by rearing species together that are not competitors. Selective rearing of predators with other species can increase the production of larger fish by controlling the survival of small fish that could compete with the larger fish.

Bottom feeding fish can disturb the sediments and re-suspend nutrients which increase the growth of plants and phytoplankton.

An example of a polyculture system:

- Silver carp feed mainly on phytoplankton.
- Bighead carp feed mainly on zooplankton.
- Grass carp and *Tilapia* feed mainly on vegetation.
- Common carp are bottom feeders and feed on molluscs, insects. They also re-suspend nutrients from the sediments.
- Catfish and perch eat small fish and prevent over-reproduction of species that breed well, for example, *Tilapia*.

Integrated multi-trophic aquaculture (IMTA)

IMTA is a polyculture system where species in different trophic levels benefit from each other.

- **Fed aquaculture**: species that are given food, for example, shrimps, salmon.
- **Inorganic extractive aquaculture**: species that absorb inorganic nutrients for growth, for example, algae/seaweed.
- **Organic extractive aquaculture**: species that catch food items such as plankton, for example, filter feeding shellfish

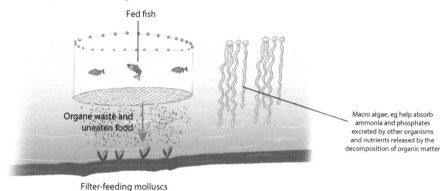

Fed fish

Organe waste and uneaten food

Macro algae, eg help absorb ammonia and phosphates excreted by other organisms and nutrients released by the decomposition of organic matter

Filter-feeding molluscs

◀ *Integrated multi-trophic aquaculture*

Aquaponics

Aquaponics combines hydroponic crop production (see pxxx) with aquaculture. Water from the aquaculture system is used in the hydroponic system. The drainage water from the hydroponic system is returned to the aquaculture system. The productivity of the hydroponic system is increased because the supply of inorganic nutrients and organic matter is increased. The aquaculture system benefits because the nutrients that could lead to deoxygenation are removed.

- **Suitable hydroponics species**: leafy salad vegetables such as lettuce, spinach, herbs, watercress.
- **Suitable aquaculture species**: *Tilapia,* carp, catfish.

Rice-fish systems

Rice is grown in flooded 'padi' fields (padi means rice in Malay). Fish can also be kept in the fields, increasing overall food production.

The extent to which aquaculture can replace fishing

After 50 years of increasing global fish catches, there has been no further increase since 1990. With the growth in demand for seafood, aquaculture production has expanded and may equal the catch of wild fish soon, see pxxx.

However, there may be problems with the sustainability of large-scale aquaculture which need to be solved.

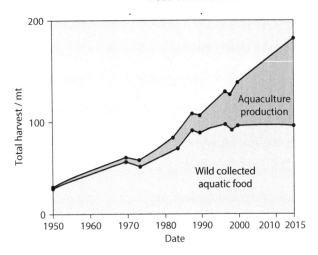

Trophic level efficiency

Raising herbivorous fish, such as *Tilapia*, can be very productive as the amount of food produced per unit area is high. Although raising carnivorous fish may be less energy-efficient, they are often more popular with customers, for example, salmon is a high-value carnivorous fish.

Fish have very low Basal Metabolic Rates because they do not use energy to keep warm or for support, so they have much higher food conversion ratios than mammal or bird livestock species. The food conversion ratio is the quantity of food required to produce a unit of growth, for example, a species that needs 3.5kg of food to produce 1 kg of new growth has an FCR of 3.5.

Food	Typical FCR
Salmon	1.1
Tilapia	1.5
Chickens	1.8
Pigs	4
Beef cattle	6

Food Conversion Rates (FCR) for different foods

Food requirements

Herbivorous fish may eat the plants and algae that grow naturally in the water. Growth may be increased by adding plant nutrients. Supplementary feeding may involve adding plant material such as crop waste.

Carnivorous fish are usually fed on fish that have a lower economic value such as salmon fed on fishmeal made from sandeels. Overfishing of sandeels has caused population decline in other species that eat sandeels, for example, puffins and terns. Some plant-based foods have been developed but the fish meat produced may be less tasty if there is no fishmeal included.

Stock collection

Some species such as Atlantic Blue Fin Tuna do not breed well in captivity, so young fish are caught in the sea then raised in large cages in the sea. Tuna aquaculture cannot continue without a wild population.

Environmental impacts and how impact can be reduced

Environmental impacts		How impacts can be reduced
Impact	**Details**	
Food supply impacts	Overfishing of wild fish to make food pellets. This reduces populations of the fish and species that feed on them such as seabirds.	Use of more plant products in food pellets or the cultivation of herbivorous fish, for example, *Tilapia*.
Habitat loss	Habitat destruction during construction, especially lagoons in mangroves.	Careful site selection (difficult for very large scale developments).
Pesticide pollution	The pesticides used to control weed and crustacean growth may kill wildlife.	Mechanical cleaning of cages and biological control with crustaceans reduces the need for pesticides.
Development of antibiotic resistant bacteria	Antibiotics used to prevent or treat diseases may lead to the development of antibiotic-resistant bacteria. The resistance may also transfer to human pathogens.	Lower stocking densities lower the risk of disease so antibiotic use can be reduced.
Control of wild predators	Culling predators such as seals and fish eating birds reduces the predator populations so fewer fish are eaten.	Better cage designs to exclude predators.
Impacts of controlling lice	Parasitic lice reduce fish growth and increase the risk of virus and fungus infections. Lice can spread to nearby wild fish populations. Lice may be controlled with chemicals such as: • Hydrogen Peroxide wash; • Azamethiphos (organophosphate pesticide); • Pyrethroid pesticides. The pesticides may kill local wildlife.	Tanks should hold fish of a single age group so lice are not transferred from old fish to young unaffected fish. Biological control with wrasse (fish) that eat lice. However, this can reduce wild wrasse populations if the wrasse are caught and moved to the fish farms. Washing fish in warm water.
Wild gene pool impacts	Fish that escape may breed with wild fish and introduce disadvantageous characteristics to the wild gene pool, for example, bright colour.	Better cage designs to reduce escapes. Eggs exposed to high pressure produce triploid fish which are sterile. (Sterile fish also grow faster.)
Introduction of non-indigenous species	Escaped non-indigenous species may colonise and become predators or competitors.	Cultivation of species that cannot breed in the wild, for example, Japanese oysters in the UK (too cold to breed).
Organic waste pollution	Organic wastes from faeces or surplus food causes deoxygenation as it decomposes.	Feeding is monitored to prevent over-feeding. Cages can be located where currents disperse wastes. Freshwater aquaculture systems may have effluent treatment works similar to sewage works. Bacteria in reed beds can also be planted to absorb nutrients and break down organic wastes.

Key principles

▶ Aquatic food resources are renewable resources but they can be depleted by over-exploitation.

▶ The productivity of marine biological resources is controlled by nutrient supplies and light levels.

▶ More effective fishing methods have made it easier to overfish populations.

▶ Improved methods make it possible to reduce environmental impacts and avoid overfishing.

▶ Aquaculture has increased aquatic food supplies but can have serious environmental impacts.

▶ New aquaculture methods may help to achieve sustainable supplies.

Chapter 13

Forest resources

Chapter topics

Forests cover about 30% of the Earth's land area. They are often the climax community in ecological succession and are found wherever conditions are suitable. These usually involve the presence of soil and a climate that does not involve prolonged dry periods or serious fires. The temperature determines the type of forest that is found.

Forests are important for human survival because they provide ecological services and resources that we need.

The natural geographical distribution of the different types of forest is controlled by the climate. See page 74, The distribution of biomes.

For more details on temperate broadleaf woodland see page 50.

For more details on tropical rainforest see page 52.

The importance of forests

Resources

A wide variety of resources are gained from forests. Some resources are extracted from existing natural forests but most are produced by cultivated plantations of species that were discovered in forests. The loss of wild forests may result in the loss of valuable species that become extinct before their importance is understood, or even before they have been discovered.

Timber

Wood is strong, has a high strength:weight ratio, flexibility, requires little processing for use and is often readily available.

▼ mahogany and teak from tropical forests
▼ oak and beech from temperate deciduous forests
▼ conifer timber from northern coniferous forests

The wood from different tree species has different properties and therefore different uses.

Wood is a globally important resource with a wide range of uses:

- Structural uses: building construction, telegraph poles, shuttering for concrete structures
- Furniture
- Tools

❶ Timber house in Central America
❷ Concrete shuttering made with tropical timber leaves the imprint of the wood grain in the concrete. The wood is often used once then thrown away

Fibres

- Most paper is made from flattened sheets of interwoven cellulose fibres from pulped wood.
- Cotton is made from the fibres that surround the seeds of the cotton bush
- Viscose (rayon) textiles are made by the chemical treatment of cellulose fibres extracted from wood

Fuel

Wood is still the fuel that is used by most people in the world for cooking

- **Fuelwood**

  Before the industrial revolution, wood was the main energy resource for almost everyone in the world. Although oil, coal and gas now provide more energy than wood, wood still provides energy for the greatest number of people, mainly in LEDCs.

Food

Trees provide fodder for livestock and fruit and nuts for human food. The animals that live in forests can provide human food such as bushmeat in LEDCs.

Many forest plant species are important in agriculture such as coffee, cacao (chocolate), bananas, papayas and Brazil nuts. Pigs and chickens were originally forest animals.

The wild varieties of cultivated species contain genes for new characteristics that may be important in future selective breeding programmes.

There may be many more species in forests that could be cultivated or domesticated.

▼ A wood stove in Africa

Medicines

Trees produce many chemicals that have medicinal uses. Some are still extracted from tree tissues while others were identified in trees but are now synthesized artificially, for example, quinine that was originally extracted from the Cinchona tree. Most forest species have not yet been researched for the medicinal compounds they may contain.

Ecosystem services

Forests provide a range of ecosystem services that influence the environment on local, regional and global scales.

Atmospheric regulation

The balance of photosynthesis and respiration in forests is important in regulating atmospheric levels of carbon dioxide and oxygen.

Forests act as a huge reservoir of carbon, mainly in the carbohydrate cellulose which is the main component of wood. If it were not stored in the wood, most of this carbon would be in the atmosphere as carbon dioxide. Cellulose is difficult to digest so wood is a carbon reservoir with a relatively long residence time compared with carbon in other living material.

Carbon sequestration is the process during which growing trees take more carbon out of the atmosphere during photosynthesis and store it in more wood. This can be used deliberately to counteract global climate change by planting more trees.

These processes that remove carbon dioxide from the atmosphere also release the oxygen that is essential for all aerobic organisms, and for the maintenance of the ozone layer.

The total mass of carbon in forest soils is greater than that in the vegetation, especially in boreal forests.

The amount of carbon in the terrestrial ecosystems

Area	Mass of carbon / 10^9 t			
	Living vegetation	Soil dead organic matter	Total	
Tropical forests	210	220	430	Total for all forests 1160
Temperate forests	60	100	160	
Boreal forests	90	480	570	
All other terrestrial ecosystems	110	1220	1330	

The total mass of carbon in forests is roughly double the mass in the atmosphere.

Carbon dioxide absorption by photosynthesis and the storage of carbon in wood increases the amount of carbon in the biomass reservoir of the carbon cycle. This helps to minimize global climate change.

Regulation of the hydrological cycle

Transpiration rates from forests are greater than from any other terrestrial ecosystem and is important in increasing precipitation rates downwind.

Interception by the foliage of forests also increases evaporation rates but decreases infiltration.

Forests help soil formation and reduce soil erosion so soil depth may be greater than for other ecosystems. The soil will retain water after it has rained and moderate the flow of water into rivers.

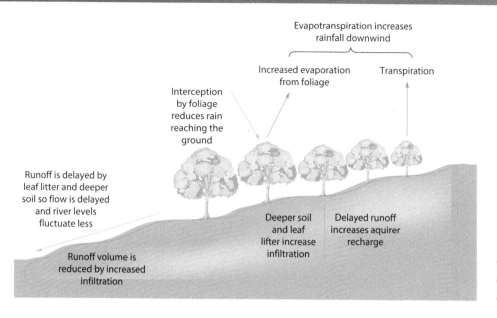

Evapotranspiration increases
rainfall downwind

Increased evaporation
from foliage

Transpiration

Interception
by foliage
reduces rain
reaching the
ground

Runoff is delayed by
leaf litter and deeper
soil so flow is delayed
and river levels
fluctuate less

Deeper soil
and leaf
lifter increase
infiltration

Delayed runoff
increases aquirer
recharge

Runoff volume is
reduced by increased
infiltration

◀ *The impact
of forests on the
hydrological cycle*

The low albedo of forests increases the absorption of sunlight and the storage of heat in the water in the wood.

Forests absorb sunlight during the day. Much of this is converted to heat which is radiated at night. This reduces the extremes of temperature between day and night.

Forest microclimate

The trees change the abiotic conditions beneath the canopy layer creating a wider range of conditions that different species may be adapted to.

- ▼ **Light**. The canopy vegetation absorbs a lot of the solar insolation, especially the red and blue wavelengths that are absorbed by chlorophyll. Plants living below the canopy have access to less light and much of this is green light that is not effectively absorbed by chlorophyll. So, these plants often have special adaptations such as denser chlorophyll, additional pigments or growth periods when the trees have lost their leaves.

- ▼ **Wind velocity**. The lower wind velocity produced by the shelter of the trees means that plants below the canopy layer use animals to help with pollination and seed dispersal rather than the wind.

- ▼ **Humidity**. High humidity levels mean that animals such as amphibians can survive more easily as their skin does not dry out.

Habitat and wildlife refuge

- ▼ Forests are the most biodiverse terrestrial ecosystems. Each species of tree supports its own unique community of species so forests with a greater variety of tree species are likely to have a greater overall biodiversity. Forests create very diverse habitats with a large variety of possible ecological niches. This is increased by stratification within the forest, which is most obvious in forests with the highest primary productivity. The trees also create variations in abiotic factors such as light levels, light wavelength, humidity, temperature and wind velocity.

- The high primary productivity of forests provides a lot of energy to support higher trophic levels in the food chain. The energy is not always available to other organisms quickly, as much is stored in the wood which will be released when the tree dies and decomposes.

Soil conservation

Forests aid soil formation and reduce soil erosion See page 158, Soil.

- Dead vegetation contributes humus and nutrients to the soil, and the food energy for detritivores and decomposers that are involved in soil formation.
- The trees help to prevent soil being washed or blown away by intercepting rainfall and reducing wind velocity.
- The living trees and leaf litter on the soil surface help to reduce wind velocity and the impact of rain drops.
- Tree roots help to hold the soil together which reduces erosion by water running over the surface.
- Humus from decomposed vegetation also binds the soil together.
- A forest soil with lots of organic matter will have lots of living organisms including worms. This increases the ease with which water infiltrates into the soil which reduces runoff and therefore the amount of soil that is washed away.

Recreation/amenity uses

Forests are important for recreational uses such as walking, orienteering, cycling and camping. Forests are also important for educational activities.

Forest exploitation and management

Forests have been managed in many ways for different purposes and with widely differing environmental impacts.

Traditional forest management

In pre-industrial societies, forests produced wood from a wide variety of different species, each having its own particular uses.

Traditional techniques involved the management of existing woodland areas to maximize yields of forest products. This rarely involved the total removal of the natural forest and often retained mixed-species forests with trees of different ages.

Uses of different tree species

The wood from different species has different properties and therefore different uses.

- Oak: timber-framed buildings, ship building
- Beech: furniture, tool handles
- Ash: furniture, roof timbers
- Holly: mathematical instruments, walking sticks
- Hazel: fencing panels, interwoven wall panels

❶ The construction of HMS victory in 1765 required over 6000 trees, mainly oak.

❷ A timber-framed building

Management methods

Standard trees

These are trees that were grown to maturity for the production of large timbers for uses such as the construction of buildings and ships.

Coppicing

This involves cutting trees to ground level on a cycle of 1 to 20 years depending on the use of the wood. The branches that regrow were used for baskets, fencing, charcoal, wall panels and roof rafters.

Pollarding

This is similar to coppicing, but the trees are cut above ground level so the regrowing branches cannot be eaten by livestock.

There is little current demand for coppiced or pollarded timber.

▲ Coppiced hazel trees

Modern commercial forestry

As a society develops to become industrial, the demand for timber changes, as does the way it is used. Demand for wood fuel may decline as people switch to fossil fuels or electricity. The species-specific uses of wood from traditionally managed woodland are often replaced by large-scale uses such as chipped wood for sheet construction material and plywood for concrete shuttering. Harvesting methods changed from selective logging or cutting of small areas to large-scale clear-felling. This reduces the wildlife biodiversity of the forest. The existing natural woodland may be replaced with plantations of selected species.

Management methods
Cultivation of non-indigenous species

The tree species selected for cultivation are often non-indigenous. They may be better adapted to the environmental conditions and are less likely to suffer damage caused by pests or disease.

Growing non-indigenous species is less likely to support indigenous wildlife species because their inter-species needs for food, pollination, seed dispersal or habitats are less likely to be met.

▲ *Clear-felling in a conifer plantation*

Examples of non-indigenous forestry plantations
UK
- ▼ Sitka Spruce and Douglas Fir (originally from North America)
- ▼ Corsican Pine (originally from Southern Europe)

Central America
- ▼ Teak (originally from Asia)

East Africa
- ▼ Eucalyptus (originally from Australia)

Single-species plantations

Growing a monoculture of one tree species can make management of a plantation easier. Activities such as planting, thinning and felling can be carried out over large areas at the same time.

Close planting

Planting all the seedlings close together makes the trees compete with each other for light so they grow tall and straight. The low light levels at ground level inhibit the growth of other plants that may compete with the trees for water or nutrients. The loss of these plants and the species that depend upon them reduces the wildlife diversity of the forest.

▲ *Close-planted conifers*

Simple age structure

Planting large areas of trees at the same time makes tree management easy. The trees will all be of similar sizes and will all need similar management activities at the same time. However, having trees of a similar size reduces the variety of abiotic factors compared with having a plantation with trees of different ages and sizes. This reduces the diversity of wildlife species that can survive.

The trees in commercial plantations are usually felled when the income will be greatest. This is normally when they are approaching full size and the growth rate is starting to decline.

This is very different from a natural forest which contain old trees with dead wood that supports many invertebrates and the species that feed on them such as woodpeckers.

Deforestation

Over 1/3 of the world's original forest area has been lost due to human activities. The loss of forests continues, especially in tropical areas, but the rate has dropped in the last 30 years.

Deforestation includes any activities that cause a reduction in forest area. There are two main causes.

▼ Deliberate removal of forests to make space for another land use eg agriculture, urban development.

▼ Unsustainable exploitation: exploitation above the Maximum Sustainable Yield

Causes of forest loss

Agriculture

Agricultural expansion causes the loss of forests in two main ways:

▼ The growth of the local population increases the demand for food, so more land must be cleared for farming.

▼ Forest clearance for commercial cash crop agriculture where the produce may be taken to cities or exported.

For example:

• Rainforest clearance in South America to grow sugar cane and soya beans or to ranch cattle.

• Rainforest clearance in SE Asia to grow palm oil.

Mineral extraction

Forest clearance for mining and the associated infrastructure affects a relatively small total area but it can have important local impacts.

Reservoirs

Reservoirs for public supply, irrigation or hydro-electric power (HEP) can replace forests. The expansion of HEP in South America has caused the loss of large areas of tropical rainforest.

Urbanisation

The expansion of urban areas can cause the direct loss of forest. It also increases the demand for fuel and food which can cause further forest loss.

Transport infrastructure

The area of forest lost by the construction of roads, railways or airports is not large, but they can have other impacts:

▼ Roads and railways can create barriers to the movement of wildlife and cause population fragmentation.

▼ Improved transport systems increase accessibility and make it easier to take out resources such as felled trees or agricultural produce that may increase the rate of forest clearance.

▼ *Woodlands clearance for urban expansion*

Unsustainable exploitation

Timber resources

Softwood produced by conifers such as pine, spruce and fir trees is often produced sustainably with replanting to replace harvested areas in areas such as Scandinavia and Canada.

Hardwood species such as teak and mahogany grow more slowly than conifers so it is more difficult to commercially manage hardwood plantations as it may take longer to produce a saleable crop. Therefore, a lot of the harvested hardwood come from mixed forests that are clear felled and may not be replanted.

Fuel

More people rely on wood as their domestic energy source than any other fuel. It is not necessarily the fuel of choice but many people in LEDCs cannot afford alternative energy sources and have to use wood, even though its exploitation may be unsustainable.

In towns and cities, there may be a greater demand for charcoal that produces less smoke when burnt. The production of charcoal involves the partial combustion of wood with a shortage of air. Much of the energy value of the wood is lost in this process which increases the rate of forest clearance to satisfy the demand for energy.

Livestock fodder

It is unusual for forest areas to be cleared to provide livestock food. However, in LEDCs, in areas of mixed woodland and grassland, farmers may cut branches off trees if there is a shortage of ground-level grazing. If this exceeds the growth of the trees then the forest may gradually be degraded and disappear.

The effects of deforestation

Loss of forest resources

Forest products are renewable but they can be depleted. Deforestation stops their production completely.

- Timber, fuel, fibres, medicines

Ecological impacts

- Reduced biodiversity
- Loss of species
- Fragmentation of remaining forest areas

Changes to hydrology

- Reduced interception and transpiration
- Increased runoff

Impact on soil

- Reduced soil formation
- less dead organic matter
- Increased soil erosion
- Less protection of soil by vegetation and leaf litter
- Reduced soil organic matter
- Reduced root binding

Climate impacts
▼ Increased albedo
▼ Reduced carbon sequestration and carbon reservoir
▼ Reduced rainfall downwind

These issues are covered in more detail in other topic areas.

Sustainable forest management

Forests can be exploited sustainably if harvesting rates and environmental impacts are carefully managed. This may involve a combination of the environmentally beneficial methods used in traditional forest management with the commercially productive methods of modern plantation forestry.

The move to better forest management has been helped by a growing understanding of the importance of forests.

Some countries have had large-scale tree planting projects, such as China, Cuba and Bhutan.

Features of sustainably managed forests

Harvesting rates
The rate of resource removal must be no greater than the Maximum Sustainable Yield.

Mixed species plantations
Wildlife biodiversity is increased by growing multiple species because there is an increase in food choices, inter-species relationships and niches.

Indigenous species
If indigenous species are cultivated it is more likely that other indigenous species will benefit eg birds and insects.

Mixed age structure
Having a plantation with trees of different ages produces a greater diversity of abiotic factors such as light levels, temperatures and wind velocity. This increases the biodiversity of other species living in the forest.

Selective logging
Clear-felling a large area at one time is easy. It can be commercially advantageous if the trees have been grown as a single species monoculture as all the trees may be ready for harvesting at the same time. In mixed-species plantations or natural forests, different trees will be ready for felling at different times. Selective logging is more expensive because it is more labour-intensive but it gains the maximum benefit from the forest timber resource over longer time periods. It is also good for wildlife because the removal of individual trees leaves smaller clearings which have a smaller impact on the survival of remaining wildlife populations. Wildlife that has lost its tree habitat will not have to move too far to find a new habitat.

Key principles
▼ Forests provide a wide range of renewable resources
▼ Forests provide a wide range of ecosystem services
▼ Wise exploitation prevents resource depletion and maintains ecosystem services
▼ Poor management has caused large areas of forest to be deforested or degraded
▼ Good forestry decisions can be used to manage forests sustainably

Sustainabilty

This chapter gives a holistic overview of environmental issues and the strategies that can be used to create sustainable lifestyles. This approach is supported by the principles and details in all the previous chapters.

Introduction

Sustainability refers to the ability to have a lifestyle that can be maintained indefinitely. On a global scale it relates to the overall impacts of the entire human population.

A commonly used definition of sustainability is that produced by the Brundtland Commission in 1987:

"Sustainable development meets the needs of the present generation without compromising the ability of future generations to meet their own needs."

Some approaches to sustainable lifestyles are founded in the moral belief that it is the 'right' thing to do. Other approaches are based on 'enlightened self-interest': that protecting the environment causes fewer difficulties than not doing so.

All human activities have an impact on the environment. The impacts of early societies only had local impacts and did not damage the processes that allow the environment to recover.

The overall environmental impact depends on two main factors: the total population and the individual impacts of each person.

Some activities that are sustainable with a small population are unsustainable if the population is too big e.g. slash and burn agriculture, fishing and the discharge of some pollutants eg sewage.

As the global human population has grown, so has the average per capita impact which is closely related to affluence.

With increasing affluence, access to energy has become easier which has made many new activities possible, many of which have greatly increased environmental impacts due to the scale of activities and the production of toxic wastes that could not be decontaminated by natural processes.

The development of new activities has rarely been restricted by an awareness that the environmental impact is unsustainable. This may be because the new opportunity is overwhelmingly attractive, due to a lack of knowledge or of understanding the impacts or because the impacts occur elsewhere or much later.

The attitude of a society to the sustainable exploitation of environmental resources is often linked to the location of the resources as well as where and when the problems occur.

Many sedentary, rural communities have a cultural belief that resources should be exploited sustainably and that the level of exploitation should be limited to satisfying needs. The problems caused by over-exploitation become obvious quickly as supplies of the resources dwindle.

Urban populations are usually supported by resources that are brought in from other areas. If resources are depleted in one area then exploitation just moves to another area without the problem being evident to the urban consumers. This has occurred with resources such as supplies of timber, energy, metal minerals and fish.

Sustainable lifestyles involve a holistic overview of the ecological support systems of Earth and an understanding of how human activities can be developed to operate by the same principles.

Many people are prepared to reduce their environmental impact by lifestyle changes such as recycling more, conserving energy or switching to renewable energy. Some of the lifestyle changes can be enacted by individuals but others need the cooperation and decision-making of groups of people or complete societies, or international cooperation and agreement so that the changed lifestyles are genuinely sustainable, not just doing a little less damage.

The principles of Earth's ecological support systems

Natural systems have developed over long time periods, based on physical resources, renewable energy and natural processes that combine to provide long-term conditions that provide relatively stable conditions that are suitable to sustain abundant, diverse life.

Dynamic equilibria

Negative feedback mechanisms which resist change

Natural processes

Climate regulation (See page 89, Global climate change.)

- increased temperatures causing increased cloud cover and a higher albedo
- increased carbon dioxide levels leading to greater photosynthesis and carbon sequestration.

Hydrological cycle

- increased evaporation leading to increased precipitation

Population regulation

- homeostatic population regulation caused by density-dependent factors.

Human activities

Natural negative feedback mechanisms that would curtail a human activity are often ignored. The human response may be to find new ways of maintain the activity. Agricultural systems often cause soil degradation, reduced water availability and the loss of natural pest predators.

Negative feedback mechanisms would reduce crop yields. The human response may be to use fertilisers, irrigation and pesticides which further reduce the natural systems that would support food production.

Positive feedback mechanisms which increase change

Natural processes

Throughout the time that humans evolved, climatic conditions on Earth have been dominated by negative feedback mechanisms, producing relatively stable conditions.

Human activities

Global Climate Change: increased temperatures may increase the following features involved in positive feedback mechanisms:

- melting of permafrost
- ocean acidification
- decline of albedo
- methane hydrate releases
- forest and peat fires
- formation of cirrus clouds
- soil decomposition rates.

Equilibrium tipping points which lead to new equilibria

Natural processes

Natural systems that are regulated by negative feedback mechanisms rarely reach tipping points because the response to changes re-establishes the previous state of equilibrium.

Large scale unusual events can cause changes that reach tipping points as they overwhelm the ability of negative feedback mechanisms to re-create the equilibrium eg the possible release of methane hydrate at the end of the Permian era that caused climate change and a mass extinction.

Human activities

Global Climate Change

- An increase in the rate of natural processes may become self-sustaining due to human activities, for example, forest fires, methane hydrate releases and permafrost melting.

Diverse systems are more likely to be resistant to change

Natural processes

High diversity natural systems:

- coral reefs
- tropical rainforests

Human activities

Human activities often produce less diverse systems. Many agroecosystems focus on the production of a limited range of food species with little attempt to maintain other species that help maintain ecological stability and productivity e.g. detritivores, pollinators, natural pest predators

Sustainability

14

Energy

Natural systems are driven by low energy-density, renewable energy resources, especially solar power

Natural processes

All the natural processes driven by solar energy are driven by low energy-density resources.
- Hydrological cycle.
- Carbon cycle.
- Nitrogen cycle.
- Atmospheric circulation.
- Thermohaline circulation.

Human activities
- Human activities are usually powered by non-renewable energy resources
- Human activities based on renewable energy resources have low carbon footprints
- Most natural processes occur at low temperatures

Natural processes
- Production of carbohydrates by photosynthesis.
- Enzymes reduce the activation energy of reactions so high temperatures are not needed.
- Decomposition.
- Nitrogen fixation.

Human activities that use high temperatures
- Many manufacturing processes.
- Haber process.
- Incineration of wastes.

Material cycles

Natural processes often link together in sequences that create cycles, with the waste products of one process being the raw materials for other processes.

Natural processes use a relatively small number of elements, which build into monomers. These build to produce a wide range of polymers eg carbohydrates, proteins.

The re-use of abundant, simple raw materials in natural cycles results in sustainable systems.

Linear human systems lead to resource depletion and waste generation.

Fossil fuels

The reliance on non-renewable energy resources cannot be sustainable. Inefficient use and their use when renewable resources are available accelerates depletion rates.

Mineral resources

Human use of minerals often causes their dispersal after use, or produces mixtures of materials which are difficult to separate. This makes recovery and re-use of materials difficult so sustainable exploitation is reduced.

Natural waste products are either non-toxic or do not build up to cause toxiity

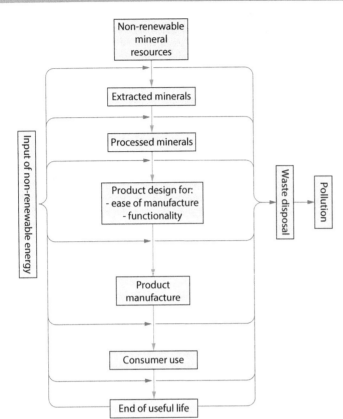

▲ *Linear human systems rely mainly on non-renewable resources and use resources once before they are discarded*

Natural processes

The molecules produced by natural processes are biodegradable and can be broken down to non-toxic products that are the raw materials for other natural processes.

Students should consider how the low toxicity of the wastes of natural systems and the natural processes that process them minimise environmental problems and provide sustainable supplies.

Human activities

Toxic metals are often used in consumer products, such as electronic items. These cannot easily be removed from end-of-life appliances.

Persistent toxins with low degradability may bioaccumulate and biomagnify, for example organochlorines, PCBs.

The circular economy

The circular economy involves an analysis of human activities and an assessment of how using the principles of natural systems would create more sustainable lifestyles. The principles below can be examined and compared with all the environmental issues already covered, to consider how a move towards a circular economy would increase sustainability.

The principles of the circular economy

Cycling of materials

Biogeochemical cycles involve interconnected physical and biological processes where each process uses the waste products of a previous process and produces wastes that are the raw materials for subsequent processes. There is no depletion of raw materials or a build-up of wastes.

Energy derived from renewable sources

Almost all natural processes are driven by renewable energy resources, especially solar energy. (See page 196, Renewable energy resources.)

Human activities should support ecosystems

Since human survival relies on the services provided by natural ecosystems, it is important that human activities do not damage them.

Diverse systems are more resistant to change

Each component in a diverse ecosystem is likely to be relatively less important, so the impact of a change is likely to be smaller.

Connected systems

Natural systems are usually connected systems where the waste product of one process is the raw material for another process.

Design of products for extended use

Making products that have long lives reduces the opportunities for the loss of materials at the end of products' lives.

Design of products for end of life reuse

Reusing or recycling materials is often easier if the items are designed so that the materials can be identified, separated and re-used or recycled more easily.

Separation of technical and biological materials

Materials such as metals and plastics require different reprocessing methods.

Optimum production rather than maximum production

Natural systems often over-produce so that the surplus supports processes upon which the whole system relies, for example, plant products which support pollinators, seed dispersal agents and soil microbes including decomposers and mycorrhizal fungi. This can be contrasted with agroecosystems which aim for maximum harvested yields of the crop.

Technologies to design new products and improve system effectiveness.

Improved designs can increase the efficiency of energy use, reduce material use and enable dismantling for re-use

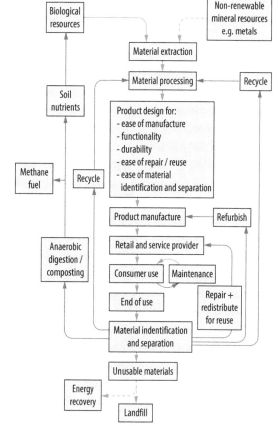

▲ *The circular economy uses renewable resources and re-uses materials whenever possilble*

Applying the circular economy to sustainable lifestyles

The extent to which the principles of the Circular Economy can be applied to the development of sustainable lifestyles can be considered in the following activities:

Land uses that support natural ecosystems

The conservation of biodiversity can be incorporated into the planning of many human activities:

Urban development

The designs and management of gardens, parks, public green spaces and buildings can provide opportunities for wildlife to colonise.

① *A wetland habitat created in an old industrial coolant lagon*

② *Housing development and wetland habitat in an old dock*

③ *Urban gardens can provide very diverse habitats for wildlife. The total garden area in the UK is over 4300km^2*

④ *A car park surface that retains vegetation and allows rainwater infiltration*

Agriculture

Agri-environmental schemes can optimise yields while benefiting wildlife. See p xxx

① *Infilling gaps in hedges increases their value as biological corridors*

② *Careful timing of mowing meadows can conserve wildflowers.*

③ *Beetle bank provide a habitat for invertebrates, inclusing predators of pests*

Forestry

Forestry management that incorporates mixed-species forests of indigenous trees often increases the wildlife value.

Fishery management

Improved fishing methods can exploit fish populations sustainably while reducing bycatch and environmental damage.

Mineral exploitation

Mining always causes habitat damage, but good management can minimise the impact and site restoration after mine closure can produce valuable land, including wildlife habitats.

▲ *A cliff in a sand quarry that is left for nesting Sand Martins.*

Waste management

Pollutants are wastes for which a new use or good disposal method was not found. Good waste management reduces pollution, including the pollution that harms wildlife.

Water supply (see page 114, The Hydrosphere)
- ◤ Good management of water catchments, aquifers and water conservation reduce the impacts of water use on wildlife.

Mineral resource management (see page 130, The Lithosphere)
- ◤ Increasing reserves by exploiting low-grade ores using low temperature processes.
- ◤ Extending product lifespans through better designs.
- ◤ No planned obsolescence.
- ◤ Replaceable parts/no built-in batteries.
- ◤ Good spare part supplies/technical support.
- ◤ Reduced unnecessary use eg excessive packaging.

Waste management (see page 143, Future mineral supplies and page 279, Solid wastes)
- ◤ Repair.
- ◤ Re-use.
- ◤ Re-purpose.
- ◤ Refurbish.
- ◤ Recycle.
- ◤ Re-design to make the above easier.

Pollution control (see page 236, Pollution)
A move from post-production treatment to non-release by changes in technology for example.
- ◤ Industrial synergy, so wastes become resources (see Kalundborg page 388)
- ◤ Better designs, so wastes can be separated
- ◤ Change from internal combustion engines to fuel cells
- ◤ Change from flue-gas desulfurisation to fuel desulfurisation/low-sulfur fuels

Energy supplies (see page 170, Energy resources)
The use of renewable energy resources and the development of low-temperature

manufacturing processes.

The development of other technologies that make the use of renewable energy easier, including storage and methods that increase the energy density.

Food production (see page 306 Agriculture and page 338, Aquatic food resources)
The inclusion of natural processes in nutrient supply, pest control and soil maintenance.

Diverse systems
As with diverse ecosystems, diverse technical systems are usually more stable e.g. societies that use a range of renewable energy resources rather than relying on one.

Initiatives to support the Circular Economy

Many governments would like to protect the environment, create more sustainable lifestyles and support the Circular Economy. However, the cost of implementing such schemes may put companies at an economic disadvantage compared with companies in countries that do not support such initiatives. A more even approach can be achieved if groups of countries use a common approach, such as the UN or EU. In a group of countries there may be better coordination and monitoring of activities than in an individual country where there is no external regulatory structure. Working as part of a group also enables countries that are protecting the environment more effectively to support those countries that are not being as successful.

EU initiatives that support a circular economy
The EU has proposed or introduced a wide range of initiatives to reduce environmental impacts and support the Circular Economy.

Conservation of biodiversity
- Better protection for ecosystems: conservation of birds, habitats and the marine environment.
- Development of green infrastructure.
- Better management of fish stocks.
- More sustainable agriculture.
- More sustainable forestry.
- Better control of introduced species.

Waste management and pollution control
- Better control of urban waste water.
- Minimal use of landfill.
- More recycling of electrical and electronic appliances.
- More recycling of used batteries.
- More control of industrial emissions.
- More use of composted materials as fertilisers.
- Reduction of food waste.
- Reduced use of packaging.
- Increased recycling of packaging.

Water
- Better management of water resources: quantity and quality.
- More reuse of water.

Energy
▼ More use of biofuels and other renewable fuels for transport.
▼ Improved energy efficiency of refrigerators and freezers.
▼ Increased use of wastes for energy generation.
▼ Increased use of renewable energy resources.

Design of manufactured appliances
▼ Improved design of products so they can be repaired to extend their useful lives.
▼ Improved design of products so the materials can be reused or recycled.
▼ Reduced use of toxic materials in electronic appliances.
▼ More use of recycled materials in road and building construction.
▼ Easier battery replacement.
▼ Reduced use of toxic materials in vehicle manufacture.
▼ Vehicle manufacture using recycled materials.
▼ Vehicle manufacture using recyclable materials.

Biocapacity and ecological footprints

Many organisations cooperate and contribute to an increased understanding of the global impact of humans on the planet. The data they collect is presented in ways that allow changes and differences to be analysed and compared easily.

The Global Footprint Network includes over 70 organisations, including national governments, research organisations and social benefit organisations. It produces information on ecological footprints, biocapacity and related issues.

The WWF publishes an annual Living Planet Report which provides a current assessment of changes in the impact of human activities on the planet and its ability to support life.

Biocapacity
Biocapacity is a measure of the biological productivity of an area. This could be the whole planet or a selected smaller area such as a country. It is calculated for five different types of area: forests, marine and inland waters, cropland, grazing land and built-up areas.

Biocapacity is affected by human management methods such as farming methods as well as the natural productivity. Although it can be increased by good human management, it can also be reduced by habitat destruction or degradation. The biocapacity that is calculated for an area does not assume that any land is reserved for the other species that could use the same area. Land that is set aside for other species and wildlife communities is called a biodiversity buffer.

Ecological footprint
An ecological footprint is the area of the Earth's surface that is needed to provide the resources that are used by the human population and to deal with the wastes produced. If the total footprint of the entire human population is less than the area of the planet, then the population can be supported sustainably. If it is larger, then the planet is being overexploited. An ecological footprint can be calculated for an individual, group of people or activity.

Global hectare (gha)

It is important to be able to compare the ecological footprint of a person, group of people or activity with the area needed to provide the resources and services required to support it. The biocapacities of different areas vary widely, so an average value is used. A global hectare refers to a hectare of land with a biocapacity that is the average of the whole planet.

Earth Overshoot Day (previously Ecological Debt Day)

The concept of overshoot is used to describe exploitation of the planet's resources that occurs at a faster rate than the replacement rate, so it will take more than a year for the Earth to recover from a year of human exploitation. Another way of considering this is that a year's worth of resources will be exhausted on Earth Overshoot Day. After that date resources are being depleted and carbon dioxide will accumulate. Earth Overshoot Day occurs earlier each year as human impacts increase. Earth Overshoot day in 2016 was estimated to be August 8th.

Carbon footprint

This is the part of an ecological footprint that relates to the emission of carbon dioxide and other greenhouse gases. It is usually expressed as a mass of carbon dioxide equivalent which allows other greenhouse gases to be included and allowance to be made for their differing strengths as greenhouse gases.

The carbon footprint can be applied at different levels such as the footprint of an individual, an organisation, a country or the entire human population. The calculation should be comprehensive, including all direct and indirect releases of greenhouse gases. For example estimates of the carbon dioxide emissions caused by a car should include a complete lifecycle analysis. This will include the obvious emissions from fuel combustion, but also the emissions released during the manufacture of the components to make the car, the items used in maintenance and its final disposal. A wider analysis would include its 'fair share' of the emissions in building and maintaining the road infrastructure: roads, carparks, road signals and street lights.

Living Planet Index

The LPI is calculated by WWF as a measure of the state of the planet's ecosystems. It compares over 18000 populations of over 3700 species of vertebrates from terrestrial, freshwater and marine ecosystems. Changes are compared with 1970 which was the first year of the study.

Case studies of sustainable development

Case study: Ol Pejeta Game Reserve, Kenya

Ol Pejeta is a large private game reserve covering 360km^2 in central Kenya.

For many years until the 1980s the area was managed as a cattle ranch where large wildlife species were not tolerated.

Big herbivores were killed for being competitors and large predators were killed to prevent livestock predation.

In the 1980s new ownership and a new management style developed: to ranch cattle and conserve wildlife.

This has become a model of pragmatic wildlife conservation alongside commercial livestock farming.

Cattle

Selection of cattle breed.

Boran cattle are very hardy, make efficient use of the available food and are resistant to many diseases.

◀ *Boran cattle*

Tick control

The cattle are 'dipped' regularly in insecticide to kill ticks. This reduces the total tick population in the reserve which improves the health of wild herbivores that therefore have fewer parasitic ticks and fewer tick-related health problems.

◀ *Insecticide spraying ('dipping')*

▼ *A cattle boma*

Bomas

The cattle are kept in small fenced areas (bomas) overnight to reduce predator losses, especially lion attacks. The bomas are moved every two or three weeks. The dung left by the cattle increases soil nutrient levels which increases plant growth, including a wide range of plants that may not otherwise have grown.

Wildlife management

Electric fences

High voltage perimeter electric fences are in place to prevent poachers from getting in and large game animals from escaping.

◀ An electric fence to keep wildlife in and poachers out

Biological corridors

▲ A biological corridor that links neighbouring conservation areas.

Although the reserve is large, many animals need to roam over larger areas in search of food or water. Biological corridors link Ol Pejeta to other conservation areas to allow animal movements. The exits from Ol Pejeta are designed to allow all species to leave or enter freely, except rhinos. They would be at risk of poaching if they left the well-protected reserve. Strong wooden posts are sunk into the ground. They are too tall for rhinos to walk over them and too close together for them to walk between them.

Checking for animal tracks and using motion-sensitive cameras help to monitor the movement of animals.

Elephant management

Elephants live in family groups led by the oldest females who have long memories of the locations of good supplies of food and water, especially in times of drought. When there is a drought, some elephants have the knowledge to break through the fences and lead the herd to better areas. The biological corridors allow the elephants to move between conservation areas without breaking fences so animals that repeatedly break fences are removed to other conservation areas if necessary.

Lion tracking

Radio collars are fitted on some of the lions in the six prides found in the reserve. This helps in collecting data on their movements and interactions with other lions and their prey species.

Drones

Ol Pejeta has used drones to monitor wildlife and search for poachers.

Endangered species

Because the reserve is well guarded and managed, populations of several endangered species have been established. For some species, the animals have been brought in from other areas.

◄Northern white rhinos.
Sudan is one of the three remaining northen white rhinos (2017). he is the only male, but produces sperms with low motility so he is unlikey to breed successfully. Neither of the two females is capable of breeding. In-vitro fertilisation using surrogate female southern white Rhinos is being considered.

Grévy's Zebra

◄ Grévy's Zebra lives in the semi-desert areas of North Africa where wildlife conservation is often ineffective. A protected popilation has been established at Ol pejeta

Ecotourism

Money paid by visitors to see the wildlife helps fund conservation projects.

Community links

The reserve is managed to ensure the local human population benefits from wildlife conservation.

Community support

Income from the reserve is used to support a range of community projects: health, education, water supplies

Employment

Local people are employed in a wide variety of roles.

Cattle

Local farmers are helped with breeding programmes to improve the quality of their cattle and increase incomes.

Sustainable development in small communities

It has sometimes proved easier for small relatively self-contained communities to become motivated and organise themselves to develop more sustainable lifestyles.

Selected community sustainability projects

▼ Eigg Scotland
▼ Samso, Denmark
▼ Gigha, Scotland
▼ BedZED, London, UK
▼ Hockerton Housing Project, Telford, UK

Case study: Eigg, UK

Eigg is small island off the west coast of Scotland, with an area of 31km² and a resident population of about 100.

In 1996 the community set up the Isle of Eigg Trust with the Scottish Wildlife Trust to buy the island from the existing landowner then manage the island for the benefit of the community, the wildlife of the island and the wider environment.

The success of the Eigg project has become a model of how to merge community and environmental priorities that has inspired and informed many other communities.

Energy

Eigg is not connected to the national electricity grid. The island's energy strategy emphasises renewable energy and the phasing out of fossil fuels.

An island electricity grid was established in 2008 to distribute electricity generated by renewable sources, with diesel generators for back-up.

▼ Three HEP generators provide electricity for the island grid, the largest having a capacity of 100kw. Some households have independent micro-hydro systems.

▼ A 50kw solar PV system provides electricity for the island grid. Some households have solar PV and photothermal systems.

❶ The solar farm on Eigg

❷ The wind farm on Eigg

❸ Surplus electricity is stored as chemical energy in a bank of lead acid batteries

❹ Kinetic energy storage using a flywheel system provides short-term energy storage

❺ An electric car

- Four wind turbines generate upto 24kw of electricity.
- Wood biomass is used for heating in many properties.
- Almost all vehicles use diesel or petrol, but some use electricity. Further developments with renewable energy and energy storage will make the move away from fossil fuels easier.
- Other projects include low-impact food production, beach litter collection and building insulation, such as a straw bale home.

Wildlife management

A range of habitats have been protected, created and managed for the benefit of particular species or communities.

1. Flag irises provide cover for nesting corncrakes
2. The sea cliffs are important nesting areas for seabirds and birds of prey
3. An Arctic Tern nesting colony was protected from the development of a new ferry terminal be relocating the access causeway
4. Conifer plantations have been removed so that bog and heath habitats can be restored
5. Rowan trees provide berries that provide winter food for migratory birds

- Hen Harriers, Golden Eagles and White Tailed Eagles all nest on Eigg
- Areas with important wild plants have been fenced for protection from grazing animals.
- Woodlands of indigenous trees have been planted such as Rowan, birch, goat willow

Waste & recycling

Recyclable waste is collected and shipped off the island for recycling.

Garden and food waste is composted and used as a garden soil improver.

The Rio Bravo Conservation and Management Area (RBCMA), Belize, Central America

The RBCMA is a relatively undamaged rainforest, although species such as Mahogany were selectively logged by the British upto the middle of the 20th century. The RBCMA is now managed by the Belizian NGO 'Programme for Belize'

The biodiversity of the RBCMA is high, with over 200 species of tree, 400 species of bird and 70 species of mammal.

Management is carried out to conserve wildlife, produce resources, sequester carbon and benefit the local and national economy.

The establishment of the rainforest reserve is good for wildlife but could threaten the local communities that used to use the area for fuelwood supplies, timber for housebuilding, farming clearings, hunting for food and the collection of medicines and fibres. A range of economic activities have been developed or encouraged. Local people are employed in forestry and ecotourism activities within the reserve. Ecotourist groups visit local restaurants, are fed with local produce and buy locally made souvenirs.

▲ *The Rio Bravo reserve protects over 100,000ha of rainforest*

Forest exploitation

Current exploitation of forest resources aims to raise money to help pay for the management of the reserve without causing long-term damage. More ecologically sensitive areas are not exploited, such as wetlands and areas close to rivers.

Tree selection

The focus is on the most economically valuable species, such as mahogany. Trees for felling are only selected in areas where there are other trees of the same species upwind of the clearing that will be created. Seeds from these trees will then recolonise the clearing.

▼ *Carvings made by local craftspeople from rainforest timber.*

Each tree that is felled is given a unique identification tag which allows the timber to be tracked from its original location to its final retail destination such as a DIY superstore in the UK. This is used to gain accreditation of sustainable exploitation from the FSC (Forest Stewardship Council).

The exploitation of other species is being developed such as zericote which is used for furniture, musical instruments and ornamental carvings.

Buffer zones near rivers

No mechanical or harvesting activities occur near rivers because of the ecological sensitivity of aquatic ecosystems.

Small trees

Small trees are not felled so that they can grow and be harvested in the future when they are larger.

Large trees

Selected large trees may be left because they will produce many seeds that will help to fill the spaces left by trees that are felled.

Restricted use of machinery

Large machines can damage the trunks and roots of trees that are not going to be felled. Restricting the use of machinery reduces this damage.

Track routes

The tracks for vehicles are planned to avoid important trees and their roots. These can include trees that are comparatively rare and trees that provide food for monkeys or birds. Previously used tracks are re-used whenever possible.

Smaller branches

Smaller branches and offcuts that have low commercial value are given to local artisans such as wood carvers or furniture makers.

Tree nurseries

Tree seedlings are raised to increase the numbers of trees that were over-exploited in the past or are ecologically important, such as fruit trees that provide food for monkeys. Tree seedlings are also given to local communities.

Control of illegal logging

Rangers patrol the reserve to control illegal logging. Illegally logged timber that is confiscated is sold to pay for conservation activities.

Community projects

Wildlife conservation projects are unlikely to be successful if there are no benefits for the local community. Programme for Belize has developed a variety of ecotourism projects so that the local communities benefit from wildlife conservation. PfB is also a major employer of rangers, forestry workers and tourism employees.

Carbon sequestration

An area of the forest is part of a research programme to monitor the sequestration of carbon as part of an assessment of the role of rainforests in reducing global climate change.

Funding for the project has come from electricity companies, airlines and individuals, all of whom wish to minimise atmospheric CO_2 levels.

▼ *Sustainably logged mahogany trees*

Case study: Kalundborg eco-industrial park, Denmark

This is an industrial symbiosis project in Denmark where companies in the area are organised in a way that mimics natural cyclical processes. Wherever possible, industries are located so that the raw materials they need are the wastes from other industries, while their wastes are needed as raw materials by other industries.

Industrial wastes and re-uses

Industry that produces waste	Waste product	Use of waste
Coal fired power station	Heat	Domestic heating Fish farm
	Sulfur dioxide	Building plaster manufacture
	Ash	Road building and cement manufacture
Fish farm	Organic sludge	Agricultural fertiliser
Biotechnology, medicine manufacture	Yeast	Pig farms
	Fermentation sludge	Agricultural fertiliser
Oil refinery	Natural gas	Burnt in coal fired power station

Case study: Large scale renewable energy electricity grids

Renewable energy is often very abundant but use may be restricted by geographical and temporal availability.

Large-scale electricity grids make it possible to distribute electricity from areas of surplus to areas of shortage.

Alternating Current (AC) grids require every power station to be generating so that it is synchronized to be in phase with all others. This can be difficult to coordinate with a scheme that involves a wide range of countries. Direct Current (DC) grids do not require the same degree of coordination.

Several large-scale DC grid projects have been proposed to harness renewable energy and distribute it to areas where it is needed:

▼ Desertec: Countries of the EU, North Africa and Middle East
▼ Pan Asian Energy Infrastructure: countries of eastern Asia.
▼ Global Renewable Energy Grid Project: high energy use areas throughout the world.

Key principles

▸ Current human lifestyles are unsustainable

▸ Resource depletion, damage to ecological processes and poor waste management are increasing problems

▸ Copying the cyclical processes of natural systems will make the development of sustainable lifestyles easier

▸ The circular economy provides a coordinated approach to achieving sustainability

Research methods

Chapter topics

▼ Scientific methodologies
▼ Population studies
▼ Abiotic factors
▼ Specialist techniques
▼ Specific scientific investigations
▼ Data analysis

Scientific research is a fundamental part of Environmental Science and good research skills are needed to collect representative data so that valid conclusions can be reached. Good decisions need good quality information to support the decision-making process.

Attributes of quality of methods and data

Quality	Description
Accuracy	A measure of how close the recorded result is to the real value.
Precision	The intervals between possible recorded results, for example, a ruler that measures in millimetres is more precise than one that measures in centimetres.
Representative sample	A subsample that accurately reflects the complete data set
Reliable method	Provides consistent, accurate results
Anomalous result	A result that differs from other results with which it was expected to be similar. Repeating the study should show whether it is a 'real' result or was caused by other variables.
Valid study	Produces precise, accurate, reliable results upon which conclusions can be based.

When designing and carrying out environmental science fieldwork, investigative enquiries and lab work a consideration of a range of factors in relation to the environmental context being investigated is necessary:

▼ appropriate risk management;
▼ the practical equipment and materials required and how to use these safely and correctly;
▼ the data to be collected and analysed:
  ▷ using appropriate apparatus/instruments to record quantitative measurements (for example, temperature, length and pH);
  ▷ using appropriate apparatus/instruments and methodologies to measure abiotic and biotic factors (for example, light intensity, humidity, population size);
  ▷ selecting the right sampling techniques (for example, pitfall traps, Tüllgren funnel, soil texture analysis, water turbidity, light traps);
  ▷ selecting the right statistical analysis techniques.

This chapter provides a summary of methodologies, skills, research methods, and statistical analysis techniques used in environmental investigations.

These activities can often be combined in complete investigations or they can be covered in a wide range of individual activities. For some methods, first-hand experience of the procedures is required. This may not be possible for the specialist techniques but the issues of planning and scientific methodologies can still be applied.

Scientific methodologies

All scientific studies are based on the same basic principles, regardless of the scientific discipline. These general principles of scientific investigations include:

- ▼ identifying a topic of interest;
- ▼ finding out what has already been learnt;
- ▼ formulating a hypothesis/null hypothesis that can be tested;
- ▼ designing and carrying out an experiment to test the hypothesis;
- ▼ designing the investigation, for example, including consideration of:
  - location of sampling sites;
  - number of samples;
  - size of samples;
  - standardised technique;
  - timing of sampling;
  - statistical analysis to assess statistical significance;
- ▼ analysing the results and drawing conclusions;
- ▼ planning further research to fill gaps in existing knowledge or develop the study further.

Careful planning is needed to ensure that the data collected can be used to conclude whether a hypothesis should be accepted or rejected.

All studies should be planned and carried out so that the statistical significance of the results can be assessed.

It is rarely possible to collect all the data that exists about a particular issue. It is more usual to collect sub-samples and use these to estimate the full situation. This will only produce reliable conclusions if the sub-samples are representative.

The planning of sub-sampling must consider factors that may affect how representative they are: location, timing, size, number.

A preliminary study should be used to test the reliability of the method.

Sampling

Sample location

If data are not being collected at a single location, then decisions will have to be made about the positioning of the sampling sites.

It is essential to avoid the introduction of bias caused by the deliberate selection of locations for convenience or to support or dismiss a hypothesis. This can usually be achieved by simple random or systematic sampling.

Random sampling:

Random sampling: if the study area has a regular shape then a grid can be laid out and the coordinates of sampling sites selected using random numbers.

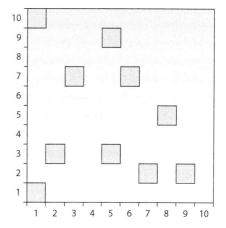

▼ *Random sampling on a site with regular shape*

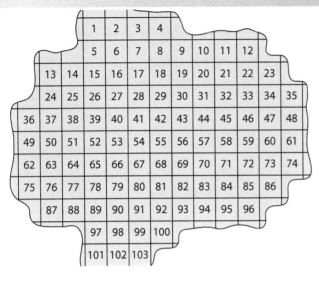

If the study area has an irregular shape then all the possible sampling sites can be numbered and selected using a random number generator.

Systematic sampling

Systematic sampling: this involves samples taken using a chosen interval distance or spacing. The choice of sampling sites is not based on choices made using observable differences in the study area.

◀ *Random sampling on a site with irregular shape*

❶ *Systematic sampling along a line transect and sampling sites in a study area*
❷ *Continuous and interrupted belt transects*

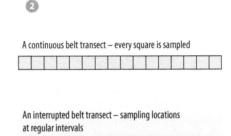

A continuous belt transect – every square is sampled

An interrupted belt transect – sampling locations at regular intervals

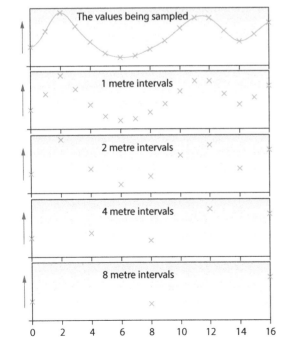

The values being sampled

1 metre intervals

2 metre intervals

4 metre intervals

8 metre intervals

The distance between sampling sites should be selected to detect variable data without collecting more data than necessary. This can be determined with a preliminary study.

Sample timing

If the factor that is being measured changes with time, then it will be necessary to sample on different occasions to produce a mean result that represents the 'typical' value or to identify trends in changing values.

The ideal time interval between samples depends upon the rate at which values change. This can be determined with a preliminary study.

◀ *Graphs to show how the distance between sampling sites affects the sensitivity of data collection. Sampling at 2m intervals does not miss variations that are identified with 1m intervals but intervals of 4 metres or more fail to detect important peaks and troughs*

Examples of time scales and variables that may be affected

Timescale	Variables
Long-term changes	Population changes, for example, tigers Area of rainforest Atmospheric CO_2 level
Seasonal changes	Presence of migratory species Populations of annual wildflowers Temperature Atmospheric CO_2 level River level
Diurnal changes (24 hours)	Light levels Temperature Atmospheric CO_2 level
Weather-related changes (minutes to weeks)	Flying insect activity Wind velocity Temperature
Other short-term changes	Road noise levels

Sample size

If the variable being measured is not homogenous then larger samples are more likely to produce representative results. The sample size needed can be determined with a preliminary study.

Number of samples

A single sample may not be representative as there may be variability between samples. Collecting multiple samples will help to eliminate the effect of variability. The number of samples needed to produce a representative mean depends upon the degree of scatter around the mean. This can be found using a preliminary study.

The degree of scatter of values around the mean can be assessed by calculating the Standard Deviation.

The number of samples collected will also depend upon how the results will be analysed. It is easier to assess the degree of statistical significance of the results with larger numbers of samples.

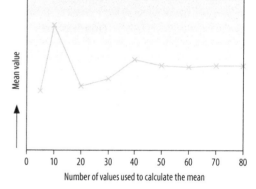

Standardisation of techniques

To allow comparison of the results that are collected at different times, in different locations, or by different researchers, they must all be collected in exactly the same way.

Other variables that may affect the results must either be controlled or monitored to assess their effects.

▲ *How the number of samples affects the reliability of a mean. in this graph, the means with fewer than 50 values are unreliable*

Population studies

Ecological monitoring is a very important part of wildlife conservation programmes. Good surveys are essential for many reasons:

▼ to find out which species are present;

▼ to monitor the habitat conditions, how they change, and which conditions individual species require;

- to monitor features of populations and how they change over time such as:
- population size;
- age structure;
- growth rates;
- breeding rates;
- territory size;
- population movements;
- reliable, representative data are important in making good conservation management decisions.

There are many different techniques that are used to monitor ecological conditions in ecosystems and the species that live there. The specific technique that is appropriate depends upon what is being measured. It is also affected by the rapid development of new technologies that may produce better results: more representative, quicker, more cost effective etc.

Standard ecological techniques

These include methods that work well and have been used for a long time, often dating back to the beginnings of scientific ecology over 100 years ago.

Quadrats

A quadrat is a study area, usually square, within which populations can be studied. The results from a number of quadrats can be scaled up to estimate the overall situation for the entire area.

Quadrat size

The size of quadrat that should be selected depends upon the habitat and groups of species being studied.

Typical quadrat sizes:

- Lichens: 10cm x 10 cm;
- Ground flora: 0.5m x 0.5m;
- Trees in a forest: 100m x 100m;
- Bird survey (presence, not population census): 10km x 10km.

Types of quadrat

- **Open frame quadrats:** these just mark out a study area. Smaller ones may be made of a metal or plastic frame. Larger ones use reference coordinates marked out by measuring tapes or GPS coordinates.
- **Grid quadrats:** these are sub-divided into smaller squares, for example, 10 x 10, each small square representing 1% of the area.
- **Point quadrat:** these are used to collect similar information to other quadrats but they do not use a square area. They can be used where ground flora is too tall for other quadrat types because it would be flattened and provide unrepresentative results: a percentage cover estimate would be inaccurate and shorter plants may be obscured by the flattened foliage of taller plants. A wooden frame supports metal rods, usually 10. Each time a rod touches a leaf it counts as 10% cover.

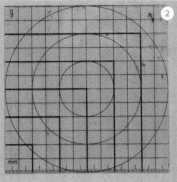

① *An open frame quadrat and a 10x10 grid quadrat.*
② *10com x 10cm quadrat for lichens*
③ *A point quadrat*

Limitations

- ⚑ Subjective judgement may be involved, for example, estimating percentage cover.
- ⚑ The quadrat frame may flatten or move plants.

Nets

A wide variety of nets can be used to capture organisms in the air, on vegetation, and in water. The net and mesh size depend upon the organisms to be collected.

Pond net

Method

- ⚑ Pond nets can be swept through the water or aquatic vegetation to capture invertebrates, amphibians, or fish.
- ⚑ Using a particular length of sweep, or number of sweeps, can be used in an attempt to standardise the method and produce comparative data.

Limitations:

- ⚑ Mobile species may escape.

▲ *Pond net*

Kick sampling

Kick sampling collects invertebrates that live on riverbeds.

Method

- ⚑ A net is held with its straight edge on the river bed and its face open to the current.
- ⚑ The riverbed in front of the net is disturbed by repeatedly scraping a boot over it. Invertebrates that are dislodged are caught in the net.
- ⚑ Controlling the number and length of kicks can be used to standardise the method.

▼ *Kick sampling*

Limitations

- ⚑ Accurate standardisation is difficult.
- ⚑ Buried organisms or those fixed on stones may not be dislodged.
- ⚑ Some organisms can swim and avoid the net.
- ⚑ The water flow rate is variable and affects the capture rate.
- ⚑ Fragile organisms may be destroyed.

Surber samplers

Surber samplers provide a more standardised technique than kick sampling.

Method

- ▼ A fixed area of riverbed is sampled within a box-like frame.
- ▼ The riverbed is disturbed using a trowel or similar tool and stones are inspected manually.
- ▼ Netting at the sides of the net opening reduces the number of organisms that escape.

Limitations

- ▼ They can only be used where the water flow is fast enough to carry organisms into the net.
- ▼ The sampler's small size can make it difficult to set on rough substrates in deep water resulting in the loss of large organisms.

▲ *Surber sampler*

Plankton net

Plankton nets catch planktonic organisms floating in water. Some plankton nets can be used to give quantitative estimates of populations

▼ *Plankton net*

Method

- ▼ A fine mesh is pulled through the water and can be used vertically or horizontally.
- ▼ The net can be fixed where there is a current or may be towed through the water.
- ▼ Different mesh sizes are used for different sizes of organisms. Phytoplankton are smaller than zooplankton so a smaller mesh size is used.

Limitations

- ▼ Nets with a coarse mesh size do not catch smaller organisms.
- ▼ Nets with a fine mesh may become clogged by phytoplankton, preventing water flowing into the net.

Sweep nets

Method

- ▼ Sweep nets are sturdy nets used to sample invertebrates in ground vegetation such as grassland. The net is swept through the vegetation so that organisms that are dislodged are caught.
- ▼ Standardisation of the method can be attempted by using the same number of sweeps of the same length.

Limitations

- ▼ Mobile species may escape, such as flying insects.

◀ *Sweep net*

Aerial insect nets

Method

▼ These are lightweight nets used to capture flying insects such as butterflies.

Limitations

▼ Successful collection depends on the agility of the researcher and the prey.

Colonisation media

Method

▼ Some species can be monitored by providing suitable habitats that they may colonise.

Limitations

▼ Not all species can be monitored as they may not use the media.

▼ Accurate population estimates are not possible as the proportion that colonise the media is not known.

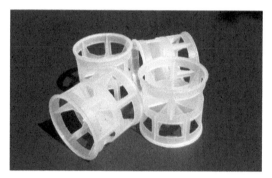

▲ *Colonisation media for aquatic invertebrates*

Pitfall traps

Pitfall traps are used to sample populations of mobile animals on the ground surface.

Method

▼ A container is placed in a hole in the ground with its open end making a close fit with the soil and the top being level with the ground surface.

▼ A cover is supported over the opening to exclude predators that may eat animals that are caught and to prevent flooding by rain.

▼ The trap is checked after a standard period of time, for example, 24 hours.

▼ A preservative fluid may be used to kill captured animals for later study.

Limitations

▼ Only mobile animals that live on the ground surface are caught.

▼ More mobile species are more likely to be caught.

▼ Trapped carnivorous animals may kill other organisms that have been caught.

▼ If a preservative is used, it may attract or repel certain species.

▼ Some species avoid traps or can escape.

▼ *A pitfall trap*

Cover to prevent large animals or rain entering

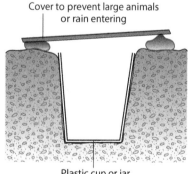

Plastic cup or jar

Beating trays

Beating trays are used to sample invertebrates present on vegetation above the ground.

Method

▼ A sheet or tray is placed beneath the vegetation which is beaten several times with a stick. The invertebrates that are dislodged fall onto the sheet and are collected for identification and counting.

▲ *Beating tray*

Limitations

◤ It is difficult to standardise the method between researchers, for example, the vigour of hitting the branches.

◤ Some species are not dislodged.

◤ Thicker branches shake less, so organisms are less likely to be dislodged.

◤ Some species fly away and are not caught.

◤ Higher branches cannot be reached.

Light traps

Light traps are used to collect night-flying insects that are attracted by bright lights, usually ultra violet lights.

Method

◤ Flying insects, especially moths that are attracted to the light fall into a container. The container is checked the following morning.

◤ The insects that have been caught are identified and counted.

Limitations

◤ Moths only fly during their adult phase and activity is affected by the weather and seasons, so the failure to find a species does not mean it is absent.

◤ The brightness and light wavelengths emitted by the light can affect their attractiveness to insects, so it may be difficult to compare results produced by different types of trap.

Three diffrent designs of light traps

Tüllgren funnel

Tüllgren funnels are used to sample mobile invertebrates in leaf litter or the soil.

Method

- ⚐ A sample of leaf litter or soil is placed on a mesh beneath a light.
- ⚐ The light and heat repel some mobile invertebrates which move downwards, pass through the mesh, and fall into a container.
- ⚐ The Tüllgren funnel is left operating for a standard period of time.
- ⚐ The invertebrates collected are identified and counted.

Limitations

- ⚐ Only species that are repelled by heat or light will be collected.
- ⚐ Some organisms may die or stop moving due to heating or desiccation before they are collected.
- ⚐ Some organisms are too large to pass through the mesh.

▲ *Tüllgren funnel*

Suction samplers

Suction samplers capture airborne insects or invertebrates that were dislodged from vegetation. Some just show the presence of the organisms but some give quantitative data.

Method

- ⚐ There are several types of suction sampler which can be used to collect invertebrates from the ground, vegetation or the atmosphere:
- ⚐ Air suction samplers capture flying insects. If the air flow rate is measured and the cross-sectional area of the collector tube is known then the number of insects per unit volume of air can be estimated.
- ⚐ Motor-driven suction samplers can be used to sample invertebrates on ground vegetation. The area of ground that is covered by the suction pipe is known, so the population density of the invertebrates can be estimated.
- ⚐ A pooter is a suction sampler used to pick up invertebrates that have been found. It is a handling method, not a population sampling technique.

Limitations

- ⚐ Some invertebrates may not be caught by an air sampler. They may sense the air sampler and fly away.
- ⚐ Some insects may not be dislodged from vegetation by a suction sampler.

❶ *Aerial insect suction sampler*
❷ *A pooter*
❸ *A motor-driven suction sampler for collecting invertebrates on ground vegetation*

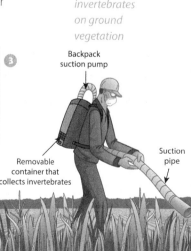

Earthworm extraction from soil

Earthworms are difficult to observe, so they must be removed from the soil for their populations to be monitored.

Soil flooding
Method

- Mark out a sample area of a suitable size 0.5m x 0.5m or 1m x 1m
- Remove vegetation that may hide worms at the surface.
- Add an irritant solution, for example, detergent or mustard in water.
- Keep adding until the soil is saturated.
- Saturate the surrounding area (so the worms are less likely to move sideways).
- Add more as the solution infiltrates into the soil.
- Collect worms that come to the surface.
- Continue collecting until no more worms appear/for suitable time period/standardised time period.
- Count/measure/weigh/identify the collected worms.

Limitations

- Irritant solution may not percolate through impermeable soils.
- Irritant solution may not reach deepest worms.
- Worms may move sideways or down.
- Worms may not move.
- Worms may die.
- Worms may move too slowly to be collected during the study period.

Soil pit extraction
Method

- A pit of a chosen area and depth is dug, for example, 0.5m x 0.5m x 0.5m.
- The soil is hand sorted and worms collected.

Limitations

- Smaller worms may be overlooked.
- Digging may disturb worms that move sideways or down, out of the sample site.

Quantitative/comparative/ numerical measures

It is important to be able to compare data about populations in different locations or at different times in the same place. A wide range of methods is available to do this, each with its own advantages and disadvantages.

Population size/density

The purpose is to estimate the numbers of organisms of a particular species within a population or per unit area.

Many different methods can be used, depending on the features of the species being studied.

For some species, it may be possible to count all the individuals in a population, for example, all the birds in a cliff nest colony.

Some species are dispersed over such large areas that sub-sampling is necessary. The data collected from the sampled areas can be extrapolated and used to estimate the population of the total area.

Some species cannot easily be observed but it may be possible to catch a sample of the population. A mark-release-recapture method may be used to estimate the total population, for example, the Lincoln Index (see below).

Abundance scales

These involve allocating species to different categories based on their relative abundance, for example, the DAFOR scale. Species are categorised into the following groups:

- Dominant
- Abundant
- Frequent
- Occasional
- Rare

The judgement of abundance is subjective and can vary between different people but it is quick and allows many areas to be studied quickly.

The results are not quantitative so statistical analysis of the results may not be possible.

Species richness/diversity

This is a measure of the number of different species found in an area. It often focuses on a particular taxon, for example, birds, ground flora, or reptiles.

To standardise the method and allow comparisons between sites, it may be used in specific sample areas, for example, tree species in 100m x 100m squares.

Species frequency

This is a measure of the dispersal of a species by recording the proportion of all samples in which it was found. A high species frequency shows the species is generally distributed.

Species density

This relates the number of species found to a specific area and makes species richness results more comparable, for example, number of species per square metre.

Percentage vegetation cover

This is estimated by observing the proportion of:

- the ground that is covered by vegetation for ground flora
- the sky that is obscured by vegetation for tree cover.

Grid quadrats are commonly used.

The Lincoln Index

The Lincoln Index estimates the total population by catching a proportion of the population.

Method

- A sample of the population is caught, counted, marked, and released.
- Some time later, a second sample is caught and counted. Individuals that already have marks from the first sample are counted.
- The Lincoln Index formula is used to estimate the total population.

The Lincoln Index formula

$$\text{Total population} = \frac{\text{Number in 1st sample} \times \text{number in 2nd sample}}{\text{Number in 2nd sample that have marks}}$$

Limitations

▶ The estimation of the population relies on some assumptions:

- individual animals are mobile and can be caught;
- the size of the population does not change during the time of the study, for example, due to births, deaths, or migration;
- being caught and marked does not affect survival rates;
- the marks do not fall off or wear away during the study;
- marked individuals mix freely with the rest of the population;
- all individuals in the population have the same chance of being caught.

Simpson's Index of Biodiversity

This is used to assess the variety and abundance of species in an area. It may be used to consider all species but it is often used for a single taxonomic group, for example, the biodiversity of ground flora or insects.

Simpson's Index of biodiversity formula

$$D = \frac{N(N-1)}{\Sigma(n(n-1)}$$

Where:

D = Index of diversity

N = total number of individuals of all species

n = number of individuals of a particular species (each species has its own n(n-1) value

Σ = sum of (all the n(n-1) value)

There are several different formulae that can be used. For this formula, a higher value indicates a higher biodiversity.

Species identification: ID keys

Method

These are often dichotomous keys where a sequence of questions narrows down the possibilities. They are based on unique visible features: size, shape, markings etc.

Limitations

▶ Some species lack characteristic features and look the same as other species.

▶ Characteristic features may not always be present, for example, flowers, seeds, breeding plumage.

Specialist techniques used in ecological research

These include methods that have been developed relatively recently, often using electronic equipment. Many are still being developed to produce improved results or so that they can be applied to new research situations.

Imagery

A rapidly expanding range of imagery systems is available to collect environmental information.

Image databases

The individuals of some species can be recognised from image databases of unique features, for example, Tiger facial

stripes, Cheetah tail markings, Whale Shark spot patterns, dolphin fin marks and injuries, zebra stripes.

Being able to identify individuals can provide information on:

◤ territory size;

◤ population movements such as migrations;

◤ lifespans;

◤ social groupings.

❶ *Cheetah tail*
❷ *Dolphin fins*
❸ *Zebra stripes*

Limitations

◤ Few species have unique features that can be used to identify individual animals.

Motion-sensitive cameras

These can be used for habitat monitoring to detect the presence or activity of animals, using visible light photography during the day or infrared photography at night.

❶ *Motion sensitive camera*
❷ *An infrared image of a giraffe*
❸ *An infrared image of zebras*

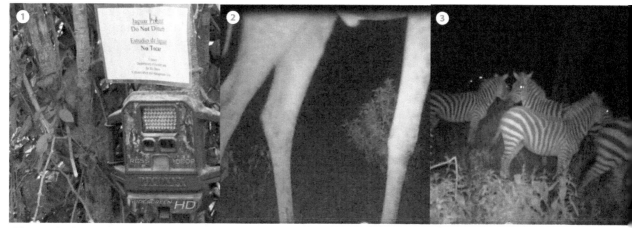

Closed circuit TV (CCTV)

CCTV cameras can be used to observe animal behaviour with a lower risk of disturbance than if researchers visit the site, for example, for monitoring birds' nests.

Marking

A range of methods is used to identify individual animals that have been previously caught, for example, rings placed on birds' legs provide information on movements and lifespan if they are caught later.

❶ *Lesser Black-backed Gull with leg rings*

❷ *Red Kite with wing tags*

DNA databases

A DNA profile can be used to identify individuals, gene pools, and other genetic relationships.

Detecting the presence of a species

The presence of some aquatic species can be detected from the DNA of the cells they shed into the water. This is called environmental DNA or eDNA.

eDNA evidence of the presence of the legally protected Great Crested Newt may prevent a development being permitted in the UK that would damage its habitat.

In the USA, the presence of non-indigenous bighead carp and silver carp is detected using eDNA.

▼ *Electrophoresis gel used to identify DNA samples from tropical timber.*

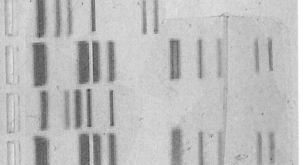

Identifying regional populations

Each separate population within a species has its own unique gene pool. It may be possible to identify where a plant or animal came from if its DNA can be compared with a DNA database for the different regional populations. This technology is being developed to track the sources of tropical timber, elephant ivory, and some commercially fished species such as cod and haddock.

Auditory monitoring

Some species that cannot be seen can be detected by the sounds they produce.

❶ *A bat detector*
❷ *A sonogram of underwater sounds*

Sonograms

Sonograms are records of the sounds made by taxa such as dolphins, bats, and some insects. They can be used as evidence of their presence, abundance and activity.

Position monitoring

A range of technologies can be used to monitor the location of individuals.

▶ Radio, GPS and acoustic transmitters can be used to track animals in air or freshwater.

▶ In seawater, acoustic transmitters are used. They give real-time information of the current position of the animal carrying the transmitter.

Geolocator tags may be used where transmitters would be too heavy, or where the battery life would be too short for a long-term study. They are small and only collect data on time and light. When the animal is re-caught, the data can be downloaded and used to work out the latitude and longitude of the animal for each day during the study. Geolocator tags are used to track the movements of birds that are too small to carry radio transmitters. The data on location can be downloaded if they are recaptured.

❶ *A Bewick's Swan with a tracking collar*
❷ *A hyena with a radio collar*
❸ *Radio tracking receiver, used to monitor lions in Kenya*

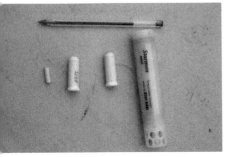

Data recorders

These collect data on a range of abiotic factors, for example, temperature, light intensity, light wavelength, salinity, and pressure. The data may be downloaded when the recorder is recovered, or by radio, or auditory transmission.

▲ *Data recorders*

Sensor carrier systems

If data is to be collected in a single location then the sensor just needs to be placed there but it is often necessary to have a carrier system to move the sensor to the study areas. Many carrier systems exist:

- ROV (Remotely Operated Vehicles), including drones;
- AUV (Autonomous Unmanned Vehicles);
- balloon;
- aircraft;
- satellites;
- animals.

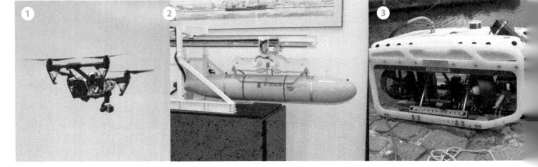

❶ *A drone*
❷ *Autosub AUV*
❸ *An aquatic ROV*

Satellite systems

Satellites are increasingly important for collecting information that increases our understanding of environmental issues and for making well-informed decisions. Sensors mounted on satellites can be used to collect large amounts of data about the Earth using different types of electromagnetic radiation:

- reflected visible light provide images of large areas of the Earth's surface. These can be used for creating maps, monitoring land use changes and monitoring environmental changes such as deforestation and flooding.
- Infrared (IR) emitted by the Earth's surface can be used to monitor vegetation density and temperature.
- weather monitoring and forecasting use sensors that detect cloud cover, humidity, wind velocity, wind direction and temperature.
- radar microwaves emitted by the satellite which reflect off the Earth's surface can be used to monitor a range of environmental features:

- wind velocity;
- sea surface altitude;
- wave height;
- oil pollution.

Microwaves can pass through clouds so the surveys are not interrupted by cloudy weather.

GPS satellites use radio waves to track the positions of mobile animals, floats in the oceans, or the location of sampling sites.

Indirect evidence

Many species leave evidence of their presence, even if they are not actually seen.

⚑ Nests/burrows.

⚑ Droppings – these can give information on diet, gender, territory size.

⚑ Feeding marks, for example, chewed nuts.

⚑ Owl pellets – these also give information on diet.

⚑ Tracks/footprints.

⚑ Territorial marks, for example, scratching posts.

Abiotic factors

Electronic meters

Many abiotic factors can be measured using electronic meters, such as:

⚑ temperature;

⚑ pH;

⚑ dissolved oxygen;

⚑ light level;

⚑ wind or water velocity.

It is important that the meter readings are accurate. To achieve this, the meter must be calibrated by adjusting its reading to be the same as a meter that is known to be accurate. If a meter cannot be adjusted then the percentage error should be noted so the results can be adjusted.

❶ *Branch where a Great Spotted Woodpecker has been feeding*
❷ *A hazel nut that has been eaten by a Hazel Dormouse*
❸ *A jaguar scratching post*

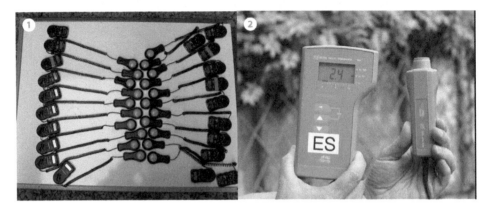

① All these light meters should give the same reading if they have been calibrated

② An electronic meter that measures levels of UV light

Light intensity

A calibrated light meter can be used to measure light intensity. The method must be standardised, especially the sensor orientation.

▼ Whirling hygrometer

Humidity

Method: Whirling hygrometer

This is the traditional method of measuring humidity. This uses two thermometers, one being dry while the other is kept wet. When they are spun, the wet bulb is cooled by the evaporation of the water, the dry bulb is not cooled. The rate of evaporation on the wet bulb depends on the humidity, so the temperature difference between the two thermometers can be compared with a table of values to estimate the humidity.

To get an accurate reading, the hygrometer must be spun until there is no further cooling.

Method: Electronic humidity meter

As with all electronic meters, they must be calibrated to ensure that the readings are accurate.

Wind velocity

This is normally measured with an electronic anemometer.

The use of an anemometer must be standardised in the following ways:

▲ An impeller-type anemometer

- distance from the ground;
- no obstacles to air flow;
- axis of rotation must be horizontal (impeller type) or vertical (rotating cup type);
- impeller type anemometers must face into the wind.

Water turbidity

Purpose/application

▼ To estimate the turbidity of water caused by suspended solid particles.

Method: Secchi disc

▼ Lower a secchi disc into the water until the black and white sectors cannot be distinguished.

▼ Record the depth of the disc (length of string below the water level).

Limitations

▼ The depth judgement is subjective.

▼ Sunlight levels may affect visibility.

▼ The water may not be deep enough for the segments to become indistinguishable.

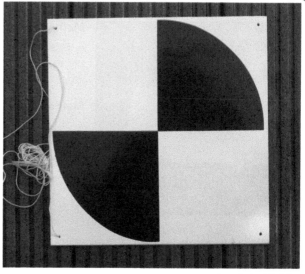

▲ *A secchi disk*

Method: Turbidity bottle

▼ Add a standard depth of water to a turbidity bottle.

▼ The hatched circles at the bottle of the bottle are observed to see which are obscured.

▼ Note the coarsest circle which cannot be distinguished.

Limitations

▼ Judging which circles can be distinguished is subjective.

▼ Light levels may affect visibility.

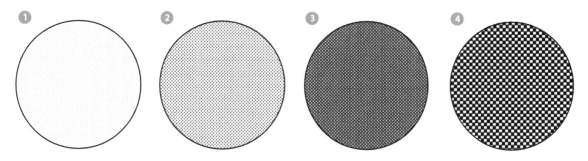

▲ *The hatched circles at the bottom of a turbidity bottle*

Concentration of ions in solution

A wide range of methods is used to measure the concentration of dissolved ions. Most methods use colourimetry where the extent of a colour change involving the ions to be measured is used to estimate the ion concentration.

Method: Test strips

The test strips have bands of the reagents that change colour when they react with the ion to be measured.

The strips are dipped into the solutions being analysed then compared with a reference colour chart.

▼ *A phosphate test strip and colour comparison chart.*

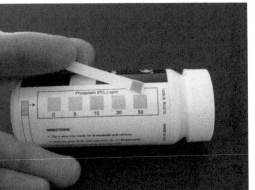

Method: Electronic colourimeter

A reagent is added to the test solution. The intensity of the colour produced is measured by a light meter that is adjusted to measure a specific wavelength of light.

Method: Ion selective electrodes

An electronic probe is put into the test solution. The electrode potential that is produced by the solution between two electrodes is used as a measure of the ion concentration.

Limitations

The presence of other ions can lead to inaccurate results.

Soil analysis

Soil sampling

If the soil is to be analysed in the lab then a representative sample must be collected. A soil auger will collect a sample of known cross-sectional area and depth. Collecting soil with a trowel produces less representative samples that cannot be compared with other samples as reliably.

Soil temperature

Method: Using a soil thermometer

- The thermometer must have a protective metal tube to prevent it breaking.
- Push the thermometer into the soil to a standard depth, for example, 10 cm.
- Protect the thermometer from direct sunlight.
- Leave it until the alcohol liquid stops moving and a constant temperature is shown.
- The temperature is read while the thermometer is still in the soil.

▲ *A soil auger collects a more standardised sample than a trowel*

Soil texture

Soil texture assesses the proportions of the mineral particles in different size categories: sand, silt, and clay.

Two methods are used to measure the proportions of sand, silt, and clay.

Soil particle sizes

Component	Particle diameter range /mm
Sand	>0.02 - 2
Silt	0.002 - 0.02
Clay	<0.002

Method: Soil sieves

- ⚐ The stack of sieves is assembled in order of mesh size, with the coarsest mesh at the top.
- ⚐ A dried, crushed soil sample is placed in the top sieve.
- ⚐ The sieve stack is shaken by hand, or mechanically, for two minutes (long enough for no more particles to fall through). The particles drop through the sieves until they reach a sieve where the holes are too small to pass through.
- ⚐ Each portion is weighed and the % composition of the three portions calculated.
- ⚐ Wet sieving is also possible. The sub-samples collected in each sieve must be dried before weighing.
  - The top sieve (mesh size >2mm) contains pebbles, twigs etc. These are not part of the soil.
  - The second sieve (0.02 – 2mm) contains sand. (Some stacks have an extra sieve to separate coarse and fine sand.)
  - The third sieve (0.002 – 0.02mm) contains silt
  - The base container holds clay.

▲ Soil sieves

Method: Sedimentation

- ⚐ Larger objects are removed from a dried soil sample by using a 2mm sieve, or by hand, for example, pebbles, twigs.
- ⚐ The soil is crushed to ensure the particles are separated.
- ⚐ A measuring cylinder is about half filled with soil, then topped up with water.
- ⚐ The top is sealed then the cylinder is shaken by repeatedly inverting it.
- ⚐ The suspension is allowed to settle.
- ⚐ The total depth of the settled soil components is measured after 2 minutes, 2 hours, and 2 days.
- ⚐ The proportion of the total volume of each textural category can then be calculated.

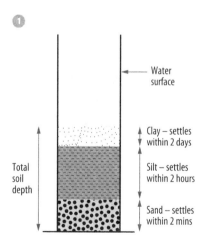

❶ Soil sedimentation to separate soil particles of different textural classes

❷ A soil triangle

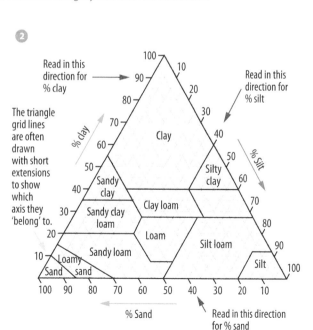

Using a soil triangle

A soil triangle is a triangular graph used to display the combined proportions of the three mineral soil components. Different areas of the graph represent soils with characteristic properties.

Soil water content

The water content of a soil can be estimated by noting the mass drop of a weighed soil sample when the water it contains is evaporated by heating.

Method

1. The soil sample is collected using a standardised technique such as a core sampler or auger.
2. The soil sample is placed in a sealed bag to prevent water loss by evaporation.
3. Larger mineral particles, organic detritus and visible organisms are removed.
4. The soil sample is placed in a pre-weighed evaporating basin or similar container.
5. The basin is heated at about 100°C for 24 hours.
6. The basin is reweighed.
7. Stages 5) and 6) are repeated until a constant mass is reached.

The percentage water content can then be calculated:

$$\text{Percentage water content} = \frac{\text{Wet soil mass - Dry soil mass}}{\text{Wet soil mass}} \times 100$$

Soil organic matter content

The organic matter content of a soil can be estimated by heating the dry soil to burn off the organic matter.

Method (follow Steps 1 -7 of the soil water content method) then:

8. A dry soil sample is placed in a pre-weighed crucible which is reweighed;
9. The crucible is heated strongly in a furnace or with a Bunsen burner;
10. The crucible is re-weighed.

If the heating temperature is above 550°C then minerals may break down, for example, calcium carbonate breaking down, releasing carbon dioxide. This would give an inaccurately high estimate of organic matter as the reduction in mass would not be caused by the loss of organic matter alone.

11. Stages 9) and 10) are repeated until a constant mass is reached. The percentage organic matter content can then be calculated:

$$\text{Percentage organic matter content} = \frac{\text{Dry soil mass - Burnt soil mass}}{\text{Dry soil mass}} \times 100$$

▶ A graph showing mass changes during an investigation to find the water and organic matter content of a soil sample.

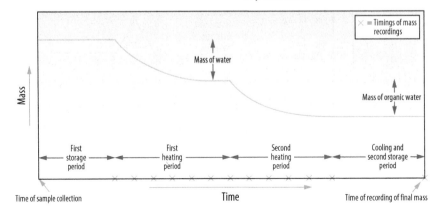

Soil bulk density

Soil bulk density is the mass of dry soil per unit volume.

The volume of a soil sample can be controlled by using a soil auger of known cross-sectional area and pushing it into the soil to a chosen depth.

The dry soil mass can be found by weighing the soil after it has been heated at about 100°C to constant weight.

pH

Several methods are used to measure pH.

Method: Colourimetry

Universal indicator is a mixture of pH indicators that show characteristic colour changes over the pH range 0 to 14. It can be used as a solution or on pH test papers.

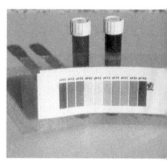

▲ Testing soil pH with universal indicator solution

- ▼ **Universal indicator solution:** pH indicator chemicals absorb different wavelengths of light at different pHs. This colour change is predictable and can be used to measure pH by comparing the colour of the indicator with a reference chart. This method is simple but is subjective because it relies upon the judgement of colour. A standard colourimetric method can be used to estimate the pH of a soil sample.
  - Add 2.5cm³ of soil to a test tube.
  - Add 1cm³ of barium sulfate (toxic), which helps the soil particles to settle.
  - Add 3.5 cm³ distilled water.
  - Add 10 drops of universal indicator solution.
  - Firmly push a bung into the tube.
  - Shake thoroughly and leave to stand for 15 minutes
  - Compare the colour of the coloured solution above the soil with a colour chart

- ▼ **Universal indicator papers:** these are strips of absorbent paper that are impregnated with universal indicator solution. The papers can be dipped into the solutions to be tested and any colour changes compared with a reference chart.
  - For soil samples, the procedure is similar to that outlined for universal indicator solution above. No universal indicator solution is added. A universal indicator paper is dipped into the settled water sample and the colour change is compared with a colour chart.
  - For water samples, the papers are simply dipped into the sample and compared with a colour chart.

Limitations

- ▼ Using colour comparison charts is subjective.

Method: Electronic pH meters

The quantitative values produced by electronic meters can be easy to interpret and compare but it is important to ensure the results are accurate, representative, and collected using a standardised method.

- ▼ The pH meter should be calibrated using buffer solutions of known pH.
- ▼ The meter should be left to stabilise for long enough to give stable readings.
- ▼ The probe should be inserted to a standard depth.

Limitations

 ◢ The need to regularly calibrate the probe with buffer solutions makes this method less convenient than universal indicator papers.

Specific practical investigations

These investigations adapt the techniques previously covered to collect data on particular environmental topics.

Without good data, collected using standardised scientific methods, it would not be possible to plan the use of environmental resources or decide how to control human impacts on the environment.

Climatic variability and the use of renewable energy

Intensity of solar power

Light intensity can be measured using an electronic light meter. As with all electronic meters, this should be calibrated to ensure it is reliable and can be used with a standardised technique.

Factors that affect the intensity of solar power include the time of day, time of year, and cloud cover.

Wind velocity

The ideal location for a wind farm is usually where the wind velocity is reliably high. The power available is not proportional to mean wind velocity as doubling wind velocity increases available power eight-fold. The effect of local factors on wind velocity can be investigated:

 ◢ distance from the ground;
 ◢ topography;
 ◢ aspect in relation to prevailing winds;
 ◢ nearby trees or buildings.

Factors affecting the rate of heat loss

The heat energy that must be added to a building, furnace, or heat store to maintain a constant temperature depends upon the rate at which heat is lost. Reducing the rate at which heat is lost will therefore reduce the rate at which heat must be added.

 ◢ **Thermal insulation**: the rate of heat loss depends upon the thermal conductivity of the surrounding material. The thicker the surrounding material, and the lower the thermal conductivity, the lower the rate of heat loss, but each additional layer has a smaller effect than the previous ones. If the value of the heat saving and the cost of the insulation are known then the optimum thickness of insulation can be calculated.

 ◢ **Volume**: the heat energy stored in a hot mass of material is lost through the external surface. As the volume increases the surface area:volume changes so the rate of heat loss also changes. The total amount of heat lost will be increased because the surface area and amount of heat stored have also gone up. However, the rate of heat loss per unit volume goes down so the temperature drops more slowly.

The principles of the effect of volume on the rate of heat loss can be investigated with a range of objects of different volumes. Factors that should be standardised:

- the material the objects are made of, for example, clay cubes, water-filled round-bottomed flasks, or PET bottles;
- 3D shape;
- colour, darkness, and texture of the surface;
- experimental conditions such as room temperature, air movements, and contact with other materials and surfaces.

The estimation of heat loss requires careful planning and interpretation. The total amount of heat energy stored can be calculated using the specific heat capacity and temperature of the materials used. However, the temperature will vary throughout the volume, being lower near the surfaces and higher in the core. It may also be higher near the top, if water-filled containers are used where convection currents may occur.

Use of biotic indices in monitoring pollution

A biotic index is a method of monitoring environmental conditions, usually pollutants, by the presence/absence, state of health/growth, and abundance/diversity of species which would normally be present.

Advantages of using biotic indices

- They monitor current pollution levels and can be used to estimate past levels.
- They can help trace the source of the pollution.
- They can be very sensitive to small changes.
- Very low levels of pollutants which bioaccumulate may be detectable in raised concentrations in organisms.
- They do not need expensive monitoring equipment.

Disadvantages of biotic indices

- Sorting samples can be time-consuming.
- Identification can be difficult for the inexperienced.

Features of good indicator species

- Easy to identify.
- Normally present if there is no pollution.
- Normally common if there is no pollution.
- Widely distributed rather than found in groups.
- Easy to find.

Ideally there will be a range of species with different sensitivities to pollution. In this case they may disappear in an order which indicates the level of pollution.

Atmospheric pollution and lichen biotic indices

The long-term effects of pollutants can be difficult to assess by measuring the levels of the pollutants that cause the damage as these can fluctuate widely. For example, the atmospheric concentrations of sulfur dioxide and other acidic gases vary widely, mainly due to the varying rate of their removal by rain. This makes it difficult to measure the concentration of pollutants such that they can be reliably correlated to the damage they cause. A better indication of the pollution problems may be achieved by measuring the impact of the pollution through the abundance and diversity of the organisms that are affected. Organisms that are sensitive to pollution give an indication of past pollutant levels as well as what is happening now.

Lichens are particularly sensitive to acidic conditions, with different species having different sensitivities so the presence or absence, size and state of health of different species can be used to produce a scale of the severity of pollution. This can be used to estimate long-term pollution conditions at different locations. Factors that should be standardised:

- the surface on which the lichens are found, as materials such as limestone or granite will also affect the pH;
- the aspect of the surface in relation to the prevailing wind and therefore exposure to rain;
- factors that influence lichen growth such as exposure to sunlight.

It is common to study lichen distribution on gravestones as their orientation normally faces west-east and the substrate can be standardised: they are often made of granite.

▼ Lichens on a gravestone in an unpolluted area.

Aquatic pollution and aquatic invertebrate biotic indices

A range of aquatic invertebrate taxa with different sensitivities to pollution are used to monitor pollution. They meet the desired criteria listed above. The following taxa are often included: Stonefly larvae, mayfly larvae, caddisfly larvae, freshwater shrimps, freshwater hoglouse, midge larvae.

The effect of pH on seed germination

High and low pH conditions denature proteins and inactivate enzymes. Each species has its own range of tolerance.

To investigate the effect of pH on germination, a number of choices must be made:

- **Choice of plant species**: some species make good experimental subjects:
  - small seeds;
  - genetic uniformity;
  - high normal germination rate;
  - rapid germination.

These species are not necessarily the ones that produce results which can be applied directly to natural ecosystems.

- **Number of seeds and replicates**: each test must use enough seeds to produce results that can be distinguished from each other if there is a real difference, but not so many that unnecessary extra work is undertaken.
- Each test must be replicated to allow anomalies to be identified and the results to be statistically valid.
- **pH range**: the range of pHs tested should cover the full range at which germination can take place. This can be established with a preliminary study using a range of widely spaced pHs. The pH range investigated in the final experiment would cover the range from the pH below the lowest pH at which germination occurred to the pH above the highest pH at which germination occurred.

- ▶ **Study duration:** the experiment should be continued until it is clear that seeds that have not germinated are not going to. The possibility that pH could delay germination must be eliminated.
- ▶ **Other variables that should be standardised**:
  - temperature: the temperature should be standardised, ideally at a constant temperature that would occur during natural germination;
  - nutrient supplies: seeds do not need to absorb nutrients to germinate. They would only need to be provided if the plants were going to be grown beyond the time at which they would have exhausted the nutrients originally present in the seed
  - using soil as a growth medium replicates the natural growth situation but may affect the experimental conditions, including the pH.

The effect of water turbidity on light penetration

Measuring the turbidity of water is an important way of monitoring soil erosion. The turbidity of water can be measured using a number of techniques in the field or in the laboratory. Secchi discs and turbidity bottles give semi-quantitative or qualitative results. Electronic meters give quantitative data.

Electronic turbidimeters

Most electronic turbidimeters measure the amount of light that is scattered by the suspended particles in a water sample, usually at 90° to the angle at which it entered the water. An increase in turbidity causes more light scatter, so the light reading rises.

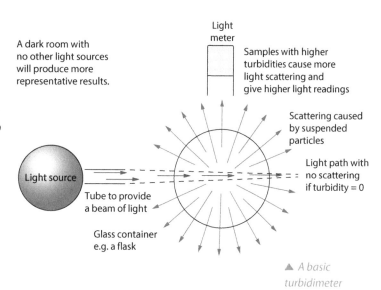

A dark room with no other light sources will produce more representative results.

Light meter

Samples with higher turbidities cause more light scattering and give higher light readings

Scattering caused by suspended particles

Light path with no scattering if turbidity = 0

Light source

Tube to provide a beam of light

Glass container e.g. a flask

▲ *A basic turbidimeter*

The light readings give relative values of the concentration of the suspended particles in the water samples. Quantitative estimates can be produced if a calibration curve is produced by measuring the light scatter from samples with known amounts of suspended matter. Factors that must be standardised:

- ▶ brightness of the light bulb;
- ▶ colour of light emitted by the lightbulb;
- ▶ distance to the sample holder;
- ▶ material used to produce the calibration samples.

The effect of inorganic nutrients on the growth of aquatic plants/algae

The inorganic nutrients washed off fields or released in sewage effluent can increase the rate of growth of plants and algae and contribute to eutrophication.

Measuring biomass growth

The increase in growth caused by the availability of nutrients may cause an increase in biomass as more sunlight is converted into carbohydrates. Living matter is mainly water, so measuring living biomass is not necessarily a good indicator of the amount of carbohydrate present. It is especially difficult with aquatic plants where surface water will affect the mass but drying it off may damage the plants. Dry biomass is a more precise measure but involves killing the plants or algae so long term studies cannot be carried out on the same organisms.

If the increase in dry biomass is estimated on several occasions over a period of time then a large number of original samples will be needed since each is destroyed when it is weighed.

For some aquatic plants, such as duckweed (*Lemna spp)*, leaf area can be used as a reasonable estimate of biomass and allows the continued use of the same plants.

Other variables that must be controlled:

- temperature;
- light levels.

If nutrient solutions need to be topped up, it is best to transfer the plants to new solutions rather than adding more nutrients to the remaining nutrient solution which will have an unknown nutrient concentration.

Factors affecting noise levels

Noise levels can be measured with an electronic sound level meter but if one is unavailable many mobile phones incorporate sound level meters. If uncalibrated meters are used then the same one should be used to collect all the results. This will ensure that the degree of error in the results is constant so they can be compared with each other.

Distance from source

The fact that noise levels decline as the distance from the source increases is predictable. Collecting quantitative data and assessing variations in noise levels from sources such as roads and airports is more difficult. Because the decibel scale is logarithmic, a simple arithmetic mean does not give a true representation of the typical sound levels.

The presence of sound absorbing or reflecting surfaces and topography can affect the noise levels, so the study sites should be as similar as possible.

Acoustic insulation

This may be investigated under laboratory conditions with a source of sound, such as a speaker, surrounded by acoustic insulation of different materials or thickness

The effectiveness of insulation around roads or airports such as baffle mounds, embankments, walls, fences, or vegetation can be compared.

The effect of slope and vegetation on rain splash erosion

Scientific experimentation relies upon good experimental design which requires a knowledge of all the variables that could influence the results. Ideally, all the variables that are not being investigated should be standardised so that the only factor that affects the dependent variable (the results) is the independent variable that is being deliberately controlled. This is easier to do under laboratory conditions than under field conditions. Factors that cannot be standardised should be measured so that their influence on the results can be assessed.

Variables that can affect rain splash erosion

- Rainfall intensity.
- Soil texture.
- Soil compaction.
- Organic matter content.
- Soil depth.
- Permeability of the material beneath the soil.
- Precipitation rate - volume per unit area per unit of time.
- Raindrop size.
- Raindrop height drop.
- Gradient.
- Vegetation cover.
- Root binding.

Many experimental procedures have limitations that are an unavoidable part of the method. It is important that these should be known and their impact on the validity of the results appreciated and noted.

▼ *An experimental system for investigating rain-splash erosion*

The effect of trees on microclimates

Trees affect the local climate in and around woodlands. Even individual trees produce microclimates. An understanding of how these microclimates are produced and the effects they have can alter management plans for urban areas and rural areas such as farmland, forestry plantations, and woodlands for wildlife conservation.

Variables that should be considered

Vegetation features:

- tree height;
- foliage characteristics;
- tree spacing;
- total area of woodland.

Features of the microclimate that can be measured:

- wind direction;
- wind velocity;
- light levels;
- humidity;
- soil moisture;
- temperature.

To measure the effect of trees on microclimates the general weather conditions must also be known to identify local differences.

Statistical analysis

It is beyond the scope of this book to include full details of how statistical tests are carried out, but it is useful to consider when they should be used and how results may be interpreted.

A simple analysis of results may show a difference in values, a link between variables or some other 'result'. Statistical analysis can help to establish whether the result is 'real' and can be trusted.

Variability of results

To increase the validity of values that are used, it is normal to take replicate readings and calculate a mean value. However, this value gives no indication of how variable the original results were. Two means may have different values but the range of original values in both data sets may overlap so much that it is not possible to be confident that they really are significantly different. Alternatively, two means may have been produced from data sets that hardly overlap and there is a significant difference between them.

▼ The scatter of values around the mean in a normally distributed sample

The degree of variability can be calculated as the Standard Deviation.

For normally distributed results, it is possible to estimate the percentage of all values that are within a particular range around the mean.

Where a graph is drawn using means, error bars may be added to show the standard deviation. This can help to assess whether the differences in mean values are statistically significant.

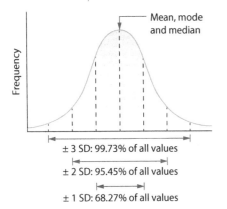

Mean, mode and median

Frequency

± 3 SD: 99.73% of all values

± 2 SD: 95.45% of all values

± 1 SD: 68.27% of all values

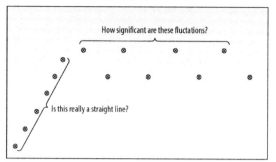

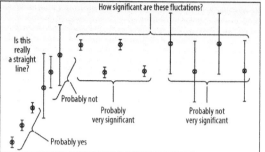

▲ *A graph drawn using means values, showing error bars*

Significance

Most scientific investigations produce quantitative results that are compared to establish the significance of any differences.

Good scientific analysis never 'proves' anything as there is always some remaining uncertainty. The key issue is the level of confidence that can be held over the significance of a conclusion.

A result is statistically significant if a result is unlikely to have occurred by random chance. The probability that the result was produced by random chance can be calculated. The lower it is, the greater the reliability of the result.

The p-value refers to the probability of an event being caused by random chance and is usually expressed as the probability that a single event was significant: 0.9, 0.95, 0.99, 0.995, or as a degree of confidence that the difference investigated is significant.

Interpreting significance

Showing that a result is significant does not mean it is important or that a causal relationship has been found. Two correlated factors may both be caused by another variable that has not been investigated.

Comparing p-values and significance levels

p-value	Significance level: % confidence that the results were NOT produced by random chance
0.1	90%
0.05	95%
0.01	99%
0.005	99.5%

Statistical tests

A wide range of statistical tests have been developed to assess statistical significance. It is very important that the test that is selected is appropriate.

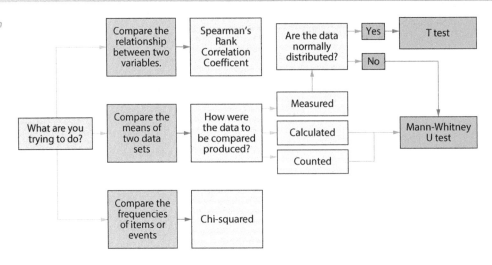

Spearman Rank Correlation Coefficient

This is used to see whether there is a consistent change in the value of one variable as another variable increases or decreases. It assesses how closely two variables are correlated by comparing the rank orders of the two variables in a variety of sampling situations.

Examples of hypotheses that can be tested using Spearman's Rank Correlation Coefficient:

- crop yield increases as fertiliser application increases;
- noise levels decrease as distance from a road increases;
- per capita energy use increases as per capita income increases;
- the number of moths increases as temperature rises;
- the number of earthworms declines as soils become more acidic.

Chi squared test

The Chi-squared test is used to compare the frequencies or numbers of things in different groups are significantly different. It cannot be used for data that can be continuously variable, such as measured or calculated data.

Examples of hypotheses that can be tested using the Chi-squared test:

- the different management practices in a range of woodlands affects the numbers of dormice;
- a range of new GM varieties of wheat produce more seeds per seed head than a traditional variety

t-test

This is used to see if there is a significant difference between two means, where the data were measured, for example, mass, length, wind speed, and dissolved oxygen concentration. It can only be used if the data are normally distributed, which may be difficult to determine with small samples. If there is uncertainty then the Mann-Whitney U test should be used instead.

Examples of hypotheses that can be tested using the t-test:

- the mean mass of lobsters is higher in areas where collection is banned;
- the dissolved oxygen level is lower in a sewage-polluted river;
- wind speed is lower in a woodland than in a clearing;
- soil water content is lower on the south side of a hedge than on the north side.

Mann-Whitney U test

This is used to see if there is a significant difference between two median values, where the data were counted, such as numbers of organisms or vehicles, or were calculated such as diversity indices.

Examples of hypotheses that can be tested using the Mann-Whitney U test:

- fewer cars use a road when road charging is introduced;
- biodiversity is higher in a hedge that is trimmed less frequently;
- more wading birds visit a nature reserve after the water level is raised;
- more bats feed over an uncut grassland than over a close-mown one;
- fewer seeds germinate at pH 5 than at pH 7.

Key principles

- Reliable information is needed to inform good decision-making.
- Sub-samples must be representative.
- Preliminary studies should be used to test the reliability of the methods used.
- All methods should be developed considering the same key questions:
  - Where should the samples be collected?
  - When should the samples be collected?
  - How big should samples be?
  - How many samples should be collected?
  - How can the method be standardised?

Index

This book is dedicated to my grandchildren:

Abigail, Ethan, and Joel

Author

Richard Genn has been teaching Environmental Science since 1981 at FE and Sixth Form colleges in Staffordshire and Hampshire. He has also worked with AQA and its predecessors since the mid-1980s as an examiner and in the preparation of teaching resources.

In 2010 he became co-founder of a sustainable development charity, Kenya 2020 (www.kenya2020.org). This works in the small rural community of Alara in Western Kenya, with the aim of increasing self-reliance and sustainability through projects in agriculture, forestry, water resources, education, and health care.

Richard also manages a woodland nature reserve, with the help of students, family, and friends. They are working on eight hectares of neglected coppiced hazel and oak woodland to increase its wildlife value, particularly for the Hazel Dormouse, Willow Tits, and woodland wildflowers.